PRENTICE HALL

Teacher's **Edition**

SCIENCE EXPLORER

Astronomy

Prentice Hall

Needham, Massachusetts
Upper Saddle River, New Jersey
Glenview, Illinois

ISBN 0-13-054089-7

2 3 4 5 6 7 8 9 10 05 04 03 02 01

PRENTICE HALL

SCIENCE EXPLORER

GET READY FOR A CONTENT-RICH, HANDS-ON EXPLORATION!

15 Books In All

PRENTICE HALL
SCIENCE EXPLORER
Earth's Waters

PRENTICE HALL
SCIENCE EXPLORER
Motion, Forces and Energy

PRENTICE HALL
SCIENCE EXPLORER
Animals

Chart your own course.

15 motivational hardcover books make it easy for you to create your own curriculum; meet local, state, and national guidelines; and teach your favorite topics in depth.

Prepare your students with rich, motivating content...

Science Explorer is crafted for today's middle grades student, with accessible content and in-depth coverage of all the important concepts.

...and a wide variety of inquiry activities.

Motivational student- and teacher-tested activities reinforce key concepts and allow students to explore science concepts for themselves.

Check your compass regularly.

Science Explorer gives you more ways to regularly check student performance than any other program available.

Utilize a variety of tools.

Integrated science sections in every chapter and Interdisciplinary Explorations in every book allow you to make in-depth connections to other sciences and disciplines. Plus, you will find a wealth of additional tools to set your students on a successful course.

Chart the course you want with 15 motivating books that easily match your curriculum.

Each book in the series contains:

- Integrated Science sections in every chapter
- Interdisciplinary Explorations for team teaching at the end of each book
- Comprehensive skills practice and application—assuring that you meet the National Science Education Standards and your local and state standards

EXPLORATION TOOLS: BASIC PROCESS SKILLS

Observing

Measuring

Calculating

Classifying

Predicting

Inferring

Graphing

Creating data tables

Communicating

LIFE SCIENCE TITLES

From Bacteria to Plants
1 Living Things
2 Viruses and Bacteria
3 Protists and Fungi
4 Introduction to Plants
5 Seed Plants

Animals
1 Sponges, Cnidarians, and Worms
2 Mollusks, Arthropods, and Echinoderms
3 Fishes, Amphibians, and Reptiles
4 Birds and Mammals
5 Animal Behavior

Cells and Heredity
1 Cell Structure and Function
2 Cell Processes and Energy
3 Genetics: The Science of Heredity
4 Modern Genetics
5 Changes Over Time

Human Biology and Health
1 Healthy Body Systems
2 Bones, Muscles, and Skin
3 Food and Digestion
4 Circulation
5 Respiration and Excretion
6 Fighting Disease
7 The Nervous System
8 The Endocrine System and Reproduction

Environmental Science
1 Populations and Communities
2 Ecosystems and Biomes
3 Living Resources
4 Land and Soil Resources
5 Air and Water Resources
6 Energy Resources

Integrated Science sections in every chapter

EXPLORATION TOOLS: ADVANCED PROCESS SKILLS

Posing questions

Forming operational definitions

Developing hypotheses

Controlling variables

Interpreting data

Interpreting graphs

Making models

Drawing conclusions

Designing experiments

EARTH SCIENCE TITLES 🔵

Inside Earth
1 Plate Tectonics
2 Earthquakes
3 Volcanoes
4 Minerals
5 Rocks

Earth's Changing Surface
1 Mapping Earth's Surface
2 Weathering and Soil Formation
3 Erosion and Deposition
4 A Trip Through Geologic Time

Earth's Waters
1 Earth: The Water Planet
2 Fresh Water
3 Freshwater Resources
4 Ocean Motions
5 Ocean Zones

Weather and Climate
1 The Atmosphere
2 Weather Factors
3 Weather Patterns
4 Climate and Climate Change

Astronomy
1 Earth, Moon, and Sun
2 The Solar System
3 Stars, Galaxies, and the Universe

PHYSICAL SCIENCE TITLES 🔵

Chemical Building Blocks
1 An Introduction to Matter
2 Changes in Matter
3 Elements and the Periodic Table
4 Carbon Chemistry

Chemical Interactions
1 Chemical Reactions
2 Atoms and Bonding
3 Acids, Bases, and Solutions
4 Exploring Materials

Motion, Forces, and Energy
1 Motion
2 Forces
3 Forces in Fluids
4 Work and Machines
5 Energy and Power
6 Thermal Energy and Heat

Electricity and Magnetism
1 Magnetism and Electromagnetism
2 Electric Charges and Current
3 Electricity and Magnetism at Work
4 Electronics

Sound and Light
1 Characteristics of Waves
2 Sound
3 The Electromagnetic Spectrum
4 Light

🔵 *Integrated Science sections in every chapter*

Turn your students into science explorers with a variety of inquiry activities.

Motivational student- and teacher-tested activities reinforce key concepts and allow students to explore science concepts for themselves. More than 350 activities are provided for each book in the Student Edition, Teacher's Edition, Teaching Resources, Integrated Science Lab Manual, Inquiry Skills Activity Book, Interactive Student Tutorial CD-ROM, and *Science Explorer* Web Site.

STUDENT EDITION ACTIVITIES

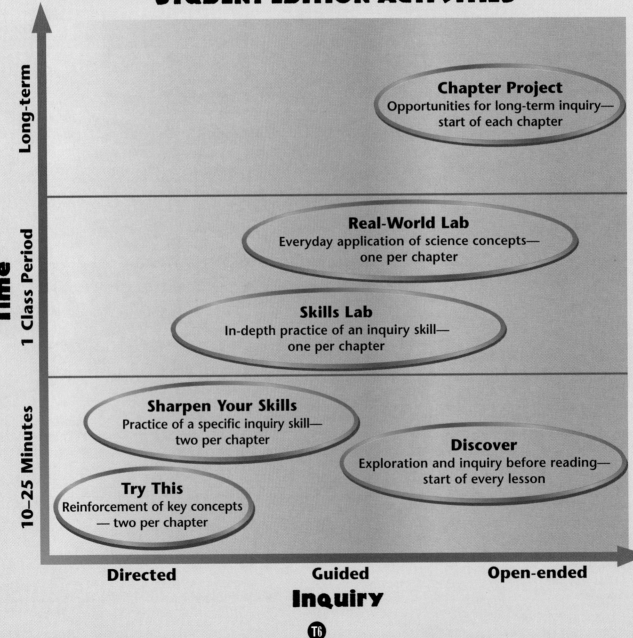

Time

Long-term

1 Class Period

10–25 Minutes

Chapter Project
Opportunities for long-term inquiry—start of each chapter

Real-World Lab
Everyday application of science concepts—one per chapter

Skills Lab
In-depth practice of an inquiry skill—one per chapter

Sharpen Your Skills
Practice of a specific inquiry skill—two per chapter

Discover
Exploration and inquiry before reading—start of every lesson

Try This
Reinforcement of key concepts—two per chapter

Directed   Guided   Open-ended
Inquiry

Check your compass regularly with integrated assessment tools.

Prepare for state exams with traditional and performance-based assessment.

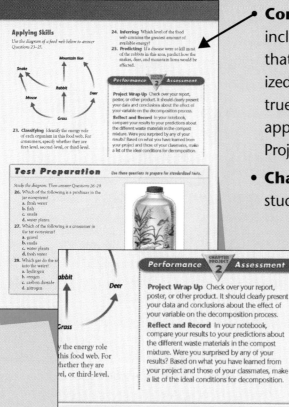

- **Comprehensive Chapter Reviews** include a wide range of question types that students will encounter on standardized tests. Types include multiple choice, enhanced true/false, concept mastery, visual thinking, skill application, and critical thinking. Also includes Chapter Project "Wrap Up."

- **Chapter Projects** contain rubrics that allow you to easily assess student progress.

- **Section Reviews** provide "Check your Progress" opportunities for the Chapter Project, as well as review questions for the section.

Additional *Science Explorer* assessment resources:
- **Computer Test Bank with CD-ROM**
- **Resource Pro® with Planning Express® CD-ROM**
- **Standardized Test Practice Book**
- **Interactive Student Tutorial CD-ROM**
- **On-line review activities** at www.phschool.com
  See pages T8 & T9 for complete product descriptions.

Self-assessment opportunities help students keep themselves on course.

- **Caption Questions** throughout the text assess critical thinking skills.

- **Checkpoint Questions** give students an immediate content check as new concepts are presented.

- **Interactive Student Tutorial CD-ROM** provides students with electronic self-tests, review activities, and Exploration activities.

- **www.phschool.com** provides additional support and on-line test prep.

Utilize a wide variety of tools.

Easy-to-manage, book-specific teaching resources

15 Teaching Resource Packages, each containing a Student Edition, Teacher's Edition, Teaching Resources with Color Transparencies, Interactive Student Tutorial CD-ROM, Guided Study Workbook, Guided Reading Audio CD, and correlation to the National Science Education Standards.

15 Teacher's Editions with a three-step lesson plan–Engage/Explore, Facilitate and Assess–that is ideal for reaching all students. Chapter planning charts make it easy to find resources, as well as to plan for block scheduling and team teaching.

15 Teaching Resource Books with Color Transparencies offer complete teacher support organized by chapter to make it easy for you to find what you need–when you need it.

15 Guided Reading Audio CD's and Audiotapes provide section summaries for students who need additional support. Available in English and Spanish.

15 Guided Study Workbooks containing blackline master worksheets for assessing, understanding, and developing study skills. Teacher's Edition available for each workbook.

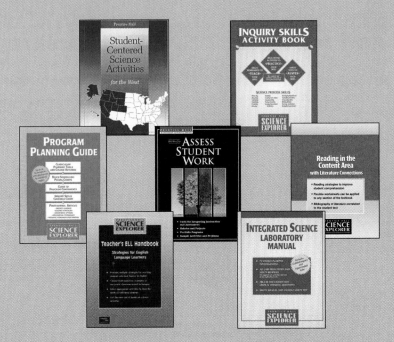

Integrated Science Lab Manual SE & TE—74 in-depth labs covering the entire curriculum, with complete teaching support.

Inquiry Skills Activity Book—additional activities that introduce basic and advanced inquiry skills and reinforce skills on an as-needed basis.

Program Planning Guide—course outlines, block scheduling pacing charts, correlations, and more.

Reading in the Content Area with Literature Connections—provides students with additional strategies for successful reading.

Standardized Test Preparation Book—provides students with hints, tips, strategies, and practice to help them prepare for state and local exams.

How to Assess Student Work—professional articles and example activities that help you design assessments, use rubrics effectively, and develop a portfolio assessment program.

Student-Centered Science Activities—five regional activity books, for the Northeast, Southeast, Midwest, Southwest, and West.

How to Manage Instruction in the Block—comprehensive collection of block scheduling resources, from managing classroom routines to checklists for monitoring and assessing small group learning.

Teacher's ELL Handbook—provides multiple strategies for reaching English language learners. Select appropriate activities to meet the needs of individual students.

Program-wide technology resources

Interactive Student Tutorial CD-ROMs—provide students with self-tests, helpful hints, and Exploration activities. Tests are scored instantly and contain a detailed explanation of all answers.

Probeware Lab Manual—provides detailed instructions for using probeware to perform selected labs. Blackline masters of labs are included.

Resource Pro® CD-ROM—electronic version of the Teaching Resources for all 15 books—ideal for creating integrated science lessons. Contains Planning Express software and Computer Test Bank. Organized by chapter to save you time.

Science Explorer Web Site—activities and teaching resources for every chapter at: www.phschool.com

Science Explorer Videotapes and Videodiscs —explore and visualize concepts through spectacular short documentaries containing computer animations. Videotapes also available in Spanish.

Lab Activity Videotapes—provide step-by-step instruction with students performing activities from every chapter. Promote and teach proper lab techniques, inquiry skills, and safety procedures.

iText—An interactive text version of the Student Edition at www.phschool.com containing animations, simulations, and videos to enhance student understanding and retention of concepts.

Interactive Physics—explore physics concepts with computer simulations that encourage what-if questions.

Computer Test Bank Book with CD-ROM—comprehensive collection of assessment resources containing Computer Test Bank Software with Dial-A-Test; provides you with unparalleled flexibility in creating tests.

ADDITIONAL RESOURCES

Materials Kits—Prentice Hall and Science Kit, Inc. have collaborated to develop a Consumable Kit and Nonconsumable Kit for each book. Ordering software makes it easy to customize!

Interdisciplinary Explorations—designed to help you connect science topics to social studies, math, language arts, and students' daily lives.

Options for Pacing *Astronomy*

The Pacing Chart below suggests one way to schedule your instructional time. The *Science Explorer* program offers many other aids to help you plan your instructional time, whether regular class periods or **block scheduling**. Refer to the Chapter Planning Guide before each chapter to view all program resources with suggested times for Student Edition activities.

Pacing Chart

	Days	Blocks		Days	Blocks
Nature of Science: Searching for the Home of Comets	1	$\frac{1}{2}$	Chapter 2 Review and Assessment	1	$\frac{1}{2}$
Chapter 1 Earth, Moon, and Sun			**Chapter 3 Stars, Galaxies, and the Universe**		
Chapter 1 Project Where's the Moon?	Ongoing	Ongoing	Chapter 3 Project Star Stories	Ongoing	Ongoing
1 Earth in Space	5	$2\frac{1}{2}$	**1** Integrating Physics: Tools of Modern Astronomy	4–5	2–$2\frac{1}{2}$
2 Phases, Eclipses, and Tides	5	$2\frac{1}{2}$	**2** Characteristics of Stars	4–5	$2\frac{1}{2}$
3 Integrating Technology: Rockets and Satellites	2	1	**3** Lives of Stars	$2\frac{1}{2}$	1–2
4 Earth's Moon	3	1–2	**4** Star Systems and Galaxies	2	1
Chapter 1 Review and Assessment	1	$\frac{1}{2}$	**5** History of the Universe	2	1
Chapter 2 The Solar System			Chapter 3 Review and Assessment	1	$\frac{1}{2}$
Chapter 2 Project Model of the Solar System	Ongoing	Ongoing	Interdisciplinary Exploration: Journey to Mars	2-3	1-2
1 Observing the Solar System	3	1–2			
2 The Sun	3	$1\frac{1}{2}$			
3 The Inner Planets	4	2			
4 The Outer Planets	5	2–3			
5 Comets, Asteroids, and Meteors	2	1			
6 Integrating Life Science: Is There Life Beyond Earth?	3	1–2			

RESOURCE PRO®

The Resource Pro® CD-ROM is the ultimate scheduling and lesson planning tool. Resource Pro® allows you to preview all the resources in the *Science Explorer* program, organize your chosen materials, and print out any teaching resource. You can follow the suggested lessons or create your own, using resources from anywhere in the program.

Thematic Overview of *Astronomy*

The chart below lists the major themes of *Astronomy*. For each theme, the chart supplies a big idea, or concept statement, describing how a particular theme is taught in a chapter.

	Chapter 1	Chapter 2	Chapter 3
Patterns of Change	Earth has day and night. The moon has phases. The seasons on Earth are caused by the revolution of Earth and the tilt of its axis. Tides are caused mainly by differences in how much the moon pulls on different parts of Earth.		Stars go through life cycles that begin with the formation of a protostar. A star's life history depends on its mass.
Scale and Structure	The moon has one fourth the radius and one eightieth the mass of Earth.	The sun is the largest body in the solar system. The outer planets, except for Pluto, are huge gas giants. The inner planets and Pluto are rocky and comparatively small.	Stars are classified according to size, color, temperature, and brightness. Stars are parts of larger systems of stars. Galaxies are part of the universe.
Unity and Diversity	The composition of rocks on the moon is similar to the composition of rocks in Earth's outer layers. But the moon has no air and no liquid water.	Students compare and contrast the objects in the solar system. Earth is unique in the solar system because it supports life.	
Systems and Interactions			Most stars are part of double, triple, or larger star systems. The Milky Way Galaxy is part of a larger system, the universe. The solar system formed about 5 billion years ago from a cloud of gas and dust.
Evolution	Moon craters and the composition of moon and Earth rocks tell us that Earth and the moon have undergone dramatic changes in their history.		The life cycle of a star is determined by its mass. According to the big bang theory, the universe formed in an enormous explosion about 10 to 15 billion years ago.
Energy	Energy constraints limit the design of rockets and force the use of multistage rockets to achieve orbital speeds.	Energy from reactions in the sun's core is transmitted as light and heat to all of the bodies in the solar system.	The electromagnetic spectrum includes all forms of electromagnetic waves. Energy is transferred between objects in the universe by means of radiation. Energy is released from a star as a result of nuclear fusion.
Stability	Earth has two high and low tides every day, due to the moon's gravitational pull. The moon's period of rotation and revolution are the same, so it always keeps the same face toward Earth.	The planets are held in constant orbits by two factors—inertia and gravity.	
Modeling	Students model the causes of the seasons and the causes of the moon phases.		Students model the construction and operation of telescopes by constructing a telescope.

Inquiry Skills Chart

The Prentice Hall *Science Explorer* program provides comprehensive teaching, practice, and assessment of science skills, with an emphasis on the process skills necessary for inquiry. The chart lists the skills covered in the program and cites the page numbers where each skill is covered.

Basic Process SKILLS

	Student Text: Projects and Labs	Student Text: Activities	Student Text: Caption and Review Questions	Teacher's Edition: Extensions
Observing	12–13, 22–23, 30–31, 78–79, 92–93, 101, 110–111	14, 24, 35, 37, 39, 41, 50, 53, 56, 58, 62, 66, 68, 84, 94, 96, 103, 108, 117, 119, 121	44, 71, 74, 81, 106	16, 18, 19, 32, 37, 64, 68, 72–73, 76, 82, 95, 105
Inferring	61, 78–79, 92–93, 101	24, 35, 37, 66, 68, 80, 84, 96, 100, 119, 121	38, 42, 44, 47, 57, 73, 77, 85, 116, 124	51, 53, 57, 68, 72, 75, 81, 86, 97, 123
Predicting	12–13, 61, 78–79, 110–111	39, 50, 53, 108, 114	32, 47, 77, 83	26, 32, 73, 76, 81, 99, 103, 123
Classifying		70		76, 105
Making Models	22–23, 30–31, 48–49, 78–79, 101, 110–111	14, 24, 28, 37, 39, 62, 73, 80, 94, 108, 117, 119, 121	91, 122	15, 20, 32–33, 37, 52, 63, 72, 82, 104, 106
Communicating	12–13, 30–31, 48–49, 92–93	17, 68, 75, 85, 88–99, 102, 107, 114	46, 90, 126	14, 35, 39, 42, 50, 52, 56, 62, 74, 76, 80, 84, 103, 117, 124
Measuring	12–13, 22–23, 78–79, 110–111	70		40, 104
Calculating	48–49, 61, 78–79, 110–111	15, 18, 25, 43, 70		32, 40, 81, 104, 119
Creating Data Tables	78–79, 110–111	58		
Graphing	61	65	127	54, 57

Advanced Process SKILLS

Posing Questions		138	47	14, 94
Developing Hypotheses	78–79	39, 138		43, 82
Designing Experiments	78–79, 110–111	139		43, 86
Controlling Variables	78–79	139		82
Forming Operational Definitions		84, 139		

	Student Text: Projects and Labs	Student Text: Activities	Student Text: Caption and Review Questions	Teacher's Edition: Extensions
Advanced Process SKILLS (continued)				
Interpreting Data	12–13, 22–23, 61, 78–79, 110–111	58, 139	91, 127	40, 63
Drawing Conclusions	22–23, 30–31, 48–49, 78–79, 101, 110–111	39, 62, 112, 139	91, 127	82, 86, 89
Critical Thinking SKILLS				
Comparing and Contrasting	22–23, 48–49, 61, 101, 110–111	62, 108, 117, 140	38, 60, 91, 127	18, 24, 27, 29, 52, 62–63, 72, 74
Applying Concepts	22–23, 61, 78–79, 101	14, 68, 94, 103, 140	15, 21, 47, 55, 86–87, 91, 100, 104, 109, 113, 116, 120, 127	16, 32, 40, 42, 71, 73
Interpreting Diagrams, Graphs Photographs, and Maps	30–31, 61, 92–93	18, 65, 112, 140	18, 27, 29, 34, 47, 51, 54, 63, 95, 105, 109, 118	121
Relating Cause and Effect	78–79, 101, 110–111	39, 141	21, 47, 60, 69, 91, 127	76, 118
Making Generalizations	30–31, 78–79	141	114, 127	63–64
Making Judgments		88, 102, 141		42, 86
Problem Solving	78–79, 110–111	88, 102, 141		42, 113
Information Organizing SKILLS				
Concept Maps		142	46, 126	94
Compare/ Contrast Tables		142	90	24, 70
Venn Diagrams		143		24, 39, 62
Flowcharts		143		112
Cycle Diagrams		143		

The *Science Explorer* program provides additional teaching, reinforcement, and assessment of skills in the Inquiry Skills Activities Book and the Integrated Science Laboratory Manual.

Throughout the *Science Explorer* program, every effort has been made to keep the materials and equipment *affordable, reusable,* and *easily accessible.*

The *Science Explorer* program offers an abundance of activity options so you can pick and choose those activities that suit your needs. To help you order supplies at the beginning of the year, the Master Materials List cross-references the materials by activity. If you prefer to create your list electronically, you can use the Materials List CD-ROM.

There are two kits available for each book of the *Science Explorer* program: a Consumable Kit and a Nonconsumable Kit. These kits are produced by **Science Kit and Boreal Laboratories,** the leader in providing science kits to schools. Prentice Hall and Science Kit collaborated throughout the development of *Science Explorer* to ensure that the equipment and supplies in the kits precisely match the requirements of the program activities.

The kits provide an economical and convenient way to get all of the materials needed to teach each book. For each book, Science Kit also offers the opportunity to buy equipment and safety items individually. For additional information about ordering materials to accompany *Science Explorer,* please call:
1-800-848-9500
or access the *Science Explorer* Internet site at: **www.phschool.com**

Master Materials List

Consumable Materials

*	Description	Quantity per class	Textbook Section(s)	*	Description	Quantity per class	Textbook Section(s)
C	Acetate Sheet 8 1/2" × 11"	5	2-4 (TT)	C	Paper Clips, Box/100	1	3-2 (Lab)
C	Alka Seltzer Pkg/2	2	1-3 (TT)	SS	Pen	5	3-2 (Lab)
C	Aluminum Foil, Roll 12" × 25"	2	3-1 (TT)	SS	Pencil	5	1-1 (Lab) 1-2 (Lab) 2-1 (TT) 2-2 (Lab) 2-5 (DIS) 3-4 (DIS)
C	Baking Soda 454 g	1	2-4 (TT)				
C	Ball, Styrofoam 3" Diameter	5	2-4 (TT)				
C	Balloons, Round 13" Pkg/10	1	1-3 (DIS) 3-5 (DIS)				
C	Battery, Carbon Zinc, Size C, 1.5 Volts	10	3-2 (TT)	SS	Pencils, Colored Pkg/12	5	3-2 (Lab)
C	Battery, Size D	20	1-1 (Lab) 3-2 (TT)	C	Peppercorns	1	2-4 (TT)
				C	Pipe Cleaners, White 12" Pkg/30	1	3-4 (TT)
SS	Box, Copier Paper	5	3-2 (Lab)	C	Sand, Fine 2.5 kg	1	1-4 (DIS)
C	Bulb, Incandescent, 100 Watt	1	1-1 (DIS) 1-2 (Lab) 3-2 (Lab)	C	Spoons, Plastic Pkg/24	1	2-6 (DIS)
				C	String, Cotton 200 ft	1	2-1 (TT) 2-4 (Lab) 2-5 (DIS)
C	Cardboard, Corrugated 32 × 32 cm	10	2-1 (TT) 3-1 (DIS)				
C	Cardboard, White 8 1/2" × 11"	5	2-2 (DIS) 2-2 (TT)	C	Sugar, Granulated 454 g	1	2-6 (DIS)
C	Clay, Modeling (Cream) lb (water-resistant)	1	2-5 DIS)	SS	Tape, Masking 3/4" × 60 yd	2	1-3 (TT) 2-3 (TT) 3-1 (TT) 2-2 (DIS) 3-2 (Lab) 3-4 (DIS)
C	Cup, Paper 100 mL	5	1-3 (TT)				
SS	Foam Holder for Eyepiece (Optional)	5	3-1 (Lab)				
SS	Graph Paper, Sheet	10	2-2 (Lab) 2-3 (SYS)	SS	Tape, Transparent Dispenser Roll 27.1 ft.	1	2-4 (TT) 3-1 (DIS) 3-1 (Lab)
C	Grid on Acetate Sheet, 4" × 5 1/2", Pkg/5	1	1-1 (Lab)	C	Thread, White 200 yd Spool	1	3-1 (DIS)
				C	Toothpicks, Flat Box/750	1	1-1 (Lab) 2-4 (TT)
SS	Marker, Black, Permanent	5	3-5 (DIS)				
SS	Paper, Sheet	45	1-1 (Lab) 1-3 (TT) 2-1 (TT) 2-2 (DIS) 2-2 (TT) 2-3 (DIS) 2-3 (TT) 2-4 (DIS) 3-2 (Lab) 3-4 (DIS)	SS	Yeast	5	2-6 (DIS)

KEY: **DIS**: Discover; **SYS**: Sharpen Your Skills; **TT**: Try This; **Lab**: Lab

Quantities based on 5 lab groups per class.

* Items designated **C** are in the Consumable Kit, **NC** are in the Nonconsumable Kit, and **SS** are School Supplied.

Master Materials List

Nonconsumable Materials

*	Description	Quantity per class	Textbook Section(s)	*	Description	Quantity per class	Textbook Section(s)
NC	Ball, Styrene 1/2"	50	3-1 (DIS)	SS	Protractor, 6" Plastic, 180 degrees	5	1-1 (Lab)
NC	Ball, Styrene 3" Diameter	5	1-1 (Lab)	SS	Quarter	5	1-2 (DIS) 2-4 (DIS)
NC	Ball, Styrofoam 4" Diameter	5	1-2 (Lab)	SS	Ruler, Plastic 12"/30 cm	5	1-2 (SYS) 2-1 (TT) 2-2 (Lab) 2-3 (DIS) 2-4 (DIS) 2-5 (DIS) 3-2 (Lab)
SS	Books	25	1-1 (Lab)				
NC	Bowl, Opaque, 2 Liters, 6 1/4" Dia. × 4 1/4" High	5	1-4 (DIS) 2-6 (DIS)				
SS	Compass with Pencil	5	2-3 (DIS) 2-4 (TT)				
SS	Film Canister	5	1-3 (TT)	SS	Scissors	5	1-3 (TT) 2-2 (DIS) 2-2 (TT) 2-4 (TT) 2-5 (DIS) 3-1 (DIS)
NC	Flashlight, Plastic (Size D)	10	1-1 (Lab) 3-2 (TT)				
NC	Flashlight, Plastic Economy (Size C)	5	3-2 (TT)				
NC	Lens, Plastic Eyepiece	5	3-1 (Lab)				
NC	Lens, Plastic Objective	5	3-1 (Lab)	NC	Sinker, Lead 1 oz	10	2-1 (DIS)
NC	Light Socket, Porcelain w/Cord, 600 Watt Capacity	1	1-1 (DIS) 1-2 (Lab) 3-2 (Lab)	NC	Stopper, Rubber Size 3, 1-Hole	5	2-4 (Lab)
				NC	Truck, Toy, Pick-Up (Pull-back Action)	5	2-1 (DIS)
NC	Marble, Large 1"	5	1-4 (DIS)	NC	Tube, Clear Plastic 3/8" × 8", .012 wall	5	2-4 (Lab)
NC	Marbles, 5/8" Pkg/20	1	1-4 (DIS)				
NC	Marbles, 9/16" Pkg/6	1	1-4 (DIS)	NC	Tubes, Cardboard (for Telescope)(set of 2 sizes)	5	3-1 (Lab)
NC	Meter Stick, Hardwood, 1/2, plain	5	1-4 (DIS) 2-4 (Lab) 3-1 (Lab) 3-2 (Lab)	SS	Umbrella	5	3-1 (TT)
				NC	Washer, Metal 1 1/2" OD, Zinc Plated	15	2-4 (Lab)
SS	Penny	5	1-2 (DIS)				
NC	Pins, Pushpins, Red Pkg/100	1	2-1 (TT)				

KEY: **DIS**: Discover; **SYS**: Sharpen Your Skills; **TT**: Try This; **Lab**: Lab
* Items designated **C** are in the Consumable Kit, **NC** are in the Nonconsumable Kit, and **SS** are School Supplied.

Equipment

*	Description	Quantity per class	Textbook Section(s)
SS	Binoculars	5	2-2 (DIS) 2-2 (TT)
SS	Calculator	5	3-2 (Lab)
SS	Fan	1	2-5 (DIS)
SS	Globe, Political	5	1-1 (DIS)
SS	Goggles, Chemical Splash-Class Set	1	1-3 (TT) 1-4 (DIS) 2-3 (TT) 2-4 (Lab)
SS	Radio, Pocket	5	3-1 (TT)
SS	Ring Stand with Clamp	5	2-2 (DIS) 2-2 (TT)
SS	Stopwatch	5	2-4 (Lab)

KEY: **DIS**: Discover; **SYS**: Sharpen Your Skills; **TT**: Try This; **Lab**: Lab
* Items designated **C** are in the Consumable Kit, **NC** are in the
Nonconsumable Kit, and **SS** are School Supplied.

PRENTICE HALL
SCIENCE EXPLORER

Astronomy

Book-Specific Resources

Student Edition
Annotated Teacher's Edition
Teaching Resources with Color Transparencies
Consumable and Nonconsumable Materials Kits
Guided Reading Audio CDs
Guided Reading Audiotapes
Guided Reading and Study Workbook
Guided Reading and Study Workbook, Teacher's Edition
Lab Activity Videotapes
Science Explorer Videotapes
Science Explorer Web Site at **www.phschool.com**

Program-Wide Resources

Computer Test Bank Book with CD-ROM
How to Assess Student Work
How to Manage Instruction in the Block
Inquiry Skills Activity Book
Integrated Science Laboratory Manual
Integrated Science Laboratory Manual, Teacher's Edition
Interactive Student Tutorial CD-ROM
Prentice Hall Interdisciplinary Explorations
Probeware Lab Manual
Product Testing Activities by Consumer Reports™
Program Planning Guide
Reading in the Content Area with Literature Connections
Resource Pro® CD-ROM (Teaching Resources on CD-ROM)
Science Explorer Videodiscs
Standardized Test Preparation Book
Student-Centered Science Activity Books
Teacher's ELL Handbook: Strategies for English Language Learners

Spanish Resources

Spanish Student Edition
Spanish Guided Reading Audio CDs with Section Summaries
Spanish Guided Reading Audiotapes with Section Summaries
Spanish Science Explorer Videotapes

Science Explorer Student Editions

From Bacteria to Plants

Animals

Cells and Heredity

Human Biology and Health

Environmental Science

Inside Earth

Earth's Changing Surface

Earth's Waters

Weather and Climate

Astronomy

Chemical Building Blocks

Chemical Interactions

Motion, Forces, and Energy

Electricity and Magnetism

Sound and Light

Acknowledgments

Activity on page 37 is from *Exploring Planets in the Classroom*. Copyright by Hawaii Space Grant Consortium, based on a concept developed by Dale Olive. Essay on page 129 by Valerie Ambroise. Copyright ©1995 by The Planetary Society.

ISBN 0-13-054088-9
2 3 4 5 6 7 8 9 10   04 03 02 01

Cover: This photo of Saturn and three of its moons is a montage of images taken by NASA's *Voyager 1*.

Teacher's Edition ISBN 0-13-054089-7

Michael J. Padilla, Ph.D.
Professor
Department of Science Education
University of Georgia
Athens, Georgia

Michael Padilla is a leader in middle school science education. He has served as an editor and elected officer for the National Science Teachers Association. He has been principal investigator of several National Science Foundation and Eisenhower grants and served as a writer of the National Science Education Standards.

As lead author of *Science Explorer*, Mike has inspired the team in developing a program that meets the needs of middle grades students, promotes science inquiry, and is aligned with the National Science Education Standards.

Ioannis Miaoulis, Ph.D.
Dean of Engineering
College of Engineering
Tufts University
Medford, Massachusetts

Martha Cyr, Ph.D.
Director, Engineering
    Educational Outreach
College of Engineering
Tufts University
Medford, Massachusetts

Science Explorer was created in collaboration with the College of Engineering at Tufts University. Tufts has an extensive engineering outreach program that uses engineering design and construction to excite and motivate students and teachers in science and technology education.

Faculty from Tufts University participated in the development of *Science Explorer* chapter projects, reviewed the student books for content accuracy, and helped coordinate field testing.

Book Author

Jay M. Pasachoff, Ph.D.
Professor of Astronomy
Williams College
Williamstown, Massachusetts

Contributing Writers

W. Russell Blake, Ph.D.
Planetarium Director
Plymouth Community Intermediate School
Plymouth, Massachusetts

Thomas R. Wellnitz
Science Teacher
The Paideia School
Atlanta, Georgia

Reading Consultant

Bonnie B. Armbruster, Ph.D.
Department of Curriculum
    and Instruction
University of Illinois
Champaign, Illinois

Interdisciplinary Consultant

Heidi Hayes Jacobs, Ed.D.
Teacher's College
Columbia University
New York, New York

Safety Consultants

W. H. Breazeale, Ph.D.
Department of Chemistry
College of Charleston
Charleston, South Carolina

Ruth Hathaway, Ph.D.
Hathaway Consulting
Cape Girardeau, Missouri

Tufts University Program Reviewers

Behrouz Abedian, Ph.D.
Department of Mechanical
    Engineering

Wayne Chudyk, Ph.D.
Department of Civil and
    Environmental Engineering

Eliana De Bernardez-Clark, Ph.D.
Department of Chemical Engineering

Anne Marie Desmarais, Ph.D.
Department of Civil and
    Environmental Engineering

David L. Kaplan, Ph.D.
Department of Chemical Engineering

Paul Kelley, Ph.D.
Department of Electro-Optics

George S. Mumford, Ph.D.
Professor of Astronomy, Emeritus

Jan A. Pechenik, Ph.D.
Department of Biology

Livia Racz, Ph.D.
Department of Mechanical Engineering

Robert Rifkin, M.D.
School of Medicine

Jack Ridge, Ph.D.
Department of Geology

Chris Swan, Ph.D.
Department of Civil and
    Environmental Engineering

Peter Y. Wong, Ph.D.
Department of Mechanical Engineering

Content Reviewers

Jack W. Beal, Ph.D.
Department of Physics
Fairfield University
Fairfield, Connecticut

W. Russell Blake, Ph.D.
Planetarium Director
Plymouth Community
    Intermediate School
Plymouth, Massachusetts

Howard E. Buhse, Jr., Ph.D.
Department of Biological Sciences
University of Illinois
Chicago, Illinois

Dawn Smith Burgess, Ph.D.
Department of Geophysics
Stanford University
Stanford, California

A. Malcolm Campbell, Ph.D.
Assistant Professor
Davidson College
Davidson, North Carolina

Elizabeth A. De Stasio, Ph.D.
Associate Professor of Biology
Lawrence University
Appleton, Wisconsin

John M. Fowler, Ph.D.
Former Director of Special Projects
National Science Teacher's Association
Arlington, Virginia

Jonathan Gitlin, M.D.
School of Medicine
Washington University
St. Louis, Missouri

Dawn Graff-Haight, Ph.D., CHES
Department of Health, Human
    Performance, and Athletics
Linfield College
McMinnville, Oregon

Deborah L. Gumucio, Ph.D.
Associate Professor
Department of Anatomy and Cell Biology
University of Michigan
Ann Arbor, Michigan

William S. Harwood, Ph.D.
Dean of University Division and Associate
    Professor of Education
Indiana University
Bloomington, Indiana

Cyndy Henzel, Ph.D.
Department of Geography
    and Regional Development
University of Arizona
Tucson, Arizona

Greg Hutton
Science and Health
    Curriculum Coordinator
School Board of Sarasota County
Sarasota, Florida

Susan K. Jacobson, Ph.D.
Department of Wildlife Ecology
    and Conservation
University of Florida
Gainesville, Florida

Judy Jernstedt, Ph.D.
Department of Agronomy and Range Science
University of California, Davis
Davis, California

John L. Kermond, Ph.D.
Office of Global Programs
National Oceanographic and
    Atmospheric Administration
Silver Spring, Maryland

David E. LaHart, Ph.D.
Institute of Science and Public Affairs
Florida State University
Tallahassee, Florida

Joe Leverich, Ph.D.
Department of Biology
St. Louis University
St. Louis, Missouri

Dennis K. Lieu, Ph.D.
Department of Mechanical Engineering
University of California
Berkeley, California

Cynthia J. Moore, Ph.D.
Science Outreach Coordinator
Washington University
St. Louis, Missouri

Joseph M. Moran, Ph.D.
Department of Earth Science
University of Wisconsin–Green Bay
Green Bay, Wisconsin

Joseph Stukey, Ph.D.
Department of Biology
Hope College
Holland, Michigan

Seetha Subramanian
Lexington Community College
University of Kentucky
Lexington, Kentucky

Carl L. Thurman, Ph.D.
Department of Biology
University of Northern Iowa
Cedar Falls, Iowa

Edward D. Walton, Ph.D.
Department of Chemistry
California State Polytechnic University
Pomona, California

Robert S. Young, Ph.D.
Department of Geosciences and
    Natural Resource Management
Western Carolina University
Cullowhee, North Carolina

Edward J. Zalisko, Ph.D.
Department of Biology
Blackburn College
Carlinville, Illinois

Teacher Reviewers

Stephanie Anderson
Sierra Vista Junior
    High School
Canyon Country, California

John W. Anson
Mesa Intermediate School
Palmdale, California

Pamela Arline
Lake Taylor Middle School
Norfolk, Virginia

Lynn Beason
College Station Jr. High School
College Station, Texas

Richard Bothmer
Hollis School District
Hollis, New Hampshire

Jeffrey C. Callister
Newburgh Free Academy
Newburgh, New York

Judy D'Albert
Harvard Day School
Corona Del Mar, California

Betty Scott Dean
Guilford County Schools
McLeansville, North Carolina

Sarah C. Duff
Baltimore City Public Schools
Baltimore, Maryland

Melody Law Ewey
Holmes Junior High School
Davis, California

Sherry L. Fisher
Lake Zurich Middle
    School North
Lake Zurich, Illinois

Melissa Gibbons
Fort Worth ISD
Fort Worth, Texas

Debra J. Goodding
Kraemer Middle School
Placentia, California

Jack Grande
Weber Middle School
Port Washington, New York

Steve Hills
Riverside Middle School
Grand Rapids, Michigan

Carol Ann Lionello
Kraemer Middle School
Placentia, California

Jaime A. Morales
Henry T. Gage Middle School
Huntington Park, California

Patsy Partin
Cameron Middle School
Nashville, Tennessee

Deedra H. Robinson
Newport News Public Schools
Newport News, Virginia

Bonnie Scott
Clack Middle School
Abilene, Texas

Charles M. Sears
Belzer Middle School
Indianapolis, Indiana

Barbara M. Strange
Ferndale Middle School
High Point, North Carolina

Jackie Louise Ulfig
Ford Middle School
Allen, Texas

Kathy Usina
Belzer Middle School
Indianapolis, Indiana

Heidi M. von Oetinger
L'Anse Creuse Public School
Harrison Township, Michigan

Pam Watson
Hill Country Middle School
Austin, Texas

Activity Field Testers

Nicki Bibbo
Russell Street School
Littleton, Massachusetts

Connie Boone
Fletcher Middle School
Jacksonville Beach, Florida

Rose-Marie Botting
Broward County
    School District
Fort Lauderdale, Florida

Colleen Campos
Laredo Middle School
Aurora, Colorado

Elizabeth Chait
W. L. Chenery Middle School
Belmont, Massachusetts

Holly Estes
Hale Middle School
Stow, Massachusetts

Laura Hapgood
Plymouth Community
    Intermediate School
Plymouth, Massachusetts

Sandra M. Harris
Winman Junior High School
Warwick, Rhode Island

Jason Ho
Walter Reed Middle School
Los Angeles, California

Joanne Jackson
Winman Junior High School
Warwick, Rhode Island

Mary F. Lavin
Plymouth Community
    Intermediate School
Plymouth, Massachusetts

James MacNeil, Ph.D.
Concord Public Schools
Concord, Massachusetts

Lauren Magruder
St. Michael's Country
    Day School
Newport, Rhode Island

Jeanne Maurand
Glen Urquhart School
Beverly Farms, Massachusetts

Warren Phillips
Plymouth Community
    Intermediate School
Plymouth, Massachusetts

Carol Pirtle
Hale Middle School
Stow, Massachusetts

Kathleen M. Poe
Kirby-Smith Middle School
Jacksonville, Florida

Cynthia B. Pope
Ruffner Middle School
Norfolk, Virginia

Anne Scammell
Geneva Middle School
Geneva, New York

Karen Riley Sievers
Callanan Middle School
Des Moines, Iowa

David M. Smith
Howard A. Eyer Middle School
Macungie, Pennsylvania

Derek Strohschneider
Plymouth Community
    Intermediate School
Plymouth, Massachusetts

Sallie Teames
Rosemont Middle School
Fort Worth, Texas

Gene Vitale
Parkland Middle School
McHenry, Illinois

Zenovia Young
Meyer Levin Junior
    High School (IS 285)
Brooklyn, New York

Contents

Astronomy

Prepare your students with rich, motivating content

Science Explorer is crafted for today's middle grades student, with accessible content and in-depth coverage. **Integrated Science Sections** support every chapter and the **Interdisciplinary Exploration** provides an engaging final unit.

Check your compass — regularly assess student progress.

Self-assessment tools are built right into the student text and **ongoing assessment** is woven throughout the Teacher's Edition. You'll find a wealth of **assessment technology** in the Resource Pro®, Interactive Student Tutorial, and Assessment Resources CD-ROMs.

Activities

Guide your students to become science explorers.

A wide range of student-tested activities, from guided to open-ended, with options for short- and long-term inquiry.

Draw upon the world around you.

Interdisciplinary Activities connect to every discipline and give science a meaningful, real-world context.

Searching for the Home of Comets

Focus on Astronomy

This four-page feature introduces the process of scientific inquiry by involving students in a high-interest, magazine-like feature about a working scientist, astronomer Jane Luu. Using Dr. Luu's investigation of the source of comets, the feature focuses on persistence, patience, and reasoning as key elements of scientific inquiry.

Comets are presented in Chapter 2 of this book. However, students need not have any previous knowledge of that chapter's content to understand and appreciate this feature.

Scientific Inquiry

◆ Before students read the feature let them read the title, examine the pictures, and read the captions on their own. Then ask: **What questions came into your mind as you looked at these pictures?** *(Students might suggest questions such as "Do comets come from a single place?" "What is astronomy?" "Why are there observatories in Hawaii?" and "What does it mean for Pluto to be on a different plane?")* Point out to students that just as they had questions about what they were seeing, scientists too have questions about what they observe.

Searching for the home of COMETS

Iᵗ's a long way from astronomer Jane Luu's office in the Netherlands to the mountaintop in Hawaii where she searches the night sky. But astronomers need dark skies, far from city lights. They also need clean, clear air to see deep into the solar system. That's why Jane Luu travels all the way to the high mountain observatory in Hawaii. Jane Luu has traveled long distances before. Born in Vietnam, she came to the United States at the age of 12.

"As a kid in Vietnam," she says, "I didn't have a single class in science. But after studying physics in college, I got a job at the Jet Propulsion Laboratory, the place where they track all the unmanned space missions. It was a summer job, pretty unimportant stuff. But when I saw the pictures taken by *Voyager I* and *Voyager II* in the mid-1980s, I thought they were spectacular. Those pictures of the planets were what made me go to graduate school in planetary astronomy."

Object in the Kuiper Belt

Dr. Jane Luu arrived in the United States from Vietnam as a young girl. Dr. Luu studied physics at Stanford University in California and astronomy at the Massachusetts Institute of Technology. She now works at Leiden University in the Netherlands.

8 ◆ J

Background

Astronomy is the study of all natural objects in space. These bodies range from comets and meteors, to planets and moons, to stars, galaxies and interstellar matter.

Within astronomy, scientists specialize in areas such as astrometry (the study of the positions and motions of objects such as stars and planets), celestial mechanics (the mathematical study of the motions of objects in space) and cosmology (the study of the development of the universe as a whole).

TALKING WITH DR. JANE LUU

What Jane Luu looks at now lies just beyond the farthest planets in our solar system. It's a ring made of millions of ice-rock pieces that circle the sun. Luu and her co-worker David Jewitt first discovered these objects in 1992. The rocky planet Pluto is the biggest object in this ring—called the Kuiper (KY pur) Belt. Pluto travels through space along with an estimated 30,000 other objects that Luu and Jewitt have named "Plutinos" (little Plutos). Objects in the Kuiper Belt sometimes escape from the belt and approach the sun. The sun's heat then makes them light up and become comets.

Q *Why did you start searching for the Kuiper Belt?*

A There were two reasons. We wanted to know if there was anything beyond Neptune besides Pluto. Why should that space be empty when there were so many planets and smaller objects nearer the sun? Scientists had predicted there would be a group of comets not too far beyond Neptune, but no one had seen these objects. There were other people trying to find the same thing, so it was a bit of a race. We're glad we won it.

Q *Where did you start looking?*

A Most things in the solar system are in a plane, a basically flat disk where the planets and the sun are. So you start looking there. Then, you want to look opposite the sun. Also, you look at a time of the year when the Milky Way, our home galaxy, isn't in the part of the sky you're

These color-enhanced images of Jupiter (above), Saturn (right), and Neptune (below) were taken from a *Voyager* spacecraft.

searching. That's so the light of all those stars doesn't make it hard to see.

Q *Once you knew where to look, what did you do?*

A We took pictures. We started in 1987 and saw the first object in 1992, five years later. In the beginning we didn't have a computer at the telescope that was fast enough to analyze the pictures. So we'd make three pictures and then take them home to analyze. We'd take images, say a half-hour apart, of the same piece of sky. Then we'd look to see if any point of light had moved

- Explain that astronomers are scientists who study objects in the universe such as stars, planets, comets, asteroids, and galaxies.
- Encourage students to tell what they already know about comets. Ask students who have seen a comet to describe how it appeared. Ask students what they know about Halley's Comet or other famous comets.
- If a student knows the difference between meteors and comets, ask the student to explain the difference to the class.
- If students have access to the Internet, they can find images of comets at **www.nasa.gov**.
- Ask: **Why is an observatory at the top of a mountain in Hawaii?** *(The sky is dark and the air is clean and clear.)* **Why is the sky dark?** *(There are no city lights nearby.)* Challenge interested students to find out the remote locations of some other observatories.
- If students seem particularly interested in the Kuiper Belt, share the information in Background below. Also suggest that they consult library books to learn more about comets. (See Further Reading, page 11.)

Background

Drs. Luu and Jewitt found the first Kuiper Belt object in August 1992, and the second in March 1993. By May 1996, 32 objects had been found by Luu, Jewitt, and other scientists. These objects are all outside Neptune's orbit. They travel in a similar plane. They have diameters ranging from 100 kilometers to 400 kilometers.

About half the objects that scientists have found so far revolve around the sun in the same amount of time that Pluto takes to revolve around the sun. Luu and Jewitt estimate that there are several thousand such objects in the Kuiper Belt.

- Using volunteers, demonstrate what it means for Pluto to be on a different plane from the other planets. Clear a large space in the classroom or take the students to a hall or field. Have one student hold a basketball or other large ball at waist-height to represent the sun. Have other students walk around this student holding tennis balls or other small balls at waist-height. Arrange students so they are in concentric circles of different radii around the "sun." Explain that the smaller balls represent planets. Point out that the sun and the planets are on one plane. Now take a different ball and walk around the "sun" while moving the ball above and below the plane of the other balls. Lead students to recognize that the plane of Pluto lies on an angle to the plane of the other planets.
- Ask: **What are the objects that Dr. Luu found in the Kuiper Belt?** (*pieces of ice-rock*)
- **What do you think it means for telescope time to be valuable?** (*Students' answers will vary. Sample: Many astronomers want to use the telescope for different projects so each astronomer is given a limited amount of time.*)
- Ask students if they have ever lived at or visited high altitudes. Invite a volunteer to explain what happens to your body when you visit a high altitude and why Dr. Luu would need an extra night to adjust to the altitude. Ask: **What does it mean for the air to be thin?** (*The air is less dense and therefore there is less oxygen to breathe.*)
- Challenge interested students to find out more about comets and the people who discovered them. Invite students to share their findings with the class.

These observatories are located on top of Mauna Kea, an inactive volcano in Hawaii.

between the three pictures. If it moves, we know it's near us in the solar system, and not a distant star. Since our first discovery in 1992, scientists have found about 60 objects in the Kuiper Belt. David and I have found about two thirds of those.

Q *Do you stay up all night?*

A Yes, we have to. Telescope time is valuable so you don't want to waste a single minute. We observe for a week or so, staying up for 5 or 6 nights in a row. It's hard work, switching from a daytime to a nighttime schedule. In Hawaii, we observe on top of Mauna Kea volcano at 14,000 feet. So we have to add an extra night at the beginning to get used to the altitude and thin air.

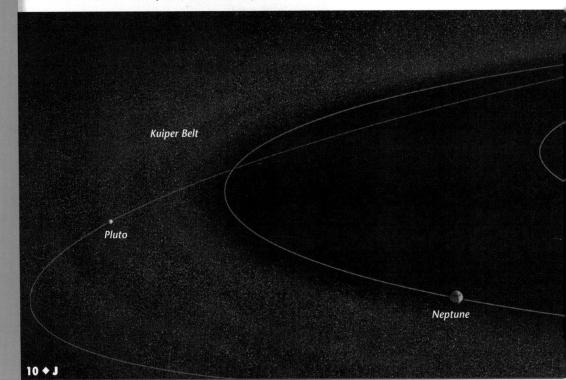

The Kuiper Belt lies beyond the part of the solar system where the planets revolve around the sun. Objects in the Kuiper Belt revolve far from Earth and the sun. Pluto's orbit is on a different plane from the other planets.

10 ◆ J

Background

In 1951, an astronomer named Gerard Kuiper theorized that the solar system contained numerous small objects revolving around the sun at or beyond Pluto's orbit. Kuiper believed that these objects would be made of material similar to comets, frozen water mixed with other frozen gases.

For years, many scientists did not take Kuiper's theory seriously. They instead believed that comets entered the solar system from interstellar space. In 1988, however, scientists used computer simulations to show that it was unlikely that comets originated from far beyond our solar system.

Even before the results of the computer simulation were published, Drs. Luu and Jewitt decided to explore whether there were objects in the solar system beyond Pluto and Neptune. Their discoveries supported Kuiper's theory.

Q *Five years is a long time to wait for a discovery. Didn't you get discouraged?*

A We told ourselves that after we'd covered a certain part of the sky without finding anything, we would stop. We were pretty near that limit. But the newer cameras could take bigger pictures of the sky. They helped us do in a month what at first had taken two years. We could see something and know right away where to look the next night.

Because I've been lucky, I've participated in discoveries. There's such a satisfaction you get when you solve a puzzle, when you find out something that nobody has known before. And it's really fun after a lot of hard work, when you've finally found what you wanted to find.

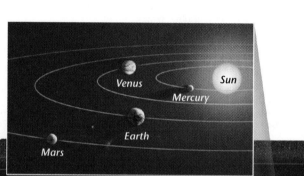

In Your Journal

Jane Luu describes working night after night for five years, observing and recording data for one part of the night sky. "It was so time-consuming, and we didn't know if anything was going to come from it." Fortunately, in the end, she was rewarded. How did Jane Luu's persistence, as well as her skill, energy, and step-by-step reasoning, lead to her success?

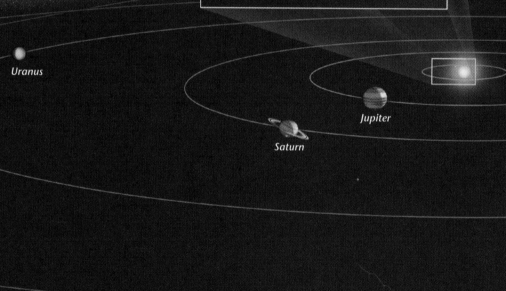

J ◆ 11

In Your Journal To help students appreciate Dr. Luu's persistence, have students recall where they were five years ago. Have students imagine that they began working on a project five years ago and worked on it every night since. Ask: **What would motivate you to keep working on your project night after night for so long?** *(Student answers will vary. Sample: the satisfaction of being the first to discover something)* Extend the discussion by asking: **What kind of person do you think would make a good astronomer?** *(Student answers will vary. Samples: patient, determined, persistent, detail-oriented)*

Introducing Astronomy

Have students look through the table of contents and the book to find the parts that relate most closely to this article. *(Chapter 2, The Solar System, particularly Section 2-5, Comets, Asteroids, and Meteors, and Chapter 3, Stars, Galaxies, Section 3-1, Tools of Modern Astronomy. There is a feature on the history of telescopes on pages 98 and 99, a lab on making a telescope on page 101, and a feature on light pollution on page 102.)* Ask: **Besides comets, what else is this book about?** *(Many other kinds of objects in the universe)* **What kinds of things do you think you will be learning about?** *(Accept all responses without comments.)*

READING STRATEGIES

Further Reading

◆ Marsh, Carole and Arthur R. Upgrenl. *Asteroids, Comets, and Meteors.* Twenty First Century Books, 1996.
◆ Sagan, Carl and Ann Druyan. *Comet.* Ballantine Books, 1997.

...

Earth, Moon, and Sun

Sections	Time	Student Edition Activities	Other Activities	
CHAPTER PROJECT 1 **Where's the Moon?** p. J13	Ongoing (2 weeks)	Check Your Progress, pp. J21, J34, J44 Project Wrap Up, p. J47	TE	Chapter 1 Project Notes, pp. J12–13
1 Earth in Space pp. J14–23 ◆ 1.1.1 Identify the effects of Earth's rotation and revolution. ◆ 1.1.2 Explain what causes the seasons.	5 periods/ $2\frac{1}{2}$ blocks	**Discover** Why Does Earth Have Day and Night?, p. J14 **Sharpen Your Skills** Calculating, p. J15 **Skills Lab: Observing** Reasons For the Seasons, pp. J22–23	TE TE TE ISLM	Building Inquiry Skills: Comparing and Contrasting, p. J18 Demonstrations, pp. J16, J19 Inquiry Challenge, p. J20 Lab J-1, "Constructing a Foucalt Pendulum"
2 Phases, Eclipses, and Tides pp. J24–34 ◆ 1.2.1 Explain what causes the phases of the moon. ◆ 1.2.2 Compare the causes of solar and lunar eclipses. ◆ 1.2.3 Explain what causes the tides.	5 periods/ $2\frac{1}{2}$ blocks	**Discover** How Does the Moon Move?, p. J24 **Sharpen Your Skills** Making Models, p. J28 **Skills Lab: Making Models** A "Moonth" of Phases, pp. J30–31	TE TE	Inquiry Challenges, pp. J26, J33 Building Inquiry Skills: Making Models, p. J32; Predicting, p. J32
3 **INTEGRATING TECHNOLOGY** **Rockets and Satellites** pp. J35–38 ◆ 1.3.1 Explain how rockets travel in space. ◆ 1.3.2 List the uses of satellites, space stations, and the Space Shuttle.	2 periods/ 1 block	**Discover** How Do Rockets Work?, p. J35 **Try This** Be a Rocket Scientist, p. J37	TE TE	Demonstration, p. J36 Inquiry Challenge, p. J37
4 Earth's Moon pp. J39–44 ◆ 1.4.1 Describe features of the moon's surface. ◆ 1.4.2 Explain what scientists learned about the moon from space exploration. ◆ 1.4.3 Describe the origin and structure of the moon.	3 periods/ 1–2 blocks	**Discover** Why Do Craters Look Different From Each Other?, p. J39 **Sharpen Your Skills** Calculating, p. J43	TE	Building Inquiry Skills: Interpreting Data, p. J40
Study Guide/Assessment pp. J45–47	1 period/ $\frac{1}{2}$ block		ISAB	Provides teaching and review of all inquiry skills

For Standard or Block Schedule The Resource Pro® CD-ROM gives you maximum flexibility for planning your instruction for any type of schedule. Resource Pro® contains Planning Express®, an advanced scheduling program, as well as the entire contents of the Teaching Resources and the Computer Test Bank.

Key: **SE** Student Edition
PLM Probeware Lab Manual
ISAB Inquiry Skills Activity Book

CHAPTER PLANNING GUIDE

Program Resources	Assessment Strategies	Media and Technology
TR Chapter 1 Project Teacher Notes, pp. J6–7 TR Chapter 1 Project Overview and Worksheets, pp. J8–11	TE Check Your Progress, pp. J21, J34, J44 TE Performance Assessment: Chapter 1 Project Wrap Up, p. J47 TR Chapter 1 Project Scoring Rubric, p. J12	Science Explorer Internet Site Audio CDs and Audiotapes, English-Spanish Section Summaries
TR 1-1 Lesson Plan, p. J13 TR 1-1 Section Summary, p. J14 TR 1-1 Review and Reinforce, p. J15 TR 1-1 Enrich, p. J16 TR Skills Lab blackline masters, pp. J29–31 SES Book A, *From Bacteria to Plants,* Chapter 5 SES Book B, *Animals,* Chapter 5	SE Section 1 Review, p. J21 SE Analyze and Conclude, p. J23 TE Ongoing Assessment, pp. J15, J17, J19 TE Performance Assessment, p. J21	Exploring Earth Science Videodisc, Unit 1 Side 1, "For the Love of Astronomy" Lab Activity Videotape, *Astronomy,* 1 Transparency 1, "Exploring the Seasons"
TR 1-2 Lesson Plan, p. J17 TR 1-2 Section Summary, p. J18 TR 1-2 Review and Reinforce, p. J19 TR 1-2 Enrich, p. J20 TR Skills Lab blackline masters, pp. J32–33 SES Book M, *Motion, Forces, and Energy,* Chapter 3 SES Book E, *Environmental Science,* Chapter 5 SES Book H, *Earth's Waters,* Chapter 4	SE Section 2 Review, p. J34 SE Analyze and Conclude, p. J31 TE Ongoing Assessment, pp. J25, J27, J29, J33 TE Performance Assessment, p. J34	Lab Activity Videotape, *Astronomy,* 2 Transparencies 2, "Exploring Phases of the Moon"; 3, "Solar Eclipse"; 4, "Lunar Eclipse"; 5, "High and Low Tides"
TR 1-3 Lesson Plan, p. J21 TR 1-3 Section Summary, p. J22 TR 1-3 Review and Reinforce, p. J23 TR 1-3 Enrich, p. J24 SES Book E, *Environmental Science,* Chapter 2	SE Section 3 Review, p. J38 TE Ongoing Assessment, p. J37 TE Performance Assessment, p. J38	Exploring Physical Science Videodisc, Unit 5 Side 1, "The Cray Computer" Exploring Physical Science Videodisc, Unit 5 Side 1, "Then and Now"
TR 1-4 Lesson Plan, p. J25 TR 1-4 Section Summary, p. J26 TR 1-4 Review and Reinforce, p. J27 TR 1-4 Enrich, p. J28	SE Section 4 Review, p. J44 TE Ongoing Assessment, pp. J41, J43 TE Performance Assessment, p. J44	Transparency 6, "Collision Theory of the Moon's Origin"
GSW Provides worksheets to promote student comprehension of content RCA Provides strategies to improve science reading skills ELL Provides multiple strategies for English language learners	SE Study Guide/Assessment, pp. J45–47 TR Performance Assessment, pp. J114–116 TR Chapter 1 Test, pp. J117–120 CTB *Astronomy,* Chapter 1 Test STP Provides standardized test practice	Computer Test Bank, *Astronomy,* Chapter 1 Test Interactive Student Tutorial CD-ROM, J-1

TE Teacher's Edition
RCA Reading in the Content Area
GSW Guided Study Workbook

TR Teaching Resources
ISLM Integrated Science Laboratory Manual
ELL Teacher's ELL Handbook

CTB Computer Test Bank
STP Standardized Test Preparation Book
SES Science Explorer Series Text

Meeting the National Science Education Standards and AAAS Benchmarks

National Science Education Standards	Benchmarks for Science Literacy	Unifying Themes
Science as Inquiry (Content Standard A) ◆ **Communicate scientific procedures and explanations** Students present their observations of the moon using words, charts, and drawings. *(Chapter Project)* ◆ **Identify questions that can be answered through scientific investigations** Students observe the moon and look for patterns in its motions and changing appearance. *(Chapter Project)* **Earth and Space Science** (Content Standard D) ◆ **Earth in the solar system** Earth has day and night and the moon has phases because of relative motions of Earth and the moon in the Solar System. *(Sections 1, 2, and 4)* ◆ **Earth's history** Cratering on the moon and the composition of moon rocks adds to our knowledge of the history of the formation of Earth. *(Section 4)* **Science and Technology** (Content Standard E) ◆ **Abilities of technological design** The space program includes many examples of both the successes and limitations of technology. *(Section 3)*	**3A Technology and Science** The space program includes many examples of both the successes and limitations of technology. *(Section 3)* **3B Design and Systems** Spacecraft are complex systems of many parts that must work together. *(Section 3)* **4B The Earth** Earth has day and night and the moon has phases because of relative motions of Earth and the moon in the Solar System. Cratering on the moon and the composition of moon rocks adds to our knowledge of the history of the formation of Earth. *(Sections 1, 2, and 4)* **4C Processes That Shape the Earth** Cratering on the moon and the composition of moon rocks adds to our knowledge of the history of the formation of Earth. *(Sections 1, 2, and 4)* **4F Motion** Newton's laws govern the motion of rockets and satellites as well as the motion of Earth and the moon. *(Section 3)* **8D Communication** Geostationary satellites and other communications satellites have made global communication possible. *(Section 3)* **11C Constancy and Change** Cratering on the moon, and the composition of moon and Earth rocks tell us that Earth and the moon have undergone dramatic changes in their history. *(Section 4)*	◆ **Energy** Energy constraints limit the design of rockets and force the use of multistage rockets to achieve orbital speeds. *(Section 3)* ◆ **Evolution** Cratering on the moon, and the composition of moon and Earth rocks tell us that Earth and the moon have undergone dramatic changes in their history. *(Section 4)* ◆ **Patterns of Change** Earth has day and night and the moon has phases because of relative motions of Earth and the moon in the Solar System. The seasons on Earth are caused by the revolution of Earth and the tilt of Earth's axis. Tides are caused by relative motions of Earth and the Moon *(Sections 1 and 2)* ◆ **Scale and Structure** The moon has one-fourth the radius and one-eightieth the mass of Earth. *(Section 4)* ◆ **Unity and Diversity** The composition of rocks on the moon is similar to the composition of rocks on Earth. But the moon has no air and no liquid water. *(Section 4)* ◆ **Stability** Earth has two high tides and two low tides every day, due to the moon's gravitational pull. The moon's period of rotation and its period of revolution are the same, so it always keeps the same face toward Earth. *(Section 2)*

Take It to the Net

 *Interactive text at www.phschool.com*

Science Explorer comes alive with iText.

- **Complete student text** is accessible from any computer with a browser.

- **Animations, simulations, and videos** enhance student understanding and retention of concepts.

- **Self-tests and online study tools** assess student understanding.

- **Teacher management tools** help you make the most of this valuable resource.

STAY CURRENT with

Find out the latest research and information about astronomy at:
www.phschool.com

Go to **www.phschool.com** and click on the Science icon.
Then click on Science Explorer under PH@school.

ACTIVITY	Time (minutes)	Materials *Quantities for one work group*	Skills
Section 1			
Discover, p. 14	15	**Nonconsumable** lamp, light bulb, globe	Making Models
Sharpen your Skills, p. 15	10	**Consumable** paper **Nonconsumable** pencil, calculator	Calculating
Skills Lab, pp. 22–23	40	**Consumable** paper **Nonconsumable** books, pencil, acetate sheet with thick grid lines drawn on it, plastic foam ball marked with poles and equator, flashlight, protractor, toothpick	Observing
Section 2			
Discover, p. 24	10	**Nonconsumable** quarters, pennies	Inferring
Sharpen your Skills, p. 28	15	**Consumable** paper **Nonconsumable** rulers, calculators	Making Models
Skills Lab, pp. 30–31	40	**Nonconsumable** floor lamp with 150-watt bulb, pencils, plastic foam balls	Making Models
Section 3			
Discover, p. 35	10	**Nonconsumable** balloons, safety goggles	Observing
Try This, p. 37	20	**Consumable** plastic or paper cup, paper, tape, film canister with a lid that snaps on inside the canister, water, fizzing antacid tablet **Nonconsumable** safety goggles	Observing
Section 4			
Discover, p. 39	20	**Nonconsumable** plastic mixing bowl about 25 cm across, sand, 3 marbles of different masses, meter stick	Developing Hypotheses
Sharpen your Skills, p. 43	10	**Consumable** No special materials are required.	Calculating

A list of all materials required for the Student Edition activities can be found beginning on page T15. You can obtain information about ordering materials by calling 1-800-848-9500 or by accessing the Science Explorer Internet site at: **www.phschool.com**

Where's the Moon?

Students have probably seen the moon in different phases, and at various times of day, throughout their lives without giving any thought to the patterns of the moon's light and motions. They may not realize that the moon's phases are a predictable cycle based on the positions of the sun, moon, and Earth.

Purpose In this project, students will make daily observations of the moon and will keep track of the moon's appearance and position in the sky. After collecting this information, students will analyze the data and look for patterns.

Skills Focus Students will be able to
◆ observe the phases of the moon;
◆ measure the direction and altitude of the moon in the sky;
◆ interpret data to explain why the moon has phases;
◆ predict when and where one would expect to see the moon based on rules developed from interpreting the data.

Project Time Line This project requires at least one month to observe all of the phases of the moon. Ideally, the project will last long enough for students to see the moon cycle begin to repeat itself. If cloudy weather makes observations difficult, you may wish to extend the observation time.

Suggested Shortcuts If the time available is less than one month, starting near a new moon should give usable results in about two to three weeks. The moon is most visible in the early evening sky between the new moon and the full moon. Before beginning the project, see Chapter 1 Project Teacher Notes on pages 8–9 in Teaching Resources for more details on carrying out the project.

Possible Materials This project requires few materials. A sample observation sheet is included in the resource materials. Students can determine directions using the eight major compass directions: N, NE, E, SE, S, SW, W, NW. If students do not have a compass, tell them to borrow one and use it to record certain landmarks around their house in each of the eight directions. They can then use these landmarks to orient themselves.

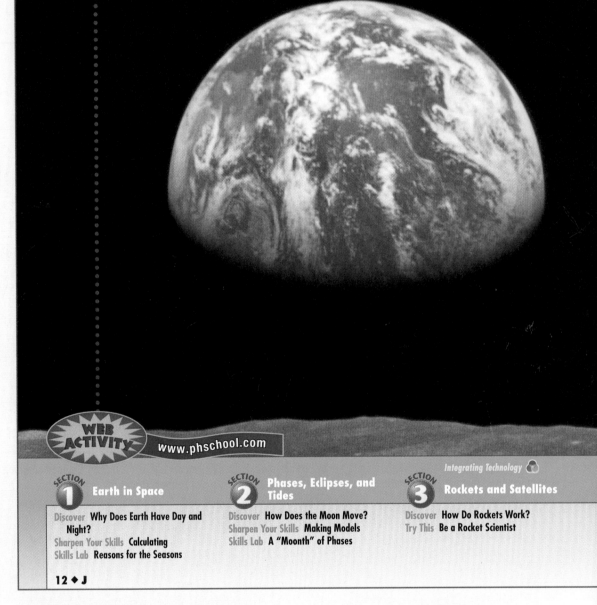

CHAPTER 1
Earth, Moon, and Sun

WEB ACTIVITY www.phschool.com

Integrating Technology

SECTION 1 Earth in Space

Discover Why Does Earth Have Day and Night?
Sharpen Your Skills Calculating
Skills Lab Reasons for the Seasons

SECTION 2 Phases, Eclipses, and Tides

Discover How Does the Moon Move?
Sharpen Your Skills Making Models
Skills Lab A "Moonth" of Phases

SECTION 3 Rockets and Satellites

Discover How Do Rockets Work?
Try This Be a Rocket Scientist

12 ◆ J

Launching the Project Ask: **When is it possible to see the moon?** If students respond that the moon is only visible at night, ask: **On a clear evening, can you always see the moon in the sky?** *(no)* **Can you ever see the moon during the day?** *(yes)* Encourage students to discuss whether they have seen a relationship between the phase of the moon, such as full or quarter, and how high it is in the sky at a particular time of night, such as 8 P.M. *(Most students will not have noticed a relationship.)*

Tell students that in this project they will investigate this relationship.

Emphasize the importance of recording data at least three times per day. Explain that it is easier to monitor movement of the moon by noting its position several times a day rather than just once. To help students get started, pass out copies of the Chapter 1 Project Worksheets on page 10–11 in Teaching Resources. You may wish to share the Chapter 1 Project Scoring Rubric with your students at this time.

Where's the Moon?

What a view! Though you would have to be in orbit around the moon to see this kind of Earthrise, you don't have to travel at all to see the moonrise from Earth. All you have to do is look in the right direction at the right time and you will see the moon rise in front of you!

In this chapter, you will explore relationships among Earth, the moon, and the sun. In your project, you will observe the position of the moon in the sky every day. These observations will show you the changing positions of Earth and the moon with respect to each other and to the sun.

Your Goal To observe the shape of the moon and its position in the sky every day for one month.

To complete the project you will
- observe and record every day the compass direction in which you see the moon and its height above the horizon
- use your observations to explain the phases of the moon
- develop rules you can use to predict where and when you might see the moon each day throughout a month

Get Started Begin by preparing an observation log. You will want to record the date and time of each observation, the direction and height of the moon, a sketch of its shape, and notes about the cloud cover or other conditions. You can also keep track of the time of moonrise each day.

Check Your Progress You'll be working on this project as you study this chapter. To keep your project on track, look for Check Your Progress boxes at the following points.

Section 1 Review, page 21: Make a map to help you determine the direction of the moon.
Section 2 Review, page 34: Observe the moon every day.
Section 4 Review, page 44: Look for patterns in your observations.

Wrap Up At the end of the chapter (page 47), you will present your observations of the moon using words, drawings, and graphs.

This amazing Earthrise above the moon's horizon was seen by astronaut Michael Collins in the *Apollo 11* moon orbiter *Columbia.*

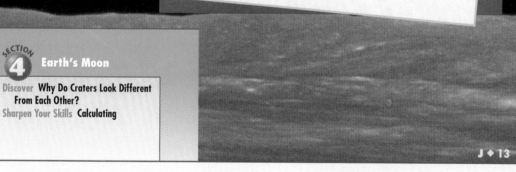

SECTION
4 **Earth's Moon**

Discover Why Do Craters Look Different From Each Other?
Sharpen Your Skills Calculating

J ◆ 13

Program Resources

- **Teaching Resources** Chapter 1 Project Teacher's Notes, pp. 6–7; Project Overview and Worksheets, pp. 8–11; Project Scoring Rubric, p. 12

Media and Technology

Audio CDs and **Audiotapes**
English-Spanish Section Summaries

WEB ACTIVITY   www.phschool.com

You will find an Internet activity, chapter self-tests for students, and links to other chapter topics at this site.

Performance Assessment

Use the Chapter 1 Project Scoring Rubric to assess students' work. Students will be assessed on
- the quality and consistency of their daily record keeping;
- the quality of their graphs and drawings and their analysis of the data;
- their ability to find patterns in the data and use these to make predictions;
- the level of their understanding as demonstrated in the presentation of their conclusions or their participation in discussion.

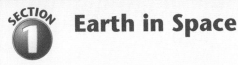

SECTION 1 Earth in Space

Objectives

After completing the lesson, students will be able to
◆ identify the effects of Earth's rotation and revolution;
◆ explain what causes the seasons.

Key Terms astronomy, axis, rotation, revolution, orbit, latitude, solstice, equinox, vernal equinox, autumnal equinox

1 Engage/Explore

Activating Prior Knowledge

Ask students to estimate what time the sun rises in the morning and sets at night. Then, have them consult a daily newspaper to check their estimates. Next, ask students to describe how the number of hours of daylight each day change during the winter and summer. *(Students should note that there are fewer hours of daylight each day in winter than in summer.)*

DISCOVER

Skills Focus making models

ACTIVITY

Materials *lamp, light bulb, globe*
Time 15 minutes
Tips Place the bulb at a height approximately level with the globe's equator. Alternatively, use flashlights and have students work in pairs. One student can hold the flashlight steady while the other turns the globe.
Expected Outcome The half of the globe facing the bulb will be lit and will move into shadow as the globe rotates.
Think It Over A complete spin of the globe represents one rotation of Earth on its axis, which equals one day. In the model, one day is 5 seconds. To model a year, students can carry the spinning globe in a circle around the bulb.

SECTION 1 Earth in Space

DISCOVER ●●●●●●●●●●●●●●●●●●●●●●●● **ACTIVITY**

Why Does Earth Have Day and Night?

1. Place a lamp with a bare bulb in the middle of a table to represent the sun. Put a globe at the end of the table about 1 meter away to represent Earth.

2. Turn the lamp on and darken the room. Which parts of the globe have light shining on them? Which parts are in shadow?

3. Find your location on the globe. Take about 5 seconds to turn the globe once. Notice when it is lit—day—at your location and when it is dark—night.

Think It Over
Making Models How does one complete turn of the globe represent one day? In this model, how many seconds represent one day? How could you use the model to represent a year?

GUIDE FOR READING

◆ What causes day and night?

◆ What causes the cycle of seasons on Earth?

Reading Tip Before you read, preview the figures and captions in the section. List any terms that are not familiar to you. Then write their definitions as you read about them.

Ancient Egyptian farmers eagerly awaited the annual spring flood of the Nile River. For thousands of years, their planting was ruled by it. As soon as the Nile's floodwaters withdrew, the farmers had to be ready to plow and plant their fields along the banks of the river. Because of this, the Egyptians wanted to predict when the flood would occur. Around 3000 B.C., people noticed that the bright star Sirius first became visible in the early morning sky every year shortly before the flood began. The Egyptians used this knowledge to predict each year's flood.

Egyptian farmers ▶

READING STRATEGIES

Reading Tip As students preview each figure and caption, suggest they ask themselves questions such as these:
◆ What is being shown in this picture?
◆ What is the main idea of the picture?
◆ What new information did I learn from the caption?

Vocabulary Point out that the term *revolution* has several meanings in addition to its scientific meaning. Provide student groups with dictionaries. Have them look up the meanings of *revolution*. Then direct each group to work together to write three original sentences that illustrate three different meanings of *revolution*.

Study and Comprehension Have students paraphrase the section that explains the cycle of seasons on Earth.

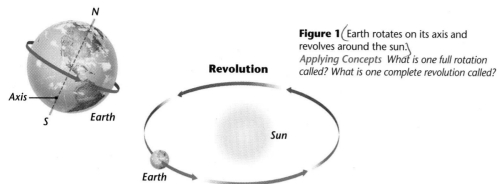

Rotation

N

Axis

S   Earth

Revolution

Earth

Sun

Figure 1 Earth rotates on its axis and revolves around the sun.
Applying Concepts What is one full rotation called? What is one complete revolution called?

Days and Years

The ancient Egyptians were among the first people to study the stars. The study of the moon, stars and other objects in space is called **astronomy.**

Ancient astronomers also studied the movements of the sun and the moon as they appeared to travel across the sky. It seemed to them as though Earth were standing still and the sun and moon were moving. Actually, the sun and moon seem to move across the sky each day mainly because Earth is rotating on its axis.

Rotation The imaginary line that passes through Earth's center and the North and South poles is called Earth's **axis.** The north end of the axis currently points toward a point in space near Polaris, the North Star. Earth's spinning on its axis is called its **rotation.** A point on the equator rotates at about 1,600 kilometers per hour. Even most commercial jet planes can't fly this fast!

Earth's rotation on its axis causes day and night. As Earth rotates eastward, the sun appears to move westward across the sky. It is day on the side of Earth facing the sun. As Earth continues to turn to the east, the sun appears to set in the west. Sunlight can't reach the side of Earth facing away from the sun, so it is night there. It takes Earth about 24 hours to rotate once on its axis. As you know, each 24-hour cycle of day and night is called a day.

Revolution In addition to rotating on its axis, Earth travels around the sun. The movement of one object around another object is called **revolution.** One complete revolution around the sun is called a year. Earth's path as it revolves around the sun is called its **orbit.** As it travels around the sun, Earth's orbit is not quite a circle. It is a slightly flattened circle, or oval shape.

☑ *Checkpoint* Why do the sun and moon seem to move each day?

Sharpen your Skills

Calculating ACTIVITY

Earth moves at a speed of about 30 km/sec as it travels around the sun. What distance, in kilometers, does Earth travel in a minute? An hour? A day? A year?

Chapter 1 **J ◆ 15**

Days and Years

Sharpen your Skills

Skills Focus calculating
Materials *paper, pencil, calculator*
Time 10 minutes
Tips Suggest students set up the problems on paper to make sure units cancel out.
Expected Outcome In 1 min, 1,800 km; in 1 h, 108,000 km; in 1 day, 2,592,000 km; in 1 yr, 946,728,000 km
Extend Students can calculate the distance Earth travels in a decade or century. **learning modality: logical/mathematical**

Program Resources

◆ **Teaching Resources** 1-1 Lesson Plan, p. 13; 1-1 Section Summary, p. 14
◆ **Guided Study Workbook** Section 1-1

Answers to Self-Assessment

Caption Question
Figure 1 One full rotation is a called a day. One complete revolution is called a year.

☑ *Checkpoint*
The sun and moon seem to move each day mainly because Earth is rotating on its axis.

Ongoing Assessment

Writing Ask students to write short paragraphs describing either the Earth's rotation or the Earth's revolution around the sun.

Days and Years, continued

Demonstration

Materials *turntable such as a lazy Susan, string, weight, ring stand, tape*

Time 15 minutes

Tips Tell students that in 1851 a French physicist named Jean Foucault used a pendulum to prove that Earth rotates. To model his pendulum, hang a small weight from the arm of a ring stand. Swing the pendulum and ask students to describe what happens. *(The weight swings back and forth in one plane.)* Place the pendulum in the center of the turntable. Mark one side of the turntable with a piece of tape. Swing the pendulum and turn the turntable slowly. Challenge students to explain how this models a pendulum at the North Pole and to explain how an experiment could prove that Earth rotates. *(The turntable is like Earth rotating around its axis. The tape mark represents a place on Earth. If a pendulum were swinging above the North Pole, the direction of its swing would appear to make one complete rotation in 24 hours.)* **learning modality: visual**

Real-Life Learning

Materials *old set of Yellow Pages separated into sections*

Time 10 minutes

Many professions or cultures require people to live by a calendar that is determined by seasonal events other than the movements of stars or planets. Assign students to small groups and have each group examine a portion of the Yellow Pages to identify occupations whose work is primarily seasonal. *(Samples: lifeguards, ski instructors, landscapers, and snow plow operators.)* **learning modality: verbal**

Calendars The Egyptian astronomers counted the number of days between each first appearance of the star Sirius. In this way, they found that there were about 365 days in each year. By dividing the year into 365 days, the ancient Egyptians had created one of the first calendars.

People of many different cultures have struggled to come up with workable calendars. Earth's orbit around the sun takes slightly more than 365 days—actually about $365\frac{1}{4}$ days. Four years of about $365\frac{1}{4}$ days each can be approximated by taking 3 years of 365 days and a fourth year of 366 days. You know this fourth year as a "leap year." During a leap year, an extra day is

SCIENCE & History

Tracking the Cycle of the Year

For thousands of years, people have used observations of the sky to keep track of the time of year.

1500 B.C.
British Isles

Ancient peoples complete Stonehenge, a monument with giant stones that mark the directions in which the sun rises and sets on the longest day of the year.

| 1500 B.C. | 900 B.C. | 300 B.C. |

1300 B.C.
China

During the Shang dynasty, Chinese astronomers made detailed observations of the sun, planets, and other objects they saw in the night sky. Chinese astronomers calculated that the length of a year is 365.25 days.

300 B.C.
Egypt

Astronomers in Alexandria, Egypt, learned to use an instrument called an astrolabe. Astrolabes were used to find the positions of stars and planets.

16 ◆ J

Background

Facts and Figures Stonehenge was built over three main periods. The first period began about 3100 B.C., and included the digging of the circular ditch and a ring of 56 pits. During the second period, about 2100 B.C., huge pillars of rock were erected in concentric circles around the center of the site. The 35-ton heel stone may have been placed during this building period. The placement of this stone was one of the most sophisticated accomplishments of the time. On the morning of the summer solstice, a person standing in the center of the circle can see the sun rising directly over this stone. During the third period, the monument was remodeled, and a circle of 30 upright stones, each weighing up to 50 tons was erected. The final phase ended around 1500 B.C.

added to February, giving it 29 days instead of its usual 28.

Dividing the year into smaller parts was difficult also. Early people used moon cycles as a sort of calendar. The time between one full moon and the next one is about $29\frac{1}{2}$ days. A year of 12 of these "moonths" only adds up to 354 days. The ancient Egyptians worked out a calendar that had 12 months of 30 days each, with an extra 5 days that were not part of any month. The Romans borrowed this calendar and made changes to it. With more changes, it eventually became the calendar we know: 11 months having 30 or 31 days each, plus one month (February) having 28 or 29 days.

Wyoming

A.D. 1450
Wyoming

The Big Horn Medicine Wheel was built by Native Americans. Individual stones are aligned with the rising and setting sun and several bright stars. The rising of these specific stars may have indicated to people when it was time to move south for the winter.

A.D. 300   **A.D. 900**   **A.D. 1500**

A.D. 900
Mexico

The Mayas studied the movement of the sun, the moon, and the planet Venus. They had two different calendars, one with 365 days for everyday use and the other with 260 days for religious uses. These calendars combined to make a 52-year cycle. The Mayas were able to predict astronomical events 3,000 years into the future.

Chapter 1   **J ◆ 17**

Encourage students to discuss how the peoples in the time line used their astronomical observations. Tell students that anything used to keep track of days, months, and year and the events that occur at those times can be a calendar. Challenge students to think about how the physical structures shown could serve as calendars. *(The giant stones at Stonehenge marked sunrise and sunset on the longest day of the year. The Big Horn Medicine Wheel marked the rising and setting of the sun and other stars.)*

In Your Journal Students should be able to research the accomplishments described in the time line in the library or on the Internet. Suggest they also look in magazines such as *Astronomy, Discover, National Geographic,* and *Natural History.* After they write their dialogues, students can perform them and record them using video or tape recorders. **learning modality: verbal**

Portfolio Students can save their recordings in their portfolios.

Ongoing Assessment

Writing Have students write brief paragraphs to explain why it was difficult for ancient peoples to come up with workable calendars. *(It was difficult to reconcile all the events—Earth's orbit around the sun takes $365\frac{1}{4}$ days, and it takes $29\frac{1}{2}$ days from one full moon to the next.)*

Using the Visuals: Figure 2

On Figure 2, guide students to compare the area of Earth's surface covered by the sun's rays at the equator and the surface covered by the same amount of light at the poles. (*At the poles, it is much larger.*) Ask students to infer how this affects the climates at those places. (*The sunlight is more spread out at the poles so it is colder. The sunlight is more concentrated at the equator, so it is warmer.*) **learning modality: visual**

Building Inquiry Skills: Comparing and Contrasting

To help students who are still mastering English understand the difference between sunlight at the equator and the poles, give small groups of students flashlights and large sheets of graph paper. Students can shine a flashlight directly above the paper and trace around the lighted area. Then they can shine the flashlight at an angle and trace around the lighted area. Guide students to determine which area represents sunlight at the equator and at the poles. (*The larger area represents the poles.*) Then ask: **Does each square receive more energy when the light shines directly or at an angle?** (*directly*) **limited English proficiency**

Math TOOLBOX

Time 20 minutes

Tips Redraw the diagram on the board so the two angles can be discussed separately. Indicate the angle of 23.5°. Explain that this is the tilt of Earth's axis. Now, erase that angle and indicate the angle of 90°. Ask: **What fraction of the circle is the angle between the sun and the horizon?** (*90° angle = one fourth of circle*) **learning modality: logical/ mathematical**

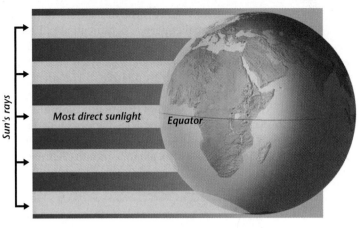

Figure 2 It is warm near the equator because sunlight hits Earth's surface directly and is less spread out. *Interpreting Diagrams Why is it colder near the poles?*

Sun's rays

Most direct sunlight

Equator

Math TOOLBOX

Angles

An angle is formed when two lines meet at a point. Angles are measured in degrees (symbol °). A full circle has 360 degrees.

23.5° from vertical

90°   90°

180°   0°

270°

Earth's axis is tilted at an angle of 23.5° from the vertical. When the sun is directly overhead at noon near the equator, its angle from the horizon is 90°. What fraction of a circle is this?

18 ◆ J

(Seasons on Earth)

Most places outside the tropics have four distinct seasons: winter, spring, summer, and autumn. But there are great differences in temperature from place to place. For instance, it is warmer near the equator than near the poles. Why is this so?

How Sunlight Hits Earth Figure 2 shows how sunlight hits Earth's surface. Notice that at the equator, sunlight hits Earth's surface directly. Closer to the poles, sunlight hits Earth's surface at an angle. Near the poles, energy from the sun is spread out over a greater area. That is why it is warmer near the equator than near the poles.

Earth's Tilted Axis If Earth's axis were straight up and down relative to the sun, as it appears in Figure 2, temperatures would remain fairly constant year-round. There would be no seasons. (Earth has seasons because its axis is tilted as it moves around the sun.)

Look at Earth's position in space in *Exploring the Seasons* on the next page. Notice that Earth's axis is tilted at an angle of 23.5° from the vertical. As Earth revolves around the sun, its axis is tilted away from the sun for part of the year and toward the sun for part of the year.

When the north end of Earth's axis is tilted toward the sun, the Northern Hemisphere has summer. At the same time, the south end of Earth's axis is tilted away from the sun. As a result, the Southern Hemisphere has winter.

Summer and winter are not affected by changes in Earth's distance from the sun. In fact, when the Northern Hemisphere is having summer, Earth is actually at its greatest distance from the sun.

Background

History of Science Early peoples such as the Sumerians of Babylon used the phases of the moon to make a calendar, counting 12 lunar months a year. The Egyptians later worked out a calendar that corresponded almost exactly to the seasons. The early Romans also used a calendar that was based on the moon. Their calendar had 355 days. An extra month was added about every fourth year. These calendars were regulated by the high priests.

However, this calendar was not very accurate. As a result, by Julius Caesar's time, the summer months were coming in springtime. Early calendars such as the Julian calendar also allowed for corrections in time. For example, the correction of one day every four years caused the calendar year to be longer than the year as measured by the seasons. As a result, the vernal equinox in 1582 occurred on March 11, instead of on March 21.

EXPLORING the Seasons

The yearly cycle of the seasons is caused by the tilt of Earth's axis as it revolves around the sun.

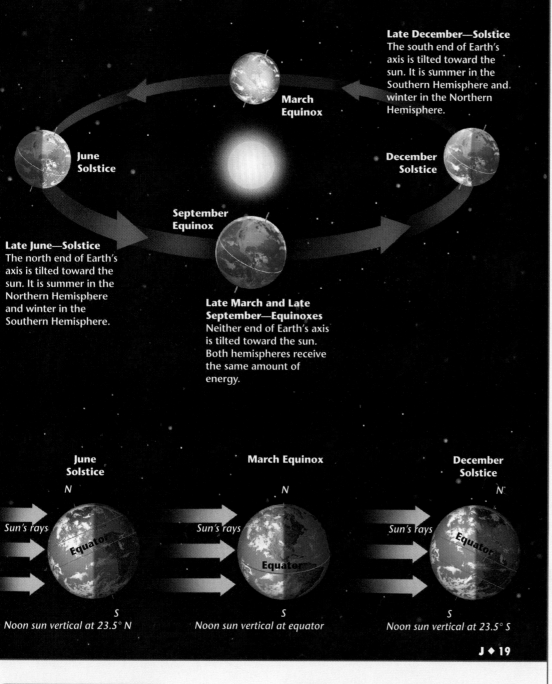

Late December—Solstice
The south end of Earth's axis is tilted toward the sun. It is summer in the Southern Hemisphere and winter in the Northern Hemisphere.

March Equinox

December Solstice

June Solstice

September Equinox

Late June—Solstice
The north end of Earth's axis is tilted toward the sun. It is summer in the Northern Hemisphere and winter in the Southern Hemisphere.

Late March and Late September—Equinoxes
Neither end of Earth's axis is tilted toward the sun. Both hemispheres receive the same amount of energy.

June Solstice
N
Sun's rays
Equator
S
Noon sun vertical at 23.5° N

March Equinox
N
Sun's rays
Equator
S
Noon sun vertical at equator

December Solstice
N
Sun's rays
Equator
S
Noon sun vertical at 23.5° S

J ◆ 19

Point out the lines showing Earth's axis and ask students what they notice about them. *(They are all tilted.)* Ask students whether the tilt is different at different points in Earth's revolution. *(The tilt is the same.)* Direct students' attention to the figure in the lower left. Ask them to list two things that cause it to be summer in the Northern Hemisphere. *(In June, the sun shines more directly on the surface. The sun is above the horizon for a longer period each day.)* Now have them look at the lower right. Ask them to list two things that cause it to be winter in the northern hemisphere. *(In December, the sun shines less directly on the surface. The sun is above the horizon for a shorter period each day.)*
learning modality: visual

Demonstration

To show students how the tilt of the Earth's axis affects the seasons, place a lamp with a bare bulb on a desk. Tilt a globe so that the Northern Hemisphere is tilted toward the lamp (sun). This represents Earth's position at the June solstice. Walk around the lamp in a circle but keep the tilt the same relative to the room, not the lamp. As you walk, stop every 90° to represent Earth's position at the equinoxes and the winter solstice. Turn the globe so the United States is facing the sun. At each position, ask students to describe the conditions in the United States. *(Sample: In December, the United States is tilted away from the sun so it is cooler.)*
learning modality: visual

Program Resources

 Science Explorer Series *From Bacteria to Plants,* Chapter 5

Media and Technology

Transparencies "Exploring the Seasons," Transparency 1

Answers to Self-Assessment

Caption Question

Figure 2 It is colder near the poles because the sunlight hits Earth at an angle and the sun's rays are spread out over a larger area.

Ongoing Assessment

Writing Have students describe the seasons in your area, when they normally occur, and why spring and fall often have similar conditions. Students can save their descriptions in their portfolios.

Inquiry Challenge

Time 30 minutes

Materials *lamp with bare bulb, plastic foam ball, modeling clay, thin wooden dowel rod*

Tips Challenge small groups of students to make models to test this hypothesis: *If Earth were not tilted, the length of the days would not change.* Once groups set up their models, turn off the lights in the room so they can demonstrate them. *(Place the lamp in the center of a desk. Insert a dowel through the center of each ball and stick each dowel into a lump of clay. Make sure the dowel is vertical. Then turn on the lamp and move the model to several positions. around the lamp. At each position, rotate the ball and observe the light and shadow on the ball. Groups should conclude that the ball is always illuminated the same, with the line between light and shadow going through each pole.)* **cooperative learning**

Addressing Naive Conceptions

Some students may think that the days seem longer in summer because of daylight-savings time. Point out that the total number of daylight hours in the Northern Hemisphere actually is greater in summer. Daylight savings time simply moves the starting time for work and school earlier in the day, so more day-light hours are available after work or school. **learning modality: verbal**

Integrating Life Science

Encourage students to think about how the change in the length of days affects humans. *(Sample: In winter, people go to bed earlier and stay inside more.)* Brainstorm a list of animals or events that are unique to each season. **learning modality: verbal**

Earth in June In June, the north end of Earth's axis is tilted toward the sun. The noon sun is directly overhead at 23.5° north latitude. **Latitude** is a measurement of distance from the equator, expressed in degrees north or south. (The equator has latitude 0° and the North Pole has latitude 90° north.)

The hemisphere that is tilted toward the sun also has more hours of daylight than the hemisphere that is tilted away from the sun. The combination of direct rays and more hours of sunlight heats the surface more than at any other time of the year. It is summer in the Northern Hemisphere.

At the same time, for any place on Earth south of the equator, the sun's energy is spread over a large area. There are also fewer hours of daylight. The combination of indirect rays and fewer hours of sunlight heats Earth's surface less than at any other time of the year. It is winter in the Southern Hemisphere.

Earth in December Look again at *Exploring the Seasons.* Around December 21, the noon sun is overhead at 23.5° south latitude. People in the Southern Hemisphere receive the most direct sunlight, so it is summer there. At the same time, the sun's rays in the Northern Hemisphere are indirect and there are fewer hours of daylight. So it is winter in the Northern Hemisphere.

Both June and December On two days each year, the noon sun is overhead at either 23.5° south or 23.5° north. Each of these days is known as a **solstice** (SAHL stis). The day when the noon sun is overhead at 23.5° south is the winter solstice in the Northern Hemisphere. It is the summer solstice in the Southern Hemisphere. This solstice occurs around December 21 each year, and is the shortest day of the year in the Northern Hemisphere. At

Figure 3 Spring is the season between the vernal equinox and the summer solstice. The warming temperatures of spring make it the best time to plant flowers like these pansies.

Background

History of Science Before calendars, some early peoples may have kept records of passing time by etching notches on sticks, or by tying knots in cords for every passing day. People also observed the changing habits of animals. A Greek epic poem from around 700 B.C. explains that people knew it was time to stop digging in their vineyards when they saw snails climb up plants. On an island near Taiwan, the Yami fisherman still use animal behavior to help them determine the seasons with their lunar-based calendar. Sometime around the month of March, the fishermen light flares and go out in their boats to look for flying fish. If the fish appear, it is time for fishing season to begin. If they do not appear, the Yami know that it is time to insert an extra month to correct their calendar. Fishing season begins the following month, and that year has 13 months instead of 12.

the same time, it is close to the longest day of the year in the Southern Hemisphere.

Similarly, around June 21, the noon sun is overhead at 23.5° north. This is the summer solstice in the Northern Hemisphere and the winter solstice in the Southern Hemisphere.

Earth in March and September Halfway between the solstices, neither hemisphere is tilted toward or away from the sun. This situation only occurs on two days of the year. On these days, the noon sun is directly overhead at the equator.

Each of these days is known as an **equinox,** which means "equal night." During an equinox, the lengths of nighttime and daytime are about the same. The **vernal equinox,** or spring equinox, occurs around March 21, and marks the beginning of spring in the Northern Hemisphere. The **autumnal equinox** occurs around September 23. It marks the beginning of fall in the Northern Hemisphere.

INTEGRATING LIFE SCIENCE In much of the United States, seasonal changes affect living things. In spring and summer, the sun shines for more hours each day and is higher in the sky. The warmer days allow many plants to begin growing leaves and flowers. Because plants grow more, animals that feed on the plants, from tiny insects to large deer, get more food.

In the fall, the nights get longer, signaling the plants to stop growing and some plants to lose their leaves. With less food available, black bears and some other animals go into a dormant state in which they use very little energy. Others, like many songbirds and waterfowl, travel to warmer climates where food is still available.

Figure 4 This hungry bear has spent the long winter in a dormant state in a cave in Alaska. *Applying Concepts Why didn't this bear remain active all winter?*

Section 1 Review

1. Explain the process that causes day and night.
2. What two factors cause the cycle of the seasons?
3. Compare rotation and revolution.
4. What do the words *solstice* and *equinox* mean? How are they related to the position of Earth's axis?
5. **Thinking Critically Relating Cause and Effect** Are changes in the distance between Earth and the sun important in causing the cycle of the seasons? Explain.

Check Your Progress CHAPTER PROJECT 1
Begin recording your daily observations of the moon. Sketch a map of the site from which you will be making observations. Which way is north? East? South? West? Each night, observe and record the moon's direction. You should also estimate the moon's altitude, or height in degrees from the horizon. You can do this by making a fist and holding it at arm's length. One fist above the horizon is 10°, two fists are 20°, and so on.

---

3 Assess

Section 1 Review Answers

1. Earth rotates on its axis once per day. As Earth rotates, half its surface is facing the sun (day) and half is facing away from the sun (night).
2. The cycle of the seasons is caused by Earth's revolution around the sun and the tilt of Earth's axis.
3. Rotation is turning around a point or an axis; revolution is movement around another object.
4. A solstice is a day when the noon sun is overhead at 23.5° south or 23.5° north. This occurs when one end of Earth's axis is tilted most directly toward the sun. *Equinox* means "equal night," and occurs when neither pole of Earth's axis is tilted toward the sun.
5. The tilt of Earth's axis, not its distance from the sun, is the cause of the cycle of seasons. During the summer months in the Northern Hemisphere, Earth is actually at its farthest point from the sun. During winter in the Northern Hemisphere, Earth is at its closest point to the sun.

Check Your Progress CHAPTER PROJECT 1
Students should be ready to begin making observations of the moon. Remind students to draw maps of their observation sites. You might want to give a brief lesson on map-making skills such as defining coordinate systems and making map keys. Make sure students have developed a method for measuring altitude. Instead of the "fist" method, you may want to have students construct astrolabes to measure the altitude of the moon.

Program Resources

◆ **Teaching Resources** 1-1 Review and Reinforce, p. 15; 1-1 Enrich, p. 16
Science Explorer Series *Animals,* Chapter 5

Answers to Self-Assessment

Caption Question
Figure 4 The amount of available food decreases in the winter season. Bears use less energy when they are dormant.

Performance Assessment

Writing Challenge students to choose a place on the globe they are not familiar with and write descriptions of the amount of sunlight received there throughout the year.

Reasons for the Seasons

Preparing for Inquiry

Key Concept The seasons are determined by the tilt of Earth's axis as Earth revolves around the sun.

Skills Objectives Students will be able to
◆ make an Earth/sun model to observe the effect of the tilt of Earth's axis on the seasons;
◆ measure and calculate light angle and area.

Time 40 minutes

Advance Planning Make sure the flashlights are working properly. Have extra batteries on hand. The room must be dim enough for the light from the flashlights to be seen. One acetate sheet can be cut into six grids.

Alternative Materials Balls with smooth, unmarked surfaces work best.

Guiding Inquiry

Invitation Ask students: **Why is it warmer in the summer?** (*Many students will hold the common misconception that Earth is closer to the sun.*) Tell students that Earth is actually a bit farther from the sun during the Northern hemisphere summer. In this activity, they will relate the tilt of Earth's axis to the seasons.

Introducing the Procedure

◆ Tell students the ball must be close enough to the flashlight so that several grid squares can be seen on the ball.
◆ Make sure students know how to use the protractor to measure the angle of Earth's axis.

Troubleshooting the Experiment

◆ Students may have difficulty maintaining the tilt of the ball at 23.5° as they move the ball. Have the partner measure the angle before recording information on the size and shape of the grid squares.
◆ Tell students to keep the axis of Earth tilted towards the same wall as the ball revolves around the light.

Skills Lab

REASONS FOR THE SEASONS

In this lab, you will use an Earth-sun model to make observations about factors that contribute to the seasons.

Problem

What effect does the tilt of Earth's axis have on the heat and light received by Earth as it revolves around the sun?

Materials (per pair of students)

books　　　flashlight　　　paper
pencil　　　protractor　　　toothpick
acetate sheet with thick grid lines drawn on it
plastic foam ball marked with poles and equator

Procedure

1. Make a pile of books about 15 cm high.
2. Tape the acetate sheet to the head of the flashlight. Place the flashlight on the pile of books.
3. Carefully push a pencil into the South Pole of the plastic foam ball, which represents Earth.
4. Use the protractor to measure a 23.5° tilt of the axis of your Earth away from your "flashlight sun," as shown in the first diagram. This represents winter.
5. Hold the pencil so that Earth is steady at this 23.5° angle and about 15 cm from the flashlight head. Turn the flashlight on. Dim the room lights.
6. The squares on the acetate should show up on your model Earth. Move the ball closer if necessary or dim the room lights more. Observe and record the shape of the squares at the equator and at the poles.

7. Carefully stick the toothpick straight into your model Earth about halfway between the equator and the North Pole. Observe and record the length of the shadow.
8. Without changing the tilt, turn the pencil to rotate the model Earth once on its axis. Observe and record how the shadow of the toothpick changes.
9. Tilt your model Earth 23.5° toward the flashlight, as shown in the second diagram. This is summer. Observe and record the shape of the squares at the equator and at the poles. Observe how the toothpick's shadow changes.
10. Rotate the model Earth and note the shadow pattern.

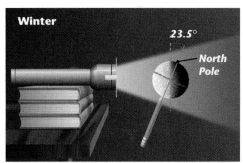

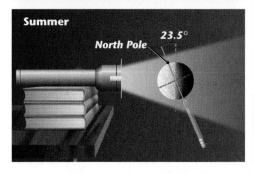

Expected Outcome

◆ The grid squares will be smaller and more square in the region of the ball where the light hits directly.
◆ The grid squares will be larger and more lengthened where the light hits at an angle.

Analyze and Conclude

1. During winter, the area near 23.5° south latitude; in summer, the region near 23.5° north latitude gets the most concentrated light.
2. Light is more concentrated in the middle zone during the summer, and more spread out during the winter.
3. The same amount of heat is spread out over a larger area.
4. The poles are consistently coolest because the energy is the most spread out there. The equator is warmest because the energy is most concentrated there.
5. The shadow will be longest during winter and shortest during summer.
6. As the angle increases, the light and heat become less concentrated and spread out over a

Analyze and Conclude

1. When it is winter in the Northern Hemisphere, which areas on Earth get the most concentrated amount of light? Which areas get the most concentrated light when it is summer in the Northern Hemisphere?

2. Compare your observations of how the light hits the area halfway between the equator and the North Pole during winter (Step 6) and during summer (Step 9).

3. If the squares projected on the ball from the acetate become larger, what can you conclude about the amount of heat distributed in each square?

4. According to your observations, which areas on Earth are consistently coolest? Which areas are consistently warmest? Why?

5. What time of year will the toothpick's shadow be longest? When will the shadow be shortest?

6. How are the amounts of heat and light received in a square related to the angle of the sun's rays?

7. **Think About It** How can you use your observations of an Earth-sun model to explain what causes the seasons?

More to Explore

You can measure how directly light from the sun hits Earth's surface by making a shadow stick. You need a stick or pole about 1 m long. With the help of your teacher, push the stick partway into the ground where it will not be disturbed. Make sure the stick stays vertical. At noon on the first day of every month, measure the length of the stick's shadow. The shorter the shadow, the more directly the sun's rays are hitting Earth. At what time of the year are the shadows longest? Shortest? How do your observations help explain the seasons?

More to Explore Over the course of time, students should notice that the length of the shadow at noon varies. The shadow grows longer and longer until the December solstice, around December 21. Then the shadow grows progressively shorter until the June solstice, on or near June 21. When the shadow is longest, the sun's rays are the most spread out and are the least effective at heating the surface.

larger area. Each square receives a smaller portion of light and heat.

7. **Think About It** During summer in the Northern Hemisphere, the rays hit the Northern Hemisphere directly. The heating effect is greater and the Northern Hemisphere is warmed. During winter the rays hit the Northern Hemisphere at an angle, so the heating effect is less.

Program Resources

◆ **Teaching Resources** Skills Lab blackline masters, pp. 29–31

Media and Technology

Lab Activity Videotape
Astronomy, 1

SECTION 2 — Phases, Eclipses, and Tides

Objectives

After completing the lesson, students will be able to
◆ explain what causes the phases of the moon;
◆ compare the causes of solar and lunar eclipses;
◆ explain what causes the tides.

Key Terms phase, eclipse, solar eclipse, umbra, penumbra, lunar eclipse, tide, gravity, spring tide, neap tide

1 Engage/Explore

Activating Prior Knowledge

Ask students to describe observations they have made of the moon. Encourage students to use descriptive language. Prompt students to recall as many things about the moon as possible by asking questions. For example, ask them if they have ever seen the moon low on the horizon, if it was full when it was low on the horizon, and if the moon is ever up in the daytime. Encourage students to think about their observations as they read this section.

DISCOVER

Skills Focus inferring
Materials *quarters, pennies*
Time 10 minutes
Tips Before students try the activity, have them predict how many times the penny will rotate during its revolution around the quarter.
Expected Outcome The penny makes one complete rotation on its axis as it revolves around the quarter.
Think It Over The moon does not appear to rotate when seen from Earth because the same face is always visible from Earth.

DISCOVER

How Does the Moon Move?

1. Put a quarter flat on your desk to represent Earth. Use a penny flat on your desk to represent the moon.
2. One side of the moon always faces Earth. Move the moon through one revolution around Earth, keeping Lincoln's face always looking at Earth. How many times did the penny make one complete rotation?

Think It Over
Inferring From the point of view of someone on Earth, does the moon seem to rotate? Explain your answer.

GUIDE FOR READING

◆ What causes the phases of the moon?
◆ What causes solar and lunar eclipses?
◆ What causes the tides?

Reading Tip As you read, write a sentence to describe what causes each of the following: phases, solar eclipses, lunar eclipses, tides.

The moon is Earth's closest neighbor in space—much closer than any planet. In fact, the average distance from Earth to the moon is only about 30 times Earth's diameter. Even so, the moon is quite far away. On average, the moon is 384,400 kilometers from Earth. If there were a highway to the moon and you could travel at 100 kilometers per hour, it would take you more than five months to get there.

The moon moves in space just as Earth does. As the moon revolves around Earth and Earth revolves around the sun, the relative positions of the moon, Earth, and sun change. **The positions of the moon, Earth, and the sun cause the phases of the moon, eclipses, and tides.**

Motions of the Moon

The moon revolves around Earth and rotates on its own axis. It takes the moon about 27.3 days to revolve around Earth. Like Earth's orbit around the sun, the moon's orbit around Earth is a flattened circle or oval shape.

The moon rotates slowly on its own axis once every 27.3 days. Because the moon also revolves around Earth every 27.3 days, a "day" and a "year" on the moon are the same length. As you saw if you

◀ Crescent moon over Fire Island, New York

READING STRATEGIES

Reading Tip Suggest students use charts like the one shown to make notes as they read. Then have them use their notes to write the sentences.

Study and Comprehension Have students review the section, then create a Venn Diagram showing the similarities and differences between solar and lunar eclipses.

What causes ___ ?	
Moon phases	
Solar eclipse	
Lunar eclipse	
Tides	

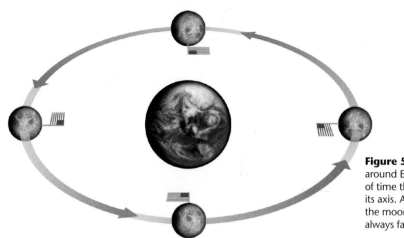

Figure 5 The moon revolves around Earth in the same amount of time the moon takes to rotate on its axis. As a result, the near side of the moon (shown with a flag) always faces Earth.

tried the Discover activity, the same side of the moon, the "near side," always faces Earth. The "far side" of the moon always faces away from Earth, so you never see it from Earth.

✓ Checkpoint How many days does it take the moon to revolve once around Earth?

Phases of the Moon

On a clear night when the moon is full, the bright moonlight can keep you awake. But the moon does not produce the light you see. Instead, it reflects light from the sun. Imagine taking a flashlight into a dark room. If you were to shine the flashlight on a chair, you would see the chair because the light from your flashlight would bounce, or reflect, off the chair. In the same way that the chair wouldn't shine by itself, the moon doesn't give off light by itself. You see the moon because sunlight reflects off it.

When you see the moon in the sky, sometimes it appears round. Other times you see only a thin sliver, or crescent. The different shapes of the moon you see from Earth are called **phases.** The moon goes through its whole set of phases each time it revolves around Earth, that is, about once a month.

What Causes Phases? Phases are caused by changes in the relative positions of the moon, Earth, and the sun. Because the sun lights the moon, half the moon is almost always in sunlight. However, since the moon revolves around Earth, you see the moon from different angles. The half of the moon that faces Earth is not always the half that is sunlit. **The phase of the moon you see depends on how much of the sunlit side of the moon faces Earth.** To understand the changing phases, refer to *Exploring Phases of the Moon* on the next page.

Social Studies CONNECTION

Before there was artificial lighting, the phases of the moon were important in planning activities. For example, the full moon nearest the autumnal equinox is called the harvest moon, and the following full moon is called the hunter's moon.

In Your Journal

Find out about an event that is determined by the phases of the moon, such as the Jewish Passover, the Christian Easter, or the Islamic fast of Ramadan. How is the date of the event calculated?

Program Resources

◆ **Teaching Resources** 1-2 Lesson Plan, p. 17; 1-2 Section Summary, p. 18
◆ **Guided Study Workbook** Section 1-2

Answers to Self-Assessment

✓ Checkpoint

It takes the moon 27.3 days to revolve around Earth.

2 Facilitate

Motions of the Moon

Including All Students

Students who are not visually oriented may need extra help understanding why the flags in Figure 5 indicate that the moon is rotating. Draw a figure similar to Figure 5 on the board. Ask: **Which way would the flags be pointing if the moon was *not* rotating?** If students have difficulty answering, draw flags on the moons to show that if the moon was not rotating, the flag at only one position would point toward Earth. **learning modality: logical/mathematical**

Phases of the Moon

Social Studies CONNECTION

A harvest moon rises at almost the same time for several nights in a row. Like all full moons, it rises at about the same time the sun sets. Ask: **Why do you think this is called the harvest moon?** (*This full moon provides extra light during the early evening hours to help farmers gather their crops.*)

In Your Journal The dates for these holidays are set using lunar references systems, and students may need additional help to calculate their dates. For example, Easter is the first Sunday after the first full moon that occurs on or after March 21. Ramadan begins and ends one month later, when the authorities decree that the twelfth new moon has been sighted by a reliable witness. Passover is from 14 to 22 of the Jewish month Nisan. **learning modality: verbal**

Ongoing Assessment

Oral Presentation Have students describe what causes the phases of the moon.

Phases of the Moon, continued

EXPLORING
Phases of the Moon

Some students may think that the far side of the moon is the same as the dark side of the moon. Explain to students that although the same side of the moon always faces Earth, the moon's position in relation to the sun is not fixed. As the moon revolves around Earth, sunlight shines on the near and far sides of the moon at different times. Point out that the diagram and the photographs are taken from different viewpoints. Direct the student's attention to the pictures of the waxing crescent moon. Ask: **If you had been observing for several days, how could you tell whether the moon was waxing or waning?** *(The waxing moon gets larger over time, while a waning moon gets smaller.)* **Where is the moon in its orbit when it is waxing?** *(On the top half of the diagram)*

Extend Ask students to find the origins of the terms *gibbous* and *waxing.* *(Gibbous is from the Latin gibbosus meaning "humpbacked." Waxing is from Old English weaxan meaning "to grow.")*
learning modality: visual

Inquiry Challenge

Materials *newspapers for the current or previous day, current calendar*
Time 20 minutes
Tips Invite students to predict the number of days between the new moon, first quarter, full moon, and third quarter. Have groups of students use the weather report from the newspaper to find the dates for each phase, then mark the dates and draw the moon phases on their calendars. Students can compare the data with their predictions. Ask questions such as: **How long does it take for the new moon to reach the first quarter?** *(About one week)* **Why do you think this is called a "quarter moon?"** *(One week is about one-quarter of the complete cycle of phases.)* **learning modality: logical/mathematical**

EXPLORING Phases of the Moon

The diagram in the center shows a view of Earth and the moon phases from above. The sun is shining from the right. The outer ring of photos shows the different amounts of the sunlit side of the moon that an observer on Earth sees as the moon revolves around Earth.

First Quarter
You see half of the lighted side of the moon.

Waxing Crescent
You see more and more of the lighted side of the moon. This is called a waxing crescent moon.

Waxing Gibbous
The moon continues to wax. The moon is called gibbous.

New Moon
The sun lights the side of the moon facing away from Earth. The side of the moon that faces Earth is dark.

Full Moon
You see the whole lighted side of the moon.

Waning Gibbous
The fraction of the lighted side of the moon that you see gets smaller each day.

Third Quarter
You can see half of the moon's lighted side.

Waning Crescent
You see a crescent again.

First week, Second week, Third week, Fourth week

26 ◆ J

Background

Facts and Figures Consider these facts about the moon.
- In 1959, the Soviet Luna 3 spacecraft photographed the hidden 41% of the moon. Until then, the far side of the moon had never been seen by anyone on Earth.
- Seen from the moon, Earth also goes through a complete cycle of phases. When an observer on Earth sees a new moon, an observer on the dark side of the moon would see a full Earth shining.
- During the first, or waxing, crescent moon, observers can often see a faint glow from the unlit part of the moon. This is caused by the light from the bright Earth being reflected off the moon.

The Cycle of the Phases During the new moon, the side of the moon facing Earth is not lit. As the moon revolves around Earth, you see more and more of the lighted side of the moon every day, until the side of the moon you see is fully lit. As the moon continues in its orbit, you see less and less of the lighted side of the moon. About 29.5 days after the last new moon, the cycle is complete, and you see a new moon again.

☑ Checkpoint *Since the moon does not produce light, how can you see it?*

Eclipses

What would you think if you were walking home from school on a sunny afternoon and the sun began to disappear? Would you be frightened? On rare occasions, the moon completely blocks the sun. The sky grows as dark as night even in the middle of a clear day. The air gets cool and the sky becomes an eerie color. If you don't know what is happening, you can become very frightened.

The moon doesn't usually go directly between Earth and the sun or directly behind Earth. As Figure 6 shows, the moon's orbit around Earth is slightly tilted with respect to Earth's orbit around the sun. As a result, in most months the moon revolves completely around Earth without the moon moving into Earth's shadow or the moon's shadow hitting Earth.

When the moon's shadow hits Earth or Earth's shadow hits the moon, an eclipse occurs. An <u>eclipse</u> (ih KLIPS) occurs when an object in space comes between the sun and a third object, and casts a shadow on that object. There are two types of eclipses: solar eclipses and lunar eclipses. (The words *solar* and *lunar* come from the Latin words for "sun" and "moon.")

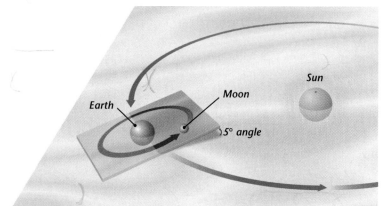

Figure 6 The moon's orbit is tilted with respect to Earth's orbit. So the moon rarely goes directly between Earth and the sun. *Interpreting Diagrams How large is the angle between Earth's orbit and the moon's orbit?*

Program Resources

🔵 **Science Explorer Series** *Motion, Forces, and Energy,* Chapter 3

Media and Technology

📺 **Transparencies** "Exploring Phases of the Moon," Transparency 2

Answers to Self-Assessment

☑ Checkpoint
Light from the sun reflects off the moon, enabling it to be seen from Earth.

Caption Question
Figure 6 The angle between Earth's orbit and that of the moon is about 5°.

Building Inquiry Skills: Comparing and Contrasting

The term *phase* is used in many different ways in science. This can be confusing to students whose native language is not English. Have all students list three ways *phase* is used in science (phases of the moon, phases of matter, color phases in a species of animal or plant) and give the appropriate definition for each one.
limited English proficiency

Eclipses

Using the Visuals: Figure 6

What phase of the moon is shown in the figure? *(Waning crescent)* Point out that around new moon the near side of the moon is the dark side and the far side is lit because the moon is between Earth and the sun. The opposite is true for the full moon. Ask students to explain what phase the moon must be in for a solar eclipse to occur and for a lunar eclipse to occur. **learning modality: visual**

Language Arts Connection

In *A Connecticut Yankee in King Arthur's Court* by Mark Twain, the main character travels back in time to the court of King Arthur. There, his knowledge of eclipses saves him from execution. Have students read the appropriate passage from Chapter 5 of the novel, in which the Yankee remembers the date on which a solar eclipse occurs. Then challenge students to write journal or diary entries about how a lack of scientific explanations might encourage superstitious beliefs. **learning modality: verbal**

Ongoing Assessment

Drawing Have students sketch the position of the moon relative to Earth and the sun at the time of new moon, first quarter, full moon, and third-quarter moon, and write brief explanations for how these phases occur.

Solar Eclipses

Cultural Diversity

Students whose native language is not English may be able to help native speakers understand some of the terms in this section. The words *solar*, *lunar*, *umbra*, and *penumbra* are derived from Latin and have cognates in languages based on Latin, such as Spanish. Ask: **What are the names for the sun and moon in other languages?** (*Sample: Spanish—el sol and la luna*) Tell students that the Latin word *umbra* means "shadow," and *penumbra* means "almost shadow." Ask: **What other words can you think of that might come from these words?** (*Sample: English—umbrella; Spanish—umbroso and umbrio mean "shady," sombra means "shadow."*) **learning modality: verbal**

Sharpen your Skills

Making Models

Materials *paper, metric rulers, calculators*

Time 15 minutes

Tips Guide students to find the other distances in terms of Earth's diameter.

Expected Outcome With Earth as 1 cm in diameter, the moon will be 2.5 mm in diameter, 30 cm away in the opposite corner of the page.

Extend Challenge students to find the distance from Earth to the sun and then estimate the distance where they would place the sun in their scale drawings. (*At about 11,725 cm*) **learning modality: logical/mathematical**

Using the Visuals: Figure 7

Ask students which side of the moon receives the light of the sun during a solar eclipse. (*Far side*) Ask: **Would people in the moon's penumbra experience a total or a partial eclipse?** (*Partial*) **learning modality: visual**

Making Models

Here is how you can draw a scale model of a solar eclipse. The moon's diameter is about one fourth Earth's diameter. The distance from Earth to the moon is about 30 times Earth's diameter. Make a scale drawing of the moon, Earth, and the distance between them. (*Hint:* Draw Earth 1 cm in diameter in one corner of the paper.) From the edges of the moon, draw and shade in a triangle just touching Earth to show the moon's umbra during a solar eclipse.

Solar Eclipses

During a new moon, the moon is almost exactly between Earth and the sun. But most months, as you have seen, the moon travels a little above or below the sun in the sky. A **solar eclipse** occurs when the moon passes between Earth and the sun, blocking the sunlight from reaching Earth. The moon's shadow then hits Earth, as shown in Figure 7. So a solar eclipse is really just a new moon in which the moon blocks your view of the sun.

Total Solar Eclipses The darkest part of the moon's shadow, the **umbra** (UM bruh), is cone-shaped. From any point in the umbra, light from the sun is completely blocked by the moon. The moon's umbra happens to be long enough so that the point of the cone can just reach a small part of Earth's surface. Only the people within the umbra experience a total solar eclipse. During a total solar eclipse, the sky is dark. You can see the stars and the solar corona, which is the faint outer atmosphere of the sun.

Partial Solar Eclipses In Figure 7, you can see that the moon casts another shadow that is less dark than the umbra. In this larger part of the shadow, called the **penumbra** (pih NUM bruh), part of the sun is visible from Earth. During a solar eclipse, people in the penumbra see only a partial eclipse. Since part of the sun remains visible, it is not safe to look directly at the sun during a partial solar eclipse (just as you wouldn't look directly at the sun at any other time).

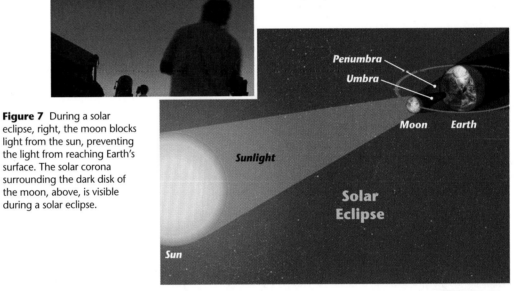

Figure 7 During a solar eclipse, right, the moon blocks light from the sun, preventing the light from reaching Earth's surface. The solar corona surrounding the dark disk of the moon, above, is visible during a solar eclipse.

Penumbra
Umbra
Moon *Earth*
Sunlight
Solar Eclipse
Sun

Background

Facts and Figures Many people have seen total lunar eclipses, but few people have the opportunity to view the total solar eclipses. The reason is that a total lunar eclipse is visible over at least half of Earth. A total solar eclipse can only be seen along a narrow path up to a few hundred miles wide and a few thousand miles long.

Astronomers can accurately predict the dates and times of future eclipses. Because a solar eclipse occurs when the new moon is near the plane of Earth's orbit, a lunar eclipse frequently occurs two weeks before and two weeks after a solar eclipse. Six and a half lunar months later, the full moon may be near the plane of Earth's orbit so more lunar and solar eclipses can occur. These periods, when the new moon or full moon is near the plane of Earth's orbit, are called eclipse seasons.

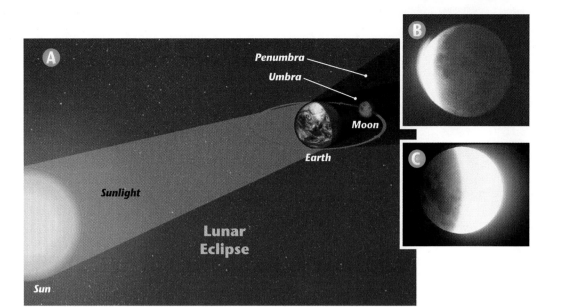

A

Penumbra

Umbra

Moon

Earth

Sunlight

Lunar
Eclipse

Sun

B

C

Lunar Eclipses

During most months, the moon goes near Earth's shadow but not quite into it. A **lunar eclipse** occurs at a full moon when Earth is directly between the moon and the sun. You can see a lunar eclipse in Figure 8. During a lunar eclipse, Earth blocks sunlight from reaching the moon. The moon is then in Earth's shadow and looks dark from Earth. Because the moon is closest to Earth's shadow during the full moon, lunar eclipses occur only at full moon.

Total Lunar Eclipses Like the moon's shadow, Earth's shadow has an umbra and a penumbra. When the moon is in Earth's umbra, you see a total lunar eclipse. You can see Earth's shadow on the moon before and after the total part of a lunar eclipse.

Unlike a solar eclipse, a lunar eclipse can be seen anywhere on Earth that the moon is visible. So you are more likely to see a total lunar eclipse than a total solar eclipse.

Partial Lunar Eclipses For most lunar eclipses, Earth, the moon, and the sun are not quite in line, and a partial lunar eclipse results. A partial lunar eclipse occurs when the moon passes partly into the umbra of Earth's shadow. The edge of the shadow appears blurry, and you can watch it pass across the moon for two or three hours.

☑ *Checkpoint* Why do lunar eclipses occur only at full moon?

Figure 8 **A.** During a lunar eclipse, Earth blocks sunlight from reaching the moon's surface. **B.** This photo of the moon was taken during a total lunar eclipse. **C.** This photo was taken during a partial lunar eclipse. *Interpreting Diagrams What is the difference between Earth's umbra and penumbra?*

Lunar Eclipses

Using the Visuals: Figure 8

Have students compare the images in B and C. Ask: **What phase is the moon in during a lunar eclipse?** *(Full moon)* Ask students to describe what happens when the moon passes into Earth's penumbra. *(Earth's shadow covers a part of the moon as shown in Figure C.)* Then ask: **Why don't we have a lunar eclipse during every full moon?** *(Because the orbit of the moon is tilted 5° to the orbit of Earth, so Earth, the moon, and the sun don't always line up.)* **Why does the moon appear reddish during a lunar eclipse?** *(The reddish color results when sunlight is bent as it passes through Earth's atmosphere and then strikes the moon.)* **learning modality: visual**

Building Inquiry Skills: Comparing and Contrasting

You may wish to have students work in groups of three or four to make a table that compares and contrasts the umbra and penumbra of the moon during a total and partial solar eclipse with the umbra and penumbra of Earth during a total and partial lunar eclipse. Members should first decide what headings to use for their table, that is, which aspects of the umbra and penumbra to compare and contrast. Suggested headings could include: "portion of the surface covered by the umbra," "phase of moon when the eclipse occurs," and "portion of Earth from which eclipse is visible." Then the group can fill in the cells of the table for a solar or lunar eclipse. **cooperative learning**

Answers to Self-Assessment
Caption Question
Figure 8 The umbra is the area of total darkness, the penumbra is the area of partial darkness.

☑ *Checkpoint*
Earth must come between the sun and the moon during a lunar eclipse; this only happens during the full moon phase.

Ongoing Assessment

Drawing Have students sketch the positions of the sun, moon, and Earth during a solar eclipse and a lunar eclipse.

Portfolio Students can save their drawings in their portfolios.

J ◆ 29

A "Moonth" of Phases

Preparing for Inquiry

Key Concept The phases of the moon are caused by the moon's position relative to Earth and the sun.

Skills Objective Students will be able to
- make a model of the Earth-moon-sun system to explore the phases of the moon;
- observe and record the phases of the model system.

Time 40 minutes

Advance Planning Collect lamps (one per group), extra bulbs (150 W bulbs work best), and plastic foam balls (one per student pair).

Guiding Inquiry

Invitation Have students think about how the moon varies in appearance in the night sky. Ask volunteers to describe variations they have seen. (*Sample: The moon may appear round (full moon), sometimes the moon can not be seen at all (new moon), or only part of the moon may visible such as a crescent moon.*)

Introducing the Procedure

- Review the photograph to make sure students understand how to position themselves.
- Suggest students make a sketch of their predictions of what they will see at each turn.

Troubleshooting the Experiment

- To model the full moon, make sure students hold the ball slightly above their heads, so the ball is not in their shadow.
- Be sure the student doing the drawing stands directly behind the one with the ball so that they get the same view.

Expected Outcome

Students should be able to identify the eight phases of the moon: new moon, waxing crescent, first quarter, waxing gibbous, full moon, waning gibbous, last quarter, waning crescent.

Skills Lab

A "Moonth" of Phases

In this lab, you will use a model of the Earth-moon-sun system to explore how the phases of the moon occur.

Problem

What causes the phases of the moon?

Materials

floor lamp with 150-watt bulb
pencils
plastic foam balls

Procedure

1. Place a lamp in the center of the room. Remove the lampshade.
2. Close the doors and shades to darken the room, and switch on the lamp.
3. Carefully stick the point of a pencil into the plastic foam ball so that the pencil can be used as a "handle."
4. Draw 8 circles on a sheet of paper. Number them 1–8.
5. Have your partner hold the plastic foam ball at arm's length in front and slightly above his or her head so that the ball is between him or her and the lamp. **CAUTION:** *Do not look directly at the bulb.*
6. The ball should be about 1 to 1.5 m away from the lamp. Adjust the distance between the ball and the lamp so that the light shines brightly on the ball.

7. Stand directly behind your partner and observe what part of the ball facing you is lit by the lamp. If light is visible on the ball, draw the shape of the lighted part of the ball in the first circle.
8. Have your partner turn 45° to the left while keeping the ball in front and at arm's length.
9. Repeat Step 7. Be sure you are standing directly behind your partner.
10. Repeat Steps 8 and 9 six more times until your partner is facing the lamp again. See the photograph for the 8 positions.
11. Change places and repeat Steps 4–10.

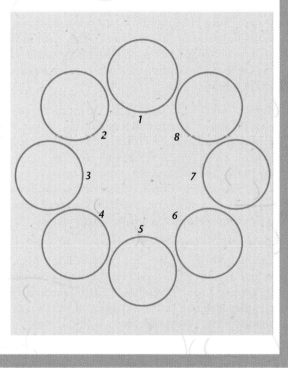

Analyze and Conclude

1. The student holding the ball represents Earth. The lamp represents the sun, and the plastic foam ball represents the moon.
2. No part
3. Position 1—new moon, position 2—waxing crescent, position 3—first quarter, position 4—waxing gibbous, position 5—full moon, position 6—waning gibbous, position 7—third quarter, position 8—waning crescent
4. For the first four turns, about 25% more of the lighted part of the ball was visible with each turn until the lighted part of the ball was completely visible (full moon). For the next four turns, about 25% less of the lighted part was visible with each turn until the dark part of the ball was completely visible (new moon) again.
5. One-half of the ball was always lit. An eclipse occurs when the moon's shadow hits Earth or Earth's shadow hits the moon. Neither of these events caused the darkness of a new moon. When the moon is between Earth and the sun, we are looking at the moon's dark side.

Analyze and Conclude

1. In your model, what represents Earth? The sun? The moon?
2. Refer back to your 8 circles. How much of the lighted part of the ball did you see when facing the lamp?
3. Label your drawings with the names of the phases of the moon. Which drawing represents a full moon? A new moon? Which represents a waxing crescent? A waning crescent?
4. How much of the lighted part of the ball did you see after each turn?
5. Whether you could see it or not, how much of the ball's surface was always lit by the lamp? Was the darkness of the new moon caused by an eclipse? Explain your answer.
6. **Think It Over** How did making a model help you understand the phases of the moon? What are some disadvantages of using models? What is another way to make a model to represent the moon's phases?

More to Explore

Design a model to show a lunar eclipse and a solar eclipse. What objects would you use for Earth, the sun, and the moon? Use the model to demonstrate why there isn't an eclipse every full moon and new moon.

45°

---

6. The model speeds up phases so you can see them in a shorter time than watching the phases for a month. The disadvantage of a model is that it does not always show the true size, measurements, or color of the real item. Another model could use a ball painted black on one hemisphere and white on the other. The white half would represent the sunlit side of the moon. A student could walk around the ball to view it from different angles and see the different phases.

Extending the Inquiry

More to Explore A solar eclipse occurs when the moon (plastic foam ball) is directly between the sun (lamp) and Earth (partner holding the ball). In this position, the new moon casts a total eclipse (shadow) on one part of Earth and a partial eclipse on another part. A lunar eclipse appears during a full moon when the moon (plastic foam ball) passes through Earth's (partner holding the ball) shadow. The moon's orbit is tilted slightly with respect to Earth's orbit around the sun.

Program Resources

◆ **Teaching Resources** Skills Lab blackline masters, pp. 32–33

Media and Technology

Lab Activity Videotape
Astronomy, 2

Safety

Remind students to be careful around the lamps and extension cords. Tell them not to look directly into the lights. Review the safety guidelines in Appendix A.

Tides

Building Inquiry Skills: Making Models

Students can model Earth by partially blowing up round balloons and knotting the stems. Instruct students to hold the balloons at the stem and the opposite end. Have them hold the balloons securely and pull on the knotted ends. Explain that the motion of pulling on a balloon is similar to the pull of the moon's gravity on Earth. Have students draw diagrams to show the balloon when it is being pulled. *(Diagrams should show that the knotted end and the opposite end both bulged, while the sides between flattened.)* Ask students: **What represents the moon in the model?** *(The hand pulling the knotted end of the balloon)* **learning modality: kinesthetic**

Building Inquiry Skills: Predicting

Provide copies of one week's worth of tide tables from a newspaper or other source. Use local tide tables if they are available. The United States National Oceanic and Atmospheric Administration (NOAA) has a Website with a tide predictor at **www.opsd.nos.noaa.gov/tp4days.html**.

Have students note the times for high and low tides each day for one week. Have them determine how much time passes between each high tide and low tide. Then ask them how many high and low tides occur during a 24-hour period. *(Note: There are lunar and solar tides, tides vary geographically, and at certain times there may be only one high and one low tide, but generally there are two high tides and two low tides each day.)* Ask: **Do the high and low tides happen at the same time every day?** *(No, the times for tides vary slightly each day, and the cycle of tides occurs approximately every 25 hours.).* Based on information from the tables, have students predict times of high and low tides for the next three days for the same location. **learning modality: logical/mathematical**

Figure 9 The Hopewell Rocks in New Brunswick, Canada, are partly covered at high tide. At low tide, people can walk along the beach between the rocks. *Predicting What would happen if these people stayed on the beach too long?*

Tides

Have you ever built a sand castle at an ocean beach? Was it washed away by the rising water? People who spend time near the ocean see the effects of **tides,** the rise and fall of water, every 12.5 hours or so. The water rises for about six hours, then falls for about six hours, in a regular cycle.

What Causes Tides?

The force of **gravity** pulls the moon and Earth (including the water on Earth's surface) toward each other. The force of gravity between two objects depends on the masses of the objects and the distance between them. **Tides occur mainly because of differences in how much the moon pulls on different parts of Earth.**

As Earth rotates, the moon's gravity pulls water toward the point on Earth's surface closest to the moon. If that were the only cause, there would be only one high tide at a time, at the point on Earth closest to the moon. Actually, there is a second high tide on the opposite side of Earth, so the explanation must be more complex. The two tides occur because of the difference in the force of gravity from one place to another.

High Tides Look at Figure 10. The force of the moon's gravity at point A, which is closer to the moon, is stronger than the force of the moon's gravity on Earth as a whole. The water near point A is pulled toward the moon more strongly than is Earth as a whole. The water flows toward point A, and a high tide forms.

The force of the moon's gravity at point B, which is farther from the moon, is weaker than the force of the moon's gravity on Earth as a whole. Earth as a whole is pulled toward the moon more strongly than the water at point B, so the water is "left behind." Water flows toward point B, and a high tide occurs there too.

☑ *Checkpoint* *Why are there high tides on opposite sides of Earth at the same time?*

Background

Integrating Science Biological clocks are internal timing mechanisms that control the cyclic patterns or rhythms of living organisms. Rhythms that occur once a solar day (24 hours) day are called *circadian rhythms;* those that occur once a lunar day (24.8 hours) are called *lunar rhythms.*

Lunar rhythms have been demonstrated under laboratory conditions during experiments with fiddler crabs. During these conditions, fiddler crabs show an activity rhythm of 24 hours and 50 minutes, which is equal to a lunar day. The patterning of the crabs' activity is linked with daily low tides, even though the laboratory has no water movements or light from the sun or moon.

High and Low Tides

Point A
Closest to the moon, the moon pulls on water at Earth's surface more strongly than on Earth as a whole. Water flows toward Point A, creating a high tide.

Point B
Farthest away from the moon, the moon pulls less strongly on the water at Earth's surface than on Earth as a whole. Earth is pulled away from this point, leaving the water behind. The water that is left behind creates another high tide.

Points C and D
Low tides occur between the two high tides.

Figure 10 Tides occur mainly because of differences in the force of gravity between the moon and different parts of Earth.

The Tide Cycle Between points A and B, water flows away from points C and D, causing low tides to occur. Figure 10 shows that at any one time there are two places with high tides and two places with low tides on Earth. As Earth rotates, one high tide stays on the side of Earth facing the moon. The second high tide stays on the opposite side of Earth. Every location on Earth sweeps through those two high tides and two low tides in a 25-hour cycle.

Spring and Neap Tides The sun's gravity also pulls on Earth's waters. Once a month, at new moon, the sun, Earth, and moon are nearly in a line. The gravity of the sun and the moon pull in the same direction. The combined forces produce a tide with the greatest difference between low and high tide, called a **spring tide.**

What do you think happens at full moon? The moon and the sun are on opposite sides of Earth. However, since there are tides on both sides of Earth, a spring tide is also produced. It doesn't matter in which order the sun, Earth, and moon line up. So spring tides occur twice a month, at the new moon and at the full moon.

Also twice a month, during the moon's first quarter and last quarter phases, the line between Earth and the sun is at right angles to the line between Earth and the moon. The sun's pull is at right angles to the moon's. This arrangement produces a tide with the least difference between low and high tide, called a **neap tide.**

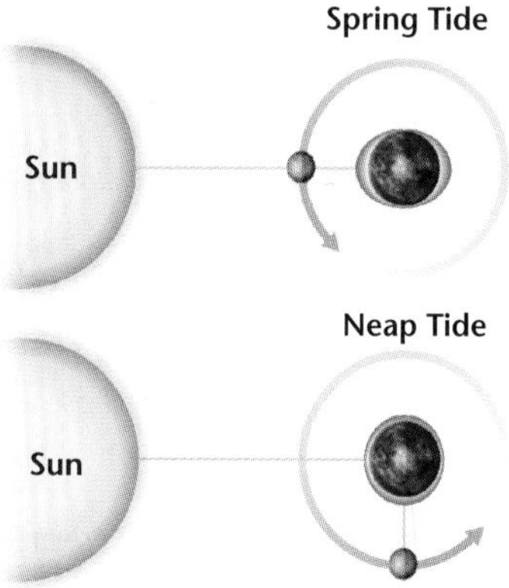

Spring Tide

Sun

Neap Tide

Sun

Figure 11 When Earth, the sun, and the moon are in a straight line (top), a spring tide occurs. When the moon is at a right angle to the sun (bottom), a neap tide occurs.

Have students choose a point on the surface of Earth in the figure. Tell them to use their fingers to trace the path that position on Earth will follow during one day as Earth rotates. Ask: **How many high tides does that location experience in one day?** *(two)* **How many low tides?** *(two)* **learning modality: visual**

Inquiry Challenge

Materials *balloons*
Time 10 minutes

ACTIVITY

Challenge students to use balloons or other available materials to make simple models to show that the combined force of the sun's and moon's gravity will be higher during a full moon, when the sun and moon are on opposite sides of Earth. *(Sample model: Partially fill a small round balloon and knot it. Compare the change in the balloons shape when it is pulled with equal force from both ends and when it is pulled with twice as much force from one end. The results should be the same.)* **learning modality: logical/ mathematical**

Integrating Life Science

Point out that organisms living in the intertidal zone spend part of each day submerged in water, and part of the day exposed to sunlight and air. In addition, these life forms must also withstand continual pounding of the ocean's waves. Interested students may investigate the body systems of intertidal animals such as snails, sea urchins, sea stars, and barnacles. **learning modality: verbal**

Media and Technology

Transparencies "High and Low Tides," Transparency 5

Answers to Self-Assessment

Caption Question

Figure 9 They could get trapped on the beach by high tide.

☑ *Checkpoint*

One high tide forms when the moon pulls on the waters near it; another high tide forms on the opposite side as the solid Earth is pulled toward the moon, leaving the waters behind.

Ongoing Assessment

Writing Have students write paragraphs to explain how the moon's gravity causes tides. Students should explain what happens at both high and low tides.

3 Assess

Section 2 Review Answers

1. As the moon revolves around Earth, phases are produced by the changing position of the moon relative to Earth and the sun.

2. During a solar eclipse, the moon is between the sun and Earth. During a lunar eclipse, Earth is between the sun and the moon.

3. There are two high tides and two low tides a day in most areas because every point on Earth rotates through two high tides and two low tides in a 25-hour cycle.

4. A "day" and a "year" on the moon are the same length because the moon revolves around Earth at the same rate that it rotates on its axis.

5. Drawings should show that during a lunar eclipse the moon is full, and on the opposite side of Earth from the sun.

Check Your Progress

CHAPTER PROJECT 1

Provide newspapers in the classroom so that students can check the times of moonrise and moonset each day. Encourage students to include small drawings in the log along with their daily observational notes. Drawings should show the phase and orientation of the moon for each observation.

Figure 12 Purple sea stars feed on barnacles at low tide in an intertidal zone in Olympic National Park in Washington State. Both animals have adaptations for keeping moist and holding on that allow them to survive the ever-changing conditions of an intertidal zone.

(Local Tide Effects) Not every place on Earth has two regular tides every day. The shapes of bays, inlets, and the ocean floor can affect the flow of water, so that the height and timing of the tides can vary even in places that are close to each other. Because low tides can expose rocks and make waters too shallow to navigate, it is very important for sailors to keep track of the tides. Even today, you sometimes read in the newspaper that a ship that had run aground at low tide was floated off on the next high tide.

Sometimes, the effects of ocean tides extend far up rivers. Water at the river's mouth flows upstream as the tide comes in. As the tide changes and goes out, the water flows downstream back into the ocean.

INTEGRATING LIFE SCIENCE (On many seashores, there is a strip of land, called an intertidal zone, that is under water at high tide but becomes dry land at low tide.) Animals that live in intertidal zones must be adapted to the constantly changing conditions. Sea stars, for example, have powerful suction structures on the undersides of their arms. These allow sea stars to firmly stick to surfaces so they don't float away when tides rush in or out. Barnacles have hard plates on their shells that can clamp shut. This way, water stays inside their shells, keeping their soft bodies moist even when the tide is out.

Section 2 Review

1. Why does the moon change its phases as the month progresses?
2. Describe the relative positions of Earth, the sun, and the moon during a solar eclipse and during a lunar eclipse.
3. Explain why there are two high tides and two low tides each day.
4. Why are a "day" and a "year" on the moon the same length?
5. **Thinking Critically Interpreting Diagrams** Make a diagram to show what phase the moon is in during a lunar eclipse.

Check Your Progress

CHAPTER PROJECT 1

Bring your log sheet to class so you can share your observations with classmates. Check the newspaper every day to find the times of moonrise and moonset and record this information. If you can, look for the moon at moonrise or moonset, even during daylight hours. Use your map to keep track of the direction in which you can see the moon.

Performance Assessment

Oral Presentation Organize the class into small groups to plan presentations that demonstrate the positions of Earth, the sun, and the moon either during a solar eclipse, a lunar eclipse, or during high and low tides.

Program Resources

◆ **Teaching Resources** 1-2 Review and Reinforce, p. 19; 1-2 Enrich, p. 20

Science Explorer Series *Earth's Waters*, Chapter 4

SECTION 3 Rockets and Satellites

DISCOVER •• ACTIVITY

How Do Rockets Work?

1. Put on your goggles. Blow up a balloon and hold its neck closed with your fingers.

2. Point the balloon toward an area where there are no people. Put your free hand behind the neck of the balloon, so the air will push against your hand. Let go of the balloon.

3. Repeat Steps 1 and 2 without your free hand behind the balloon.

Think It Over

Observing In which direction does the air rush out? In which direction does the balloon go? Does the balloon need to push against something in order to move? Explain your answer.

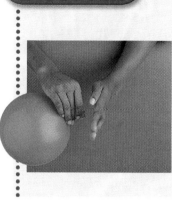

Curiosity about Earth's "neighborhood" in space has led to moon missions, space shuttle missions, space stations, and Mars missions. But without rockets, none of these accomplishments would have been possible.

How Rockets Work

A rocket works in much the way that a balloon is propelled through the air by releasing gas. A rocket moves forward when gases expelled from the rear of the rocket push it in the opposite direction. It's a basic law of physics that for every force, or action, there is an equal and opposite force, or reaction. For example, the force of the air going out the back of a balloon is an action force. An equal force, the reaction, pushes the balloon forward.

In a rocket, fuel is burned to make a hot gas. This hot gas is forced out of narrow nozzles in the back of the rocket, propelling the rocket forward.

GUIDE FOR READING

♦ How do rockets travel in space?

♦ What are satellites and space stations used for?

Reading Tip Before you read, rewrite the headings in the section as *how, why,* or *what* questions. As you read, look for answers to those questions.

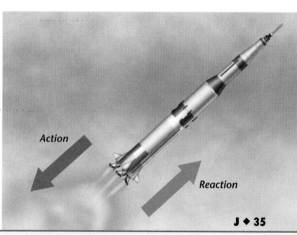

Action

Reaction

Figure 13 Hot gas is propelled out of the back of a rocket engine. The force of the gas in one direction (action) produces an opposing force (reaction) that propels the rocket forward.

J ♦ 35

READING STRATEGIES

Reading Tip Suggest students write their how, why, and what questions in columns under those headings. Encourage them to answer the questions based on what they already know, and revise their answers as they read.

Program Resources

♦ **Teaching Resources** 1-3 Lesson Plan, p. 21; 1-3 Section Summary, p. 22
♦ **Guided Study Workbook** Section 1-3

INTEGRATING TECHNOLOGY

SECTION 3 Rockets and Satellites

Objectives

After completing the lesson, students will be able to
♦ explain how rockets travel in space;
♦ list the uses of satellites, space stations, and the Space Shuttle.

Key Terms satellite, geosynchronous orbit

1 Engage/Explore

Activating Prior Knowledge

Many students will have watched a space shuttle launch on television or will have seen rockets being launched in news specials, documentaries, or movies. Invite volunteers to describe what happens when a rocket is launched. Ask them to consider the motion of the rocket in their responses. (*Sample: Engines are fired, large clouds of gas come from the rocket boosters, the rocket or space shuttle pulls away from Earth.*) Ask students what forces are at work when a rocket lifts off from the ground. (*Gas pushed out the bottom of the rocket pushes against the rocket.*)

•••••••• DISCOVER ••••••••

Skills Focus observing
Materials *balloons, safety goggles*
Time 10 minutes
Tips Remind students to try to blow up the balloons to the same size each time so they can compare their results.
Expected Outcome The balloons will move across the room in both trials.
Think It Over The air rushes out the neck of the balloon, and the balloon goes in the opposite direction. The balloon does not need to push against something to move, because it is the action-reaction pair of forces that makes it move, not the push of air off your hand.

2 Facilitate

How Rockets Work

Using the Visuals: Figure 13
Explain that the force of gases expelled by the rocket boosters creates a thrust or push that causes the rocket to move away. Ask: **What action is shown in the diagram?** (*The force of the gas coming from the back of the rocket engine*) **What reaction?** (*The force making the rocket move away in the opposite direction*)
learning modality: visual

Multistage Rockets

Demonstration

Time 15 minutes

Materials *2 long balloons, nylon fishing line, 2 plastic drinking straws, plastic foam cup, masking tape, scissors*

Tips Thread the straws on the fishing line and tie the line securely across the room. Cut the top off a cup ring. Inflate one balloon about three quarters full and hold the neck tight so no air can escape. Do not tie the neck. Have a volunteer help you place the neck of the balloon through the plastic foam ring and hold it tightly closed. Inflate the second balloon so that the round end extends a short way through the ring. After some practice, you will be able to inflate the second balloon so it presses the neck of the first balloon against the ring and holds it shut. Hold the neck of the second balloon firmly, and tape each balloon to one of the straws on the line. When you release the balloon, the escaping air will propel the balloons down the line. When the first balloon runs out of air, it will release the other.
learning modality: kinesthetic

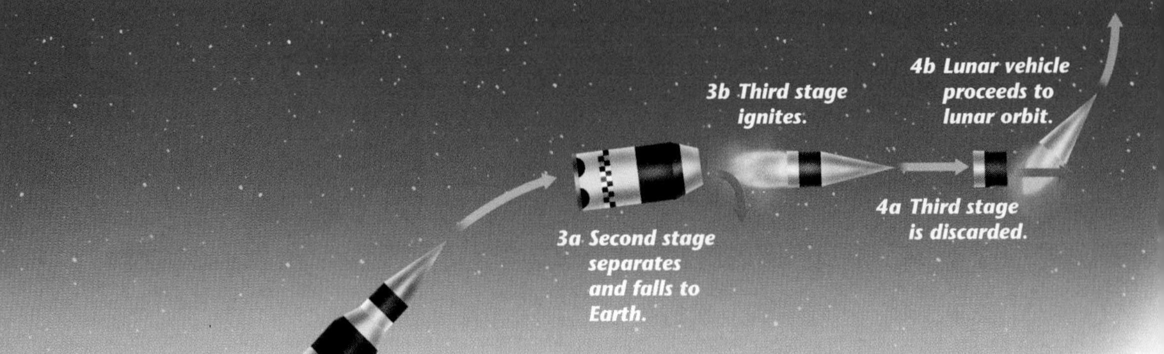

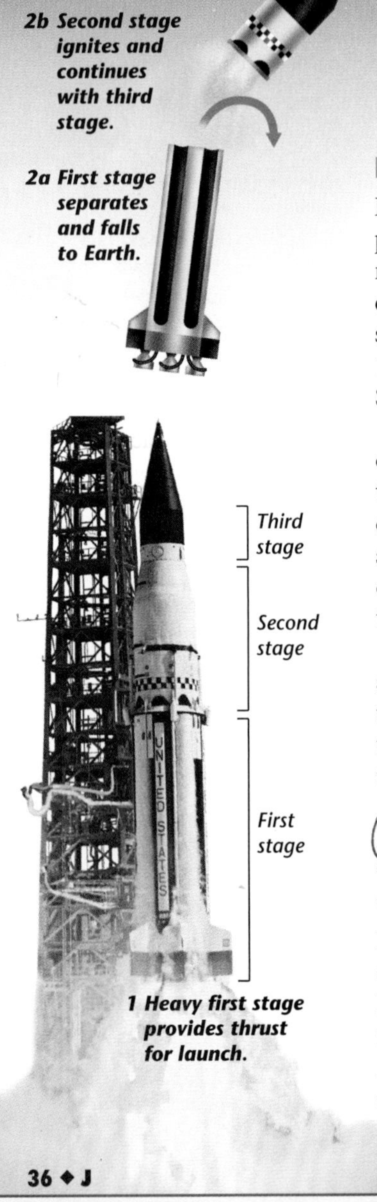

3b Third stage ignites.

4b Lunar vehicle proceeds to lunar orbit.

3a Second stage separates and falls to Earth.

4a Third stage is discarded.

2b Second stage ignites and continues with third stage.

Figure 14 Multistage rockets have three stages, or sections. Each of the first two stages burns all its fuel and then drops off. The next stage then takes over. Only part of the third stage reaches the rocket's destination.

2a First stage separates and falls to Earth.

Third stage

Second stage

First stage

1 Heavy first stage provides thrust for launch.

Multistage Rockets

Early rockets, built by the Chinese around the year 1000, used gunpowder as fuel. But gunpowder burns quickly and explosively. A rocket designed to travel out of Earth's atmosphere needs a different sort of fuel that burns slowly and continuously. The American scientist Robert H. Goddard experimented with liquid fuels in the 1920s. He showed that a liquid fuel can provide continuous power. Some solid fuels also burn slowly and continuously.

Another problem remained, however. A rocket can carry only so much fuel. Once the fuel is used up, the rocket falls back to Earth. In 1903, a Russian named Konstantin Tsiolkovsky came up with the idea of multistage rockets. As each stage, or section, of a rocket uses up its fuel, the empty fuel container drops off. Then the next stage ignites and continues up toward the rocket's destination.

The development of powerful multistage rockets in the 1950s and 1960s made it possible to send rockets to the moon and farther into space. Figure 14 shows a rocket similar to the Saturn V that carried the astronauts to the moon. You will learn more about the moon landings in Section 4.

Artificial Satellites

The world was astounded on October 4, 1957, when the Soviet Union launched the first artificial satellite into orbit around Earth. A **satellite** is any natural or artificial object that revolves around an object in space, just as the moon revolves around Earth. This satellite, *Sputnik 1*, revolved around Earth every 96 minutes. Three months later, the United States launched *Explorer 1* into orbit. On April 12, 1961, Yuri Gagarin, a Soviet cosmonaut, orbited Earth, becoming the first person in space.

Background

History of Science Artificial satellites used for communications are generally very reliable. However, on May 19, 1998, a satellite called *Galaxy 4* went out of service when its onboard control system failed and the satellite rolled out of position. Its failure interrupted communications systems all over the United States and the Caribbean.

Because a majority of pager companies in the United States relied on *Galaxy 4*, approximately 40 million pager users lost service. In addition, television and radio networks used *Galaxy 4* to transmit feeds to their stations, so these transmissions were interrupted too. The problem also halted the operation of bank automated teller machines and the systems customers use at gas stations to pay with credit cards. To reestablish service, the company that owns *Galaxy 4* had to reposition another satellite.

Since 1957, thousands of artificial satellites, including space stations, have been launched into orbit. **Satellites and space stations are used for communications, navigation, collecting weather data, and research.**

Satellites Artificial satellites are used to relay telephone calls, to measure Earth's atmosphere, and to photograph weather systems, crops, troops, and ships. In addition, two dozen Global Positioning Satellites give off signals that can be picked up by small receivers on Earth. The receiver can then tell you where you are on Earth's surface.

Some satellites are in **geosynchronous orbits,** which means they revolve around Earth at the same rate that Earth rotates. Geosynchronous satellites above the equator seem to hover over a given point on Earth. Geosynchronous satellites are used to relay television signals and to map weather patterns.

Space Stations A space station is a large satellite in which people can live for long periods. The first space station, the Soviet Union's *Salyut,* was launched in 1971. In 1973, the United States launched *Skylab,* which carried a series of telescopes and scientific experiments. The former Soviet Union, of which Russia was part, launched the *Mir* space station in 1986. Astronauts from many countries, including Americans, visited *Mir.* Sixteen countries, including the United States and Russia, are cooperating on the International Space Station, which is now being built in orbit and will eventually provide living quarters and labs for up to seven astronauts.

☑ *Checkpoint* What is a geosynchronous orbit?

Figure 15 The International Space Station is a cooperative project involving 16 countries, including the United States, Russia, Japan, and Canada. This is an artist's conception of the station in orbit.

Be a Rocket Scientist

You can build a rocket.

1. Use a plastic or paper cup as the rocket body. Cut out a paper nose cone and tape it to the closed end of the cup.

2. Obtain an empty film canister with a lid that snaps on inside the canister. Go outside to do Steps 3–5.

3. Fill the canister about one-quarter full with water.

4. Put on your goggles. Now add half of a fizzing antacid tablet to the film canister and quickly snap on the lid.

5. Place the canister on the ground with the lid down. Place your rocket over the canister and stand back.

Observing
What action happened inside the film canister? What was the reaction of the rocket?

Artificial Satellites

TRY THIS

Skills Focus observing
Materials *plastic or paper cup, paper, tape, film canister with a lid that snaps on inside the canister, water, fizzing antacid tablet, safety goggles*
Time 20 minutes
Tips Caution students not to place sharp objects on the rocket.
Expected Outcome The rocket will lift off and shoot 2 to 5 meters into the air.
Observing Gas pressure builds up inside the canister due to the reaction of the antacid and water. Pressure continues to build until it blows off the lid of the canister and launches the rocket.
Extend Challenge students to design and launch rockets powered by two, three, or more film canisters. **learning modality: logical/mathematical**

Inquiry Challenge

Pair students and have them use physical activity  to model how a satellite with a geosynchronous orbit can stay above the same point on Earth. One student turns very slowly in place at about one turn per minute, while the partner walks around the first student in a circle at a rate of one step per second so that the turning student always faces the walking student. There will be only one radius where this will happen. Ask the students to describe what is happening. Now have the walking student move faster and walk in a smaller circle while the turning student turns at the same rate. Ask the students to describe what happens. (*The first case models a geosynchronous orbit. The second case models a low Earth orbit.*) **learning modality: kinesthetic**

Answers to Self-Assessment

☑ *Checkpoint*

A geosynchronous orbit is one in which the satellite revolves around Earth at the same rate that Earth rotates on its axis.

Ongoing Assessment

Oral Presentation Ask students to describe how satellites are launched into orbit.

Space Shuttles

Addressing Naive Conceptions

Many students may think that the shuttle is far from Earth when in orbit. In fact, the shuttle was designed for low-Earth orbits of less than 480 km. To help students visualize this, use a paper ruler to measure a distance on the surface of a globe approximately 480 km from your location. Mark the ruler and hold it perpendicular to the globe to show the highest altitude of the orbiting shuttle.
learning modality: visual

3 Assess

Section 3 Review Answers

1. The rocket's exhaust gases go in one direction and the rocket moves in the opposite direction.
2. Any three: Communications, weather monitoring, navigation, and research
3. Only part of the third stage of the rocket reaches the final destination.
4. Space shuttles cost less than the *Saturn V* rockets and can be reused.

Students may be able to interview their parents or grandparents about the first moon landing. Encourage students to prepare a list of who, what, when, where, why, and how questions before the interview. Students could also write their interviews as magazine articles. Provide examples of interviews from newspapers and magazines for students to use as a style guide.

Figure 16 The Space Shuttle *Discovery* is launched into space by its own rockets as well as by rockets attached to it. *Inferring What is one advantage of a reusable space vehicle?*

Space Shuttles

The Saturn V rockets that carried astronauts to the moon in the 1960s and 1970s were very expensive. In addition, they could not be reused because each stage burned up as it fell back through Earth's atmosphere. In the late 1970s, the National Aeronautics and Space Administration (NASA) developed the reusable space shuttles. They are called shuttles because they can go back and forth, or shuttle, between Earth and space. Since the first shuttle was launched in 1981, space shuttles have been the main way that the United States launches astronauts and equipment into space.

NASA is studying several ideas for building better and less expensive ways of launching people and cargo into space. The ideal vehicle would be an aerospace plane that could take off from a runway, travel into space, and land again on a runway.

Section 3 Review

1. How does a rocket work?
2. Describe three uses of satellites and space stations.
3. Which stage of a multistage rocket reaches the final destination?
4. **Thinking Critically Comparing and Contrasting** What is one way that Saturn V rockets and space shuttles are different?

Science at Home

Interview someone who remembers the space programs of the 1950s and 1960s. Prepare your questions in advance, such as: How did you feel when you heard that *Sputnik* was in orbit? How did you feel when the first Americans went into space? Did you watch any of the space flights on television? You may want to record your interview, then write it out in a question-and-answer format.

Performance Assessment

Drawing Create a poster showing how a space station or satellite is launched into orbit and then used for practical applications on Earth.
 Students can save their posters in their portfolios.

Media and Technology

Exploring Physical Science Videodisc Unit 5, Side 1, "The Cray Computer"; "Then and Now"

Chapter 8

Answers to Self-Assessment

Caption Question
Figure 16 Reusable vehicles are less expensive.

DISCOVER ⋯⋯⋯⋯⋯⋯⋯⋯⋯ ACTIVITY

Why Do Craters Look Different From Each Other?

The moon's surface has pits in it, called craters.

1. Put on your goggles. Fill a large plastic basin with 2 cm of sand.

2. Drop marbles of different masses from about 20 cm high. Take the marbles out and view the craters they left.

3. Predict what will happen if you drop marbles from a higher point. Smooth out the sand. Now drop marbles of different masses from about 50 cm high.

4. Take the marbles out and view the craters they left.

Think It Over
Developing Hypotheses In which step do you think the marbles were moving faster when they hit the sand? If objects hitting the moon caused craters, how did the speeds of the objects affect the sizes of the craters? How did the masses of the objects affect the sizes of the craters?

Would you want to take a vacation on the moon? Before you answer, think about these facts. There is no air or liquid water on the moon. Temperatures on the moon's surface range from 100°C, the boiling point of water, to –170°C, well below freezing.

To stay at a comfortable temperature and carry an air supply, the astronauts who landed on the moon had to wear bulky space-suits. Each spacesuit had a mass of 90 kilograms, about as much as the astronaut himself! Because the moon's gravity is only about one-sixth as strong as Earth's, however, the astronauts were able to leap about like basketball stars despite their heavy spacesuits. What do you think now? Do you still want to go?

GUIDE FOR READING

◆ What features of the moon can be seen with a telescope?

◆ How did the Apollo landings help scientists learn about the moon?

Reading Tip As you read, write down ways in which the moon's surface is similar to Earth's surface.

Figure 17 Astronaut John W. Young jumps up from the moon's surface as he salutes the flag on April 21, 1972. The machine on the left is the *Apollo 16* lunar lander.

READING STRATEGIES

Study and Comprehension As they read, have students fill in a Venn diagram of the similarities and differences between the moon's surface and Earth's surface. Remind students to list shared features in the area where the two circles overlap. Invite volunteers to write their Venn diagrams on the board.

Program Resources

◆ **Teaching Resources** 1-4 Lesson Plan, p. 25; 1-4 Section Summary, p. 26
◆ **Guided Study Workbook** Section 1-4

Objectives

After completing the lesson, students will be able to
◆ describe features of the moon's surface;
◆ explain what scientists learned about the moon from space exploration;
◆ describe the origin and structure of the moon.

Key Terms telescope, crater, maria

1 Engage/Explore

Activating Prior Knowledge

Hold up a rock. Tell students to imagine that the rock is as large as a building and is traveling through space. Ask them to imagine the rock falling through Earth's atmosphere and landing in an open desert. Ask: **What do you think would happen?** *(Sample: The rock would leave a large depression in the desert sand or explode on impact.)*

⋯⋯⋯ DISCOVER ⋯⋯⋯

Skills Focus developing hypotheses
Materials *plastic basin or mixing bowl about 25 cm across, sand, 3 marbles of different masses, meter stick*
Time 20 minutes
Tips After Step 2, have students measure the depth and diameter of the craters made.
Expected Outcome The size of the craters will increase with mass and with height.
Think It Over The marbles are moving faster in Step 3. The more massive the impacting object or the faster it hits, the larger the resulting crater will be.

2 Facilitate

The Structure and Origin of the Moon

Using the Visuals: Figure 19

Explain that computer simulations are visual representations of information that are created by computers. Have students organize the information in the figure into a flowchart. Ask: **According to this theory, what is the moon made of?** (*Material from the object that collided with Earth and the material that was broken off Earth*) **learning modality: logical/mathematical**

Building Inquiry Skills: Interpreting Data

Pair students and have them measure the diameter of a quarter. Students should then measure the distance from the classroom clock to a position on the opposite side of the room. From that position, one student can hold the quarter at arm's length and close one eye, then move the coin closer until it appears to completely cover the clock. The other student can measure the distance from the partner's eye to the coin. Have students convert their measurements to a common unit, then use the following proportion to calculate the diameter of the clock:

$$\frac{\text{diameter of coin}}{\text{diameter of clock}} = \frac{\text{distance from eye to coin}}{\text{distance from eye to clock}}$$

Ask students how scientists could use this method to find the diameter of the moon. **learning modality: logical/mathematical**

Figure 18 The diameter of the moon is a little less than the distance across the United States.

Figure 19 This computer simulation shows the collision theory of the moon's origin. In this theory, a large object struck Earth. The resulting debris formed the moon.

The Structure and Origin of the Moon

The moon is 3,476 kilometers in diameter, a little less than the distance across the United States. This diameter is only one fourth Earth's diameter. However, the moon contains only one-eightieth as much mass as Earth. Though Earth has a very dense core, the outer layers are less dense. The moon's average density is about the same as the density of Earth's outer layers.

People have long wondered how the moon formed. Scientists have suggested many possible hypotheses. For example, did Earth at one time spin so fast that the material the moon is made of was thrown off? Was the moon formed elsewhere in the solar system and captured by Earth's gravitational pull as it came near? Was the moon formed near Earth at the same time that Earth formed? Scientists have found reasons to reject all of these ideas.

The theory of the moon's origin that best fits the evidence is called the collision theory. It is illustrated in Figure 19. About 4.5 billion years ago, when Earth was very young, an object at least as large as Mars collided with Earth. Material from the object and Earth's outer layers was thrown into orbit around Earth. Eventually, this material combined to form the moon.

Looking at the Moon From Earth

For thousands of years, people could see shapes on the surface of the moon, but didn't know what caused them. The ancient Greeks thought that the moon was perfectly smooth. It was not until about 400 years ago that scientists could study the moon more closely.

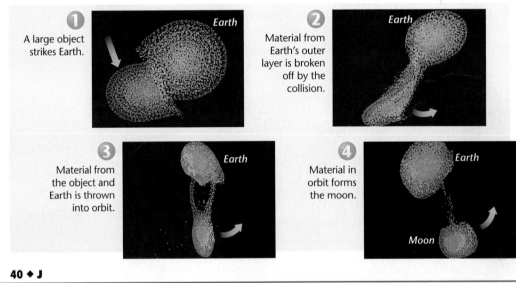

① A large object strikes Earth. *Earth*

② Material from Earth's outer layer is broken off by the collision. *Earth*

③ Material from the object and Earth is thrown into orbit. *Earth*

④ Material in orbit forms the moon. *Earth* *Moon*

Plato

Sea of Rains

Archimedes

Sea of Serenity

Copernicus

Sea of Tranquillity

Figure 20 Astronomers have given names to many of the moon's craters and maria. Copernicus is one of the largest craters.

In 1609, the Italian astronomer Galileo Galilei heard about a device that made distant objects appear closer. Galileo soon made his own **telescope** by putting two lenses in a wooden tube. The lenses focused the light coming through the tube, making distant objects seem closer. When Galileo pointed his telescope at the moon, he was able to see much more detail than anyone had ever seen before. **Features on the moon's surface include craters, highlands, and maria.**

Galileo saw that much of the moon's surface is covered with round pits called **craters.** Some craters are hundreds of kilometers across. For 300 years, scientists thought that the craters on the moon had been made by volcanoes. But about 50 years ago, scientists concluded that the craters on the moon were caused by the impacts of meteoroids, rocks from space.

Galileo inferred that some of the other features he saw were highlands, or mountains. The peaks of the highlands and the rims of the craters cast dark shadows, which Galileo could see.

The moon's surface also has dark, flat areas, which Galileo called **maria** (MAH ree uh), the Latin word for "seas." Each one is a "mare" (MAH ray). Galileo thought that the maria might be oceans. Scientists now know that there are no oceans on the moon. The maria are low, dry areas that were flooded with molten material billions of years ago. Since you always see the same maria from Earth, you can tell that the moon always shows the same face to Earth.

✓ *Checkpoint* What are maria?

Visual Arts CONNECTION

When Galileo observed the moon, he drew pictures like the one below. Galileo had been trained as an artist, so he interpreted his observations as an artist would. Light and shadow are used in art to create the appearance of three-dimensional forms.

Galileo saw the areas of light and shadow on the moon and concluded that the surface of the moon was not smooth.

In Your Journal

Under a bright light, set up an arrangement of objects. Sketch the outline of the objects. Then observe where the shadows fall. Shade in those areas. Notice how adding shading makes your drawing look more real.

Including All Students

Students who are mastering English may need extra help using the text to identify the features in Figure 20. Choose one feature in the figure and have a volunteer read its description from the text. Then ask questions such as: **Is the Sea of Tranquillity really an ocean?** *(no)* **What is it?** *(It is one of the maria, dark, flat parts of the moon's surface.)* Repeat for the other labeled features. **limited English proficiency**

Visual Arts CONNECTION

Tell students that although Galileo did not invent the telescope, he constructed the first refracting telescope designed for viewing features in space. Refracting telescopes use a combination of lenses to magnify an image. In addition to the moon's features, Galileo was able to view and sketch the moons of Jupiter, the Milky Way, sunspots, and the shape of Saturn and its rings. Ask students why they think that Galileo's observations were of such great historical importance. *(Sample: No one had ever viewed these features before.)*

In Your Journal Show students examples of paintings that use light and shadow to produce three-dimensional effects. Provide a variety of objects with interesting shapes such as bottles, fruit, models, toys, or carvings with relief for students to sketch. **learning modality: visual**

Media and Technology

📽 **Transparencies** "Collision Theory of the Moon's Origin," Transparency 6

Answers to Self-Assessment

✓ *Checkpoint*

Maria are large flat plains on the moon's surface.

Ongoing Assessment

Writing Ask students to explain how scientists think the moon was formed.

Building Inquiry Skills: Applying Concepts

Divide students into small groups of three or four. Tell them they are going to pretend they are NASA scientists during the early 1960s, when President Kennedy made his famous challenge to the nation. Have students brainstorm a list of factors that they, as scientists, need to consider when landing a human on the moon. Encourage students to consider requirements for survival, landing safely, and returning to Earth. Ask: **What five items would you bring with you to the moon?** *(Sample: oxygen, water, spacesuit to wear on the moon, fuel for return trip, books)* Have students share their lists and discuss their reasons for selecting the items. **cooperative learning**

Social Studies Connection

Students may enjoy watching or listening to the first moon landing. Many recordings are available at local libraries, on the Internet (visit the Science Explorer website for information **www.phschool.com**) and also on many multimedia encyclopedias. Encourage students to listen and imagine they are back in the year 1969, watching or listening to the moon landing for the first time. Ask students to describe how they would have felt during the tense last moments of the landing. **learning modality: verbal**

Using the Visuals: Figure 22

Ask students to describe the lunar surface shown in the photograph. Then ask them to describe challenges they think NASA scientists had to consider when creating a vehicle that could explore the moon's terrain. Ask: **Why does the lunar buggy need such large soft wheels?** *(To go over rocks and through small craters)* **learning modality: visual**

"I believe that this nation should commit itself to achieving the goal, before this decade is out, of landing a man on the moon and returning him safely to Earth." With these words from a May 1961 speech, President John F. Kennedy launched an enormous program of space exploration and scientific research.

Exploring the Moon Between 1964 and 1972, the United States and the Soviet Union sent dozens of rockets to explore the moon. Until spacecraft went to the moon, no one knew what its surface was like. Would spacecraft landing on the moon sink deep into thick dust and be lost? When *Surveyor* spacecraft landed on the moon, they didn't sink in, thus showing that the surface was solid. Lunar orbiters then photographed the moon's surface, so scientists could find a flat, safe spot for a rocket to land.

The Moon Landings In July 1969 three astronauts circled the moon in *Apollo 11*. Once in orbit around the moon, Neil Armstrong and Buzz Aldrin got into a tiny Lunar Module called *Eagle*, leaving Michael Collins in orbit in the Command Module. On July 20, 1969, the *Eagle* descended toward a flat area on the moon's surface called the Sea of Tranquillity. Armstrong and Aldrin were running out of fuel, so they had to find a safe landing spot fast. Billions of people held their breaths as they waited to learn if the astronauts had landed safely on the moon. Finally, a red light flashed on the control panel. "Contact light! Houston, Tranquillity Base here. The *Eagle* has landed," Armstrong radioed to Earth.

After the landing, Armstrong and Aldrin left the *Eagle* to explore the moon. When Armstrong first set foot on the moon, he said, "That's one small step for man, one giant leap for mankind." Armstrong meant to say "That's one small step for *a* man," meaning himself, but in his excitement he never said the "a."

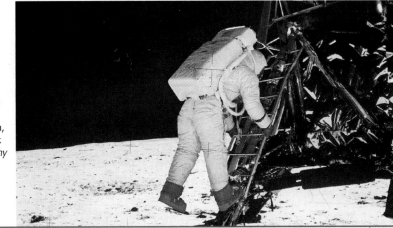

Figure 21 On July 20, 1969, *Apollo 11* astronaut Neil Armstrong became the first person to walk on the moon. He took this photograph of Buzz Aldrin, the second person to walk on the moon. *Inferring Why was it important for the lunar module to land on a flat spot?*

Background

History of Science Each Apollo project had a three-passenger Command Module (CM) and a two-passenger Lunar Module (LM). *Apollo 13* was launched at 13:13 on April 11, 1970. It looked like it was going to be the smoothest flight of the program, but two days into the flight, at 21:08 on April 13, an oxygen tank blew up. The CM's supply of electricity, light, and water was lost. The crew decided to use the LM to pilot the crippled CM around the moon and back to Earth. Astronauts had enough oxygen, but they had to conserve water, power, and food. They also had to find a way to remove carbon dioxide from the spacecraft. Mission Control found a way to do this using materials on board. On April 17, after surviving 3.6°C cold and losing a total of almost 15 kg through dehydration, the crew in the LM landed in the Pacific Ocean near Samoa.

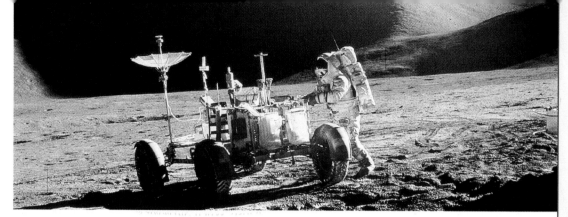

Figure 22 Astronauts on later missions had a lunar buggy to help them explore the moon's surface.

On the Surface of the Moon Everything the *Apollo 11* astronauts found was new and exciting. Even looking at their footprints taught the astronauts lessons about the moon's soil. The astronauts bounded around the surface, picking up samples of rocks to bring back to Earth for scientists to study.

In later missions, the astronauts were able to stay on the moon for days instead of hours. They even had a lunar buggy to ride around in. The astronauts were also able to land near the highlands, which were more interesting to study than the flat mare where *Apollo 11* landed.

Moon Rocks and Moonquakes The astronauts brought back to Earth 382 kilograms of moon rocks, about half the mass of a small car. **Much of what scientists have learned about the moon came from detailed study of the moon rocks gathered by astronauts.** Almost all of the rocks were formed from the cooling of molten material, so the moon's surface must once have been very hot. Some of the rocks showed that they had been broken apart by impacts and then reformed. So scientists concluded that meteoroids had bombarded the moon's surface.

The astronauts brought measuring instruments to the moon to record some of the meteoroid impacts. One type of device, known as a seismometer, is used to detect earthquakes on Earth. The seismometers on the moon detected extremely weak moonquakes, the result of changes deep under the moon's surface.

Until the *Apollo* astronauts landed, scientists knew very little about the moon's interior. Another kind of instrument the astronauts left behind measured the amount of heat flowing out from the moon's interior, in order to study what the inside of the moon is like. This instrument showed that the moon has cooled almost completely since it was formed.

☑ *Checkpoint* What did scientists discover about the interior of the moon as a result of the moon landings?

Sharpen your Skills

Calculating ACTIVITY

If you went to the moon for a vacation, your weight would only be about one sixth of your weight on Earth. To find your weight on the moon, divide your weight by 6.

If you had to wear a spacesuit that weighed as much as you do, what would be your total weight on the moon?

---

3 Assess

Section 4 Review Answers

1. Craters, highlands, and maria
2. The Apollo astronauts collected moon rocks, brought seismometers to detect moon quakes, and measured heat flow in the moon's interior.
3. The craters were formed by the impact of meteoroids on the moon's surface.
4. Scientists once thought that some of the moon's craters were formed by volcanoes because they resembled volcanic craters. The Apollo astronauts measured the heat flow beneath the moon's surface and found that the moon has cooled almost completely since it was formed, so the presence of volcanoes seems unlikely.

Check Your Progress
CHAPTER PROJECT 1

At this stage, students will be looking for patterns in their observational data. Encourage them to look for changes throughout the day in addition to comparing their observations over the course of the project. Suggest they look for some of the surface features that they studied in Section 4. Provide moon maps and charts showing what features are likely to be visible. Binoculars will help students spot the highlands, craters, and maria. The elevated walls of craters are most likely to be visible during the crescent and quarter phases.

Figure 23 The far side of the moon is much rougher than the side that faces Earth.
Observing What are the round features in this photograph called?

Photographs of the Moon The *Apollo* astronauts circled the moon by rocket and photographed all parts of its surface. The pictures show that the far side of the moon is rougher than the near side and has very few maria.

The American *Clementine* spacecraft went to the moon in 1994. It took photographs of the moon through different filters chosen to show what types of minerals are on the moon. The name *Clementine* was chosen because it is the name of the prospector's daughter in the old song "My Darlin' Clementine."

In 1998, the American *Lunar Prospector* spacecraft went to the moon. *Lunar Prospector* mapped the entire moon from an altitude of only 100 kilometers. *Lunar Prospector* found evidence that there is ice frozen into the lunar soil near the moon's poles.

Section 4 Review

1. Name the three kinds of features that Galileo saw on the moon's surface.
2. What did the *Apollo* astronauts do on the moon?
3. How did the craters form on the moon?
4. **Thinking Critically Inferring** Why did scientists once think there were volcanoes on the moon? What evidence from the *Apollo* landings makes this unlikely?

Check Your Progress
CHAPTER PROJECT 1

Compare your observations of the moon early in the day with observations later that day. How does the moon appear to move in the sky during the course of the day? What happens to the appearance of the moon between earlier and later observations? Is there a pattern for each day? (*Hint:* See whether the same pattern holds true for observations later in the month.)

44 ◆ J

Performance Assessment

Drawing Have students make a diagram of the moon using shadows to indicate the presence of craters and other features. Students may label the features and write a brief caption to go with each feature.

 Students can save their sketches in their portfolios.

Program Resources

◆ **Teaching Resources** 1-4 Review and Reinforce, p. 27; 1-4 Enrich, p. 28

Answers to Self-Assessment

Caption Question
Figure 23 The round features are craters.

SECTION 1 — Earth in Space

Key Ideas

- Astronomy is the study of the moon, stars, and other objects in space.
- Earth's rotation on its axis causes day and night.
- One complete revolution of Earth around the sun is called a year.
- Earth has seasons because its axis is tilted as it revolves around the sun.

Key Terms

astronomy	latitude
axis	solstice
rotation	equinox
revolution	vernal equinox
orbit	autumnal equinox

SECTION 2 — Phases, Eclipses, and Tides

Key Ideas

- The moon revolves around Earth and rotates on its own axis.
- The phase of the moon you see depends on how much of the sunlit side of the moon faces Earth.
- A solar eclipse occurs when the moon passes between Earth and the sun, blocking the sunlight from reaching Earth.
- A lunar eclipse occurs when Earth is directly between the moon and the sun, blocking the sunlight from reaching the moon.
- Tides occur mainly because of differences in how much the moon pulls on different parts of Earth.

Key Terms

phase	lunar eclipse
eclipse	tide
solar eclipse	gravity
umbra	spring tide
penumbra	neap tide

SECTION 3 — Rockets and Satellites

INTEGRATING TECHNOLOGY

Key Ideas

- A rocket moves in one direction when gases are expelled from it in the opposite direction.
- Satellites and space stations are used for communications, navigation, collecting weather data, and research.

Key Terms

satellite	geosynchronous orbit

SECTION 4 — Earth's Moon

Key Ideas

- Features on the moon's surface include craters, highlands, and maria.
- Much of what scientists have learned about the moon came from detailed study of the moon rocks.

Key Terms

telescope	crater	maria

Organizing Information

Concept Map Copy the concept map about how Earth moves in space onto a sheet of paper. Then complete it and add a title. (For more on concept maps, see the Skills Handbook.)

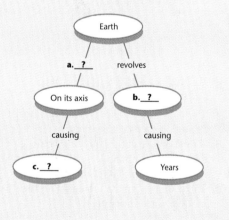

Organizing Information

Concept Map Sample title: *How Earth Moves;* **a.** rotates **b.** around the sun **c.** day and night

Media and Technology

- **Interactive Student Tutorial CD-ROM** J-1
- **Computer Test Bank** *Astronomy,* Chapter 1 Test

Program Resources

- **Teaching Resources** Chapter 1 Project Scoring Rubric, p. 12; Chapter 1 Performance Assessment, pp. 114–116; Chapter 1 Test, pp. 117-120

Reviewing Content
Multiple Choice
1. c 2. a 3. d 4. d 5. c

True or False
6. rotation 7. seasons 8. true 9. true
10. lunar seas or maria

Checking Concepts
11. A flattened oval
12. Yes, because seasons are caused by sunlight hitting different hemispheres of a planet at different angles over the year.
13. They are the same.
14. The moon must enter Earth's shadow for a lunar eclipse to take place. In most months, when the moon is full it is near Earth's shadow but not in it. This is because the moon's orbit is slightly tilted relative to the plane of Earth's orbit around the sun.
15. Everyone who can see the moon can see a lunar eclipse, in which the moon goes into Earth's shadow, while only those in a narrow band on Earth's surface can see a total solar eclipse.
16. Closest to the moon, the moon's gravitational pull on water at Earth's surface is stronger than its pull on Earth as a whole, and water flows toward that point. Furthest from the moon, the moon pulls more strongly on Earth as a whole than on water at Earth's surface, creating a high tide at that point as well.
17. Rockets work on the law of action and reaction.
18. A large object collides with Earth, material from Earth's outer layer breaks off, material from Earth and the object are thrown into orbit, the material combines to form the moon.
19. Scientists learned that the moon's surface was once very hot and that it had been bombarded by meteoroids.
20. Students should give detailed descriptions of the surface of the moon, and of objects they would see in the sky (including Earth). New rock samples might tell whether the rocks contain minerals that could be mined.

Reviewing Content

For more review of key concepts, see the Interactive Student Tutorial CD-ROM.

Multiple Choice
Choose the letter of the answer that best completes each statement.

1. The movement of Earth around the sun once a year is Earth's
   a. orbit.
   b. rotation.
   c. revolution.
   d. axis.
2. The darkest part of a shadow is the
   a. umbra.
   b. penumbra.   *partial*
   c. eclipse.
   d. phase.
3. When Earth's shadow falls on the moon, the shadow causes a
   a. new moon.
   b. solar eclipse.
   c. full moon.
   d. lunar eclipse.
4. A satellite in geosynchronous orbit revolves around Earth once each
   a. hour.
   b. week.
   c. month.
   d. day.
5. The craters on the moon were caused by
   a. highlands.   b. volcanoes.
   c. meteoroid impacts.   d. maria.

True or False
If the statement is true, write true. If it is false, change the underlined word or words to make the statement true.

6. Earth's spinning on its axis is called <u>revolution</u>.
7. The tilt of Earth's axis as Earth revolves around the sun causes <u>eclipses</u>.
8. A total eclipse of the <u>sun</u> occurs only during a new moon.
9. Many <u>artificial satellites</u> orbit Earth.
10. The cooling of molten material on the moon formed the <u>craters</u>.

Checking Concepts

11. Describe the shape of Earth's orbit.
12. Mars's axis is tilted at about the same angle as Earth's axis. Do you think Mars has seasons? Explain your answer.
13. How does the time it takes the moon to rotate on its axis compare with the time it takes the moon to revolve around Earth?
14. Why isn't there a lunar eclipse every month?
15. Why do more people see a total lunar eclipse than a total solar eclipse?
16. Why is there a high tide on the side of Earth closest to the moon? On the side of Earth furthest from the moon?
17. What basic law of physics explains how a rocket moves forward?
18. Describe the events that formed the moon, according to the collision theory.
19. What did scientists learn by studying the rocks astronauts brought back from the moon?
20. **Writing to Learn** Imagine that trips to the moon are resuming. You are an astronaut going to the moon. Write a paragraph describing what you see as you arrive. What does the sky look like? What could the rocks you find help scientists learn?

Thinking Critically

21. **Relating Cause and Effect** How do the changing positions of the moon, Earth, and sun cause spring tides or neap tides on Earth?
22. **Applying Concepts** At what time does the full moon rise? Is it visible in the eastern sky or the western sky?
23. **Posing Questions** Suppose you were assigned to design a spacesuit for astronauts to wear on the moon. What questions about the moon would you need to have answered in order to design the spacesuit?

Thinking Critically

21. At new moon and full moon, the moon, sun, and Earth are lined up. The sun and moon's gravity combine to produce spring tides. At lunar first and third quarters, the moon and sun are at right angles. The sun and moon's gravity partly cancel out and neap tides result.

22. The full moon rises at sunset because it has to be opposite the sun in the sky for the face we see to be fully lighted. It therefore rises in the east as the sun sets in the west.
23. Sample questions: What are the temperatures like? What kinds of terrain will the astronauts have to cover? Is there any air to breathe or will we need to bring our own?

Applying Skills

Use the illustration below to answer Questions 24–26. (Hint: The tilt of the Earth's axis is 23.5°.)

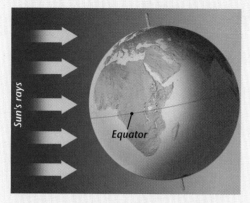

Sun's rays

Equator

24. **Interpreting Diagrams** On which hemisphere are the sun's rays falling most directly?
25. **Inferring** In the Northern Hemisphere, is it the summer solstice, winter solstice, or one of the equinoxes? How do you know?

26. **Predicting** Six months after this illustration, Earth will have revolved halfway around the sun. Show in a sketch which end of Earth's axis will be tilted toward the sun.

Performance CHAPTER PROJECT 1 **Assessment**

Project Wrap Up Now you are ready to present your log, map, and drawings. Here are some ways you can graph your data: time of moonrise for each date; how often you saw the moon at each compass direction; how often you saw the moon at a specific time. Display your graphs. Discuss any patterns you discovered with your classmates. With your classmates, predict when and where you can see the moon.

Reflect and Record In your journal, write about the easiest and hardest parts of this project. What would you do differently if you observed the moon for another month? What observation(s) surprised you? Why?

Test Preparation

Use these questions to prepare for standardized tests.

Study the diagram. Then answer Questions 27–30. Numbers 1, 2, 3, and 4 on the diagram indicate locations of the moon in its orbit around Earth.

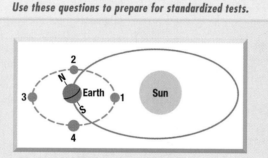

27. About how much time does it take the moon to revolve once around Earth?
    a. one day
    b. 7 days
    c. 27 days
    d. one year
28. Which of the following phases is the moon in at location 1?
    a. new   b. crescent
    c. half   d. full
29. At which location(s) could a lunar eclipse occur?
    a. 1 only   b. 3 only
    c. 1 and 3   d. 2 and 4

30. Only one side of the moon is visible from earth because
    a. the moon does not rotate on its axis.
    b. the moon does not revolve around Earth.
    c. the moon is in a geosynchronous orbit around Earth.
    d. the moon revolves once and rotates once in the same period of time.

Applying Skills

24. Northern Hemisphere
25. Summer solstice. The north end of Earth's axis is tilted toward the sun.
26. Students' sketches should show the southern end of Earth's axis tilted toward the sun.

Performance CHAPTER PROJECT 1 **Assessment**

Project Wrap Up Have students make graphs showing the different patterns, so all information is available for the class. Encourage students to discuss the patterns they see in the graphs. Emphasize these patterns:

◆ In the course of a day, the moon position changes from the eastern sky, through southern, to western. (Because of Earth's rotation).
◆ Moonrise gets progressively later throughout the cycle.
◆ The moon will be seen mostly in the southern half of the sky, rising more easterly and setting more westerly.
◆ The lit portion of the moon starts on the right side and waxes until full; as it wanes, the right side becomes slowly dark.

Reflect and Record Students may have had trouble determining compass direction or altitude. It may have been frustrating not to see the moon when they looked for it. Students might be surprised to discover that their results confirm that the full moon always rises at about the same time as sunset.

Test Preparation

27. c **28.** a **29.** b **30.** d

Program Resources

◆ **Inquiry Skills Activity Book** Provides teaching and review of all inquiry skills
◆ **Standardized Test Preparation Book** Provides standardized test practice
◆ **Reading in the Content Area** Provides strategies to improve science reading skills
◆ **Teacher's ELL Handbook** Provides multiple strategies for English language learners

CHAPTER 2

The Solar System

Sections	Time	Student Edition Activities	Other Activities	
CHAPTER PROJECT 2 **Model of the Solar System** p. J49	Ongoing (3 weeks)	Check Your Progress, pp. J55, J69, J77 Project Wrap Up, p. J91	TE	Chapter 2 Project Notes, pp. J48–49
1 Observing the Solar System pp. J50–55 ◆ 2.1.1 Explain how the heliocentric and geocentric models of the solar system differ. ◆ 2.1.2 Explain how scientists such as Kepler and Copernicus contributed to the current understanding of the solar system. ◆ 2.1.3 Explain the two factors that keep the planets in their orbits.	3 periods/ 1–2 blocks	**Discover** How Do Mass and Speed Affect an Object's Motion?, p. J50 **Try This** A Loopy Ellipse, p. J53	TE TE	Building Inquiry Skills: Comparing and Contrasting, p. J52; Modeling, p. J52 Including All Students, p. J52
2 The Sun pp. J56–61 ◆ 2.2.1 Describe how the sun produces its energy. ◆ 2.2.2 List and describe the layers of the sun's atmosphere. ◆ 2.2.3 Identify features of the sun's surface.	3 periods/ $1\frac{1}{2}$ blocks	**Discover** How Can You Safely Observe the Sun?, p. J56 **Try This** Viewing Sunspots, p. J58 **Real-World Lab: You and Your Environment** Stormy Sunspots, p. J61	TE ISLM	Demonstration, p. J57 Lab J-2, "Measuring the Diameter of the Sun"
3 The Inner Planets pp. J62–69 ◆ 2.3.1 Describe the main characteristics of the inner planets.	4 periods/ 2 blocks	**Discover** How Does Mars Look From Earth?, p. J62 **Sharpen Your Skills** Graphing, p. J65 **Try This** Remote Control, p. J68	TE TE TE	Integrating Earth Science, p. J63 Building Inquiry Skills: Observing, p. J64, p. J68 Demonstration, p. J65
4 The Outer Planets pp. J70–79 ◆ 2.4.1 Describe the main characteristics of the gas giant planets. ◆ 2.4.2 Compare Pluto with the other planets.	5 periods/ 2–3 blocks	**Discover** How Large Are the Outer Planets?, p. J70 **Try This** Model Saturn, p. J73 **Skills Lab: Developing Hypotheses** Speeding Around the Sun, pp. J78–79	TE TE TE	Building Inquiry Skills: Making Models, p. J72; Relating Cause and Effect, p. J76 Using the Visuals, p. J74 Language Arts, p. J75
5 Comets, Asteroids, and Meteors pp. J80–83 ◆ 2.5.1 Describe the characteristics of comets and asteroids. ◆ 2.5.2 Describe the formation of meteoroids.	2 periods/ 1 block	**Discover** Which Way Do Comet Tails Point?, p. J80	TE	Building Inquiry Skills: Predicting, p.J81; Hypothesizing, p. J82
6 ☁ _INTEGRATING LIFE SCIENCE_ **Is There Life Beyond Earth?** pp. J84–88 ◆ 2.6.1 Identify the conditions needed for living things to exist on Earth. ◆ 2.6.2 State why Mars and Europa are thought to be good places to look for signs of life.	3 periods/ 1–2 blocks	**Discover** Is Yeast Alive or Not?, p. J84 **Sharpen Your Skills** Communicating, p. J85	TE TE TE	Cultural Diversity, p. J85 Building Inquiry Skills: Making Judgments, p. J86 Including All Students, p. J86
Study Guide/Assessment pp. J89–91	1 period/ $\frac{1}{2}$ block		ISAB	Provides teaching and review of all inquiry skills

For Standard or Block Schedule The Resource Pro® CD-ROM gives you maximum flexibility for planning your instruction for any type of schedule. Resource Pro® contains Planning Express®, an advanced scheduling program, as well as the entire contents of the Teaching Resources and the Computer Test Bank.

Key: **SE** Student Edition
PLM Probeware Lab Manual
ISAB Inquiry Skills Activity Book

CHAPTER PLANNING GUIDE

Program Resources	Assessment Strategies	Media and Technology
TR Chapter 2 Project Teacher Notes, pp. J34–35 TR Chapter 2 Project Overview and Worksheets, pp. J36–39	TE Check Your Progress, pp. J55, J69, J77 TE Performance Assessment: Wrap Up, p. J91 TR Chapter 2 Project Scoring Rubric, p. J40	Science Explorer Internet Site Audio CDs and Audiotapes, English-Spanish Section Summaries
TR 2-1 Lesson Plan, p. J41 TR 2-1 Section Summary, p. J42 TR 2-1 Review and Reinforce, p. J43 TR 2-1 Enrich, p. J44	SE Section 1 Review, p. J55 TE Ongoing Assessment, pp. J51, J53 TE Performance Assessment, p. J55	Exploring Earth Science Videodisc, Unit 1 Side 1, "For the Love of Astronomy" Interactive Student Tutorial CD-ROM, J-2
TR 2-2 Lesson Plan, p. J45 TR 2-2 Section Summary, p. J46 TR 2-2 Review and Reinforce, p. J47 TR 2-2 Enrich, p. J48 TR Real-World Lab blackline masters, pp. J65–66	SE Section 2 Review, p. J60 SE Analyze and Conclude, p. J61 TE Ongoing Assessment, pp. J57, J59 TE Performance Assessment, p. J60	Exploring Earth Science Videodisc, Unit 1 Side 1, "Sunny Days"; Exploring Physical Science Videodisc, Unit 4 Side 2, "Wired to the Sun" Transparency 7, "Exploring the Sun" Lab Activity Videotape, *Astronomy*, 3
TR 2-3 Lesson Plan, p. J49 TR 2-3 Section Summary, p. J50 TR 2-3 Review and Reinforce, p. J51 TR 2-3 Enrich, p. J52 SES Book F, *Inside Earth,* Chapter 1	SE Section 3 Review, p. J69 TE Ongoing Assessment, pp. J63, J65, J67 TE Performance Assessment, p. J69	Transparency 8, "The Inner Planets"
TR 2-4 Lesson Plan, p. J53 TR 2-4 Section Summary, p. J54 TR 2-4 Review and Reinforce, p. J55 TR 2-4 Enrich, p. J56 TR Skills Lab blackline masters, pp. J67–69	SE Section 4 Review, p. J77 SE Analyze and Conclude, p. J79 TE Ongoing Assessment, pp. J71, J73, J75 TE Performance Assessment, p. J77	Transparency 9, "The Outer Planets" Lab Activity Videotape, *Astronomy*, 4
TR 2-5 Lesson Plan, p. J57 TR 2-5 Section Summary, p. J58 TR 2-5 Review and Reinforce, p. J59 TR 2-5 Enrich, p. J60 SES Book G, *Earth's Changing Surface,* Chapter 4	SE Section 5 Review, p. J83 TE Ongoing Assessment, p. J81 TE Performance Assessment, p. J83	Audio CDs and Audiotapes, English-Spanish Summary 2-5 Interactive Student Tutorial CD-ROM, J-2
TR 2-6 Lesson Plan, p. J61 TR 2-6 Section Summary, p. J62 TR 2-6 Review and Reinforce, p. J63 TR 2-6 Enrich, p. J64	SE Section 6 Review, p. J87 TE Ongoing Assessment, p. J85 TE Performance Assessment, p. J87	Exploring Life Science Videodisc, Unit 1 Side 2, "Evolution of Cells"
GSW Provides worksheets to promote student comprehension of content RCA Provides strategies to improve science reading skills ELL Provides multiple strategies for English language learners	SE Study Guide/Assessment, pp. J89–91 TR Performance Assessment, pp. J121–123; Test, pp. J124–127 CTB *Astronomy,* Chapter 2 Test STP Provides standardized test practice	Computer Test Bank, *Astronomy,* Chapter 2 Test Interactive Student Tutorial CD-ROM, J-2

TE Teacher's Edition   **TR** Teaching Resources   **CTB** Computer Test Bank
RCA Reading in the Content Area   **ISLM** Integrated Science Laboratory Manual   **STP** Standardized Test Preparation Book
GSW Guided Study Workbook   **ELL** Teacher's ELL Handbook   **SES** Science Explorer Series Text

Meeting the National Science Education Standards and AAAS Benchmarks

National Science Education Standards	Benchmarks for Science Literacy	Unifying Themes
Science as Inquiry (Content Standard A) ◆ **Develop descriptions, explanations, predictions, and models using evidence** Students design scale models of the solar system. *(Chapter Project; Section 4)* **Physical Science** (Content Standard B) ◆ **Transfer of energy** Energy from the sun is the source of energy in our solar system. *(Section 2)* **Earth and Space Science** (Content Standard D) ◆ **Structure of the Earth system** Earth's structure is the basis for understanding the structure of other planets. *(Section 3)* ◆ **Earth in the solar system** The heliocentric model of the solar system is the basis for our modern understanding. *(Section 1)* **Science in Personal and Social Perspectives** (Content Standard F) ◆ **Risks and benefits** Space exploration has many benefits but is very costly and risky. *(Science and Society)* **History and Nature of Science** (Content Standard G) ◆ **History of science** The struggle that occurred when society changed from a geocentric to a heliocentric model of the solar system is an example of the development of a scientific paradigm. *(Section 1)*	**1A The Scientific World View** Students learn about the observations and hypotheses that led to the shift from a geocentric to a heliocentric system of planets. *(Section 1)* Investigations into potential life on other planets are described. *(Section 6; Science and Society)* **2C Mathematical Inquiry** Applied mathematics helped scientists predict the existence of the planet Neptune. *(Sections 1, 4)* **4A The Universe** Each category of solar system object has distinct characteristics that reveal information about the nature of that object. *(Sections 1, 2, 3, 4, 5; Skills Lab; Real-World Lab)* **4B The Earth** The structure of Earth is used as the basis for making inferences about other planets. *(Section 3)* **4E Energy Transformation** The energy released by nuclear fusion in the sun's core is converted into light, heat, and other forms of energy at the sun's surface. *(Section 2; Real-World Lab)* **4G Forces of Nature** Gravity holds satellites in orbit around planets and the planets and other objects in orbit around the sun. *(Sections 1, 3, 4, 5)* **11B Models** Students construct scale models of the planets and sun. *(Chapter Project)*	◆ **Energy** Energy from reactions in the sun's core is transmitted as light and heat to all of the bodies in the solar system. *(Sections 2, 3, 4, 5; Skills Lab; Real-World Lab)* ◆ **Scale and Structure** Our understanding of the structure of the solar system depends on accurate observations. The sun is the largest body in the solar system. The outer planets, except for Pluto, are huge gas giants. The inner planets and Pluto are rocky and comparatively small. *(Sections 1, 2, 3, 4; Chapter Project)* ◆ **Unity and Diversity** Students compare the similarities of objects in the solar system and contrast their differences. The idea that conditions for life should be the same on all planets is considered, yet studies reveal that Earth is unique in the solar system because it supports life. *(Section 6)* ◆ **Stability** The planets are held in constant orbits by the force of the sun's gravity. *(Sections 1, 2; Skills Lab)*

Take It to the Net

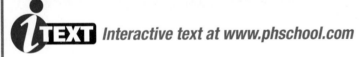 **Interactive text at www.phschool.com**

Science Explorer comes alive with iText.

- **Complete student text** is accessible from any computer with a browser.
- **Animations, simulations, and videos** enhance student understanding and retention of concepts.
- **Self-tests and online study tools** assess student understanding.
- **Teacher management tools** help you make the most of this valuable resource.

STAY CURRENT with  **SCIENCE NEWS**®

Find out the latest research and information about astronomy at:
www.phschool.com

 **www.phschool.com**

Go to **www.phschool.com** and click on the Science icon. Then click on Science Explorer under PH@school.

ACTIVITY	Time (minutes)	Materials *Quantities for one work group*	Skills
Section 1			
Discover, p. 50	10	**Nonconsumable** toy trucks, rocks	Predicting
Try This, p. 53	15	**Consumable** white paper, corrugated cardboard, 30-cm string **Nonconsumable** 2 pushpins, ruler, pencil	Predicting
Section 2			
Discover, p. 56	15	**Consumable** thin cardboard, masking tape **Nonconsumable** binoculars, ring stand, ruler, scissors, white paper	Observing
Try This, p. 58	10/day over 10 days	**Consumable** thin cardboard, masking tape, white paper **Nonconsumable** binoculars, ring stand, ruler, scissors	Interpreting Data
Real-World Lab, p. 61	30	**Consumable** graph paper **Nonconsumable** pencil, ruler	Graphing, Interpreting Data
Section 3			
Discover, p. 62	10	**Nonconsumable** compass, ruler	Observing
Sharpen Your Skills, p. 65	15	**Consumable** graph paper **Nonconsumable** colored pencils	Graphing
Try This, p. 68	15	**Consumable** tape, paper **Nonconsumable** goggles	Inferring
Section 4			
Discover, p. 70	15	**Consumable** lined paper, butcher paper or poster board, string **Nonconsumable** quarter, ruler, compass, pushpin	Classifying
Try This, p. 73	20	**Consumable** clear plastic sheet, tape, baking soda, peppercorn, glue (optional) **Nonconsumable** 8-cm plastic foam sphere, ruler, scissors, compass, 5 toothpicks	Making Models
Skills Lab, p. 78	45	**Consumable** string, 1.5 m **Nonconsumable** one-hole rubber stopper; plastic tube, 6 cm; stopwatch; weight or several washers; meter stick	Developing Hypotheses
Section 5			
Discover, p. 80	10	**Consumable** 3 10-cm lengths of string **Nonconsumable** modeling clay, pencil, small fan	Inferring
Section 6			
Discover, p. 84	15	**Consumable** yeast, warm water, sugar **Nonconsumable** bowl, thermometer, spoon, stopwatch or clock	Forming Operational Definitions

A list of all materials required for the Student Edition activities can be found beginning on page T15. You can obtain information about ordering materials by calling 1-800-848-9500 or by accessing the Science Explorer Internet site at: **www.phschool.com**

Model of the Solar System

Movies, books, and television shows have given most people a distorted understanding of the sizes of objects and distances between objects in the solar system. The Chapter Project will help students understand that the distances between the planets are very large relative to the sizes of the planets.

Purpose By creating scale models of the solar system, students will begin to understand the vastness of space, including the size of planets and the great distances between them. They will also discover difficulties in scaling the size of objects and distance between objects into the same scale measurements.

Skills Focus After completing the Chapter 2 project, students will be able to

◆ convert large numbers to the established scale;

◆ compare scaled distances and diameters to familiar distances and diameters;

◆ establish scale models to show the actual size of the solar system;

◆ discover why it can be difficult to build a scale model of the solar system's distance.

Suggested Shortcuts Allow students to do the mathematical calculations in groups. Since many distances in the solar system are given in astronomical units, an easy way to establish a scale is to let 1 AU = 1 m. Students can then brainstorm familiar objects that are comparable to the estimated planet sizes. If students have not had much experience with scaling, providing in-class time will allow you to assist students. Additionally, you may decide to allow students to build the models in groups, or you can lead the class in one large model-building project.

Project Time Line This project requires about four weeks. Students will work on a different model each week, and the final week will be reserved for presentation preparation. Models should be completed sequentially, beginning with the planet sizes, then moving to the distance between the planets, and ending with the combination model. Students should complete the appropriate portion of the worksheets and get approval from

CHAPTER
2 The Solar System

This artist's conception shows the *Cassini* space probe arriving near Saturn's rings in 2004.

WEB ACTIVITY www.phschool.com

48 ◆ J

you before they begin each phase of model building. Toward the end of the third week, students should prepare their class presentation. The project should end with the presentations and a class discussion. Before beginning the project, see Chapter 2 Project Teacher Notes on pages 34–35 in Teaching Resources for more details on carrying out the project. Also, distribute the students' Chapter 2 Project Overview and Worksheets and Scoring Rubric on pages 36–40 in Teaching Resources.

Possible Materials For model building, students will need meter sticks or metric rulers and calculators. Since models of solar system distance usually involve large numbers, students may also need maps of their local community. Familiar objects such as tennis balls, beach balls, pieces of fruit (grapefruit, orange, etc.), marbles, dried beans, and ball bearings will make good planets, depending on the required diameters. Allow students to be creative in thinking about objects they can use to model relative planet sizes.

PROJECT 2

Model of the Solar System

If you could drive from Earth to the sun at 100 kilometers per hour, your trip would take 170 years. And most distances in the solar system are even greater! The *Cassini* space probe left Earth for Saturn in 1997 traveling much faster than highway speed, but will not arrive at Saturn's rings until 2004. Sizes in the solar system can be huge, too. Compared with some of the other planets in the solar system, Earth is very small. Saturn, for example, is about 10 times Earth's diameter.

In this chapter, you will get to know many of the objects in the solar system. To help you understand the huge distances and sizes, you will design three different scale models of the solar system.

Your Goal To design scale models of the solar system.

To complete this project, you will
- ◆ design a model to show the planets' distances from the sun
- ◆ design a model to show the planets' sizes relative to the sun
- ◆ test different scales to see if you can use the same scale for both size and distance in one model

Get Started Begin by previewing the tables with distances and diameters on pages 63 and 71. Brainstorm with a group of classmates how you will build your models. Prepare a data sheet to record your calculations of scaled-down distances and diameters.

Check Your Progress You will be working on this project as you study this chapter. To keep your project on track, look for Check Your Progress boxes at the following points.

Section 1 Review, page 55: Design a model to show distances.
Section 3 Review, page 69: Design a model to show diameters.
Section 4 Review, page 77: Design one scale model that shows both sizes and distances.

Wrap Up At the end of the chapter (page 91), you will present your design to the class.

Program Resources

- ◆ **Teaching Resources** Chapter 2 Project Teacher's Notes, pp. 34–35; Project Overview and Worksheets, pp. 36–39; Project Scoring Rubric, p. 40

Media and Technology

🎧 **Audio CDs** and **Audiotapes**
English-Spanish Section Summaries

WEB ACTIVITY www.phschool.com

You will find an Internet activity, chapter self-tests for students, and links to other chapter topics at this site.

Other tools that may assist students in their model building are available from *The Astronomical Society of the Pacific*, 390 Ashton Avenue, San Francisco, CA 94112, USA.

Launching the Project When introducing the project, bring in a scale model of an object familiar to all students (e.g., the Statue of Liberty). Ask: **How does the size of this model compare to the real object?** Discuss scaling. Take measurements of features of the model, and compare these to measurements of features on the actual object. If the model is proportional, the scaling should be the same for each measurement taken. Ask: **How big is Earth?** Discuss size. If you travel once around Earth, you would cover about 40,000 km. The United States is about 4,000 km across. It takes about four or five days to make this journey by car, yet this is only 1/10 the distance around the Earth! Ask: **How could you compare size and distance in space with travel speeds on Earth?** Compare average travel speeds. (*Walking 3.6 km/hr, car 80 km/hr, jet 1,436 km/hr, light 300,000 km/sec*) Since the distance from Earth to the moon is about 386,000 km, it takes about 1.5 sec for light to travel this distance. Ask students how long it would take a jet to fly there.

Allow time for students to read the description of the project in their text and the Chapter Project Overview on pages 36–37 in Teaching Resources. Pass out copies of the Chapter 2 Project Worksheets on pages 38–39 in Teaching Resources for students to review.

Performance Assessment

The Chapter 2 Project Scoring Rubric on page 40 of Teaching Resources will help you evaluate how well students complete the Chapter 2 Project. Students will be assessed on
- ◆ how accurately they did their mathematical calculations;
- ◆ how well they selected model scales;
- ◆ how well they can discuss the concepts of size and scaling;
- ◆ the thoroughness and organization of their presentation.

By sharing the Chapter 2 Project Scoring Rubric with students at the beginning of the project, you will make it clear to them what they are expected to do.

Objectives

After completing the lesson, students will be able to

♦ explain how the heliocentric and geocentric models of the solar system differ;

♦ explain how scientists such as Kepler and Copernicus contributed to the current understanding of the solar system;

♦ explain the two factors that keep the planets in their orbits.

Key Terms geocentric, heliocentric, ellipse, inertia

1 Engage/Explore

Activating Prior Knowledge

Show students a photograph of the night sky that shows stars and the moon. Ask them to identify the objects they see. Then ask: **Where was the sun when this picture was taken?** (*The sun could not be seen from the spot where the picture was taken because it was on the other side of Earth.*) Reinforce the idea that the objects in our solar system are moving.

DISCOVER

Skills Focus predicting
Materials *toy truck, rocks*
Time 10 minutes
Tips A toy car, roller skate, or skateboard may be substituted for the truck. Remind students to push the truck gently at first. When they add rocks to the truck, students should be careful not to pile them so high that they fall out when the truck is pushed.
Expected Outcome Students should observe that it is harder to stop the truck when the truck is moving faster and when it has more mass.
Think It Over It would be easier to stop the truck if the partner pushed it more slowly. It would be harder to stop the truck if more mass was added.

DISCOVER ·············· ACTIVITY

How Do Mass and Speed Affect an Object's Motion?

1. Have your partner push a toy truck across the table toward you. Stop the truck with your hands.

2. Repeat Step 1, but have your partner push the truck a little faster. Was it easier or harder to stop the truck than in Step 1?

3. Now add some rocks or other heavy objects to the truck and repeat Step 1. Your partner should push the truck at the same speed as in Step 1. How hard was it to stop the truck this time compared to Step 1?

4. Repeat Step 2 with the rocks still in the truck. How hard was it to stop the truck this time?

Think It Over
Predicting How hard would it be to stop the truck if your partner pushed it more slowly? If you added more mass to the truck?

GUIDE FOR READING

♦ How do the heliocentric and geocentric descriptions of the solar system differ?

♦ What did Kepler discover about the orbits of the planets?

♦ What two factors keep the planets in their orbits?

Reading Tip As you read, make a list of the evidence that supports the heliocentric system.

Have you ever lain outdoors on a starry night, gazing up at the stars? As you watch, the stars seem to move across the sky. The sky seems to be rotating right over your head. In fact, from the Northern Hemisphere, the sky appears to rotate completely around Polaris, the North Star, once every 24 hours.

Now think about what you see every day. During the day, the sun appears to move across the sky. From here on Earth, it seems as if Earth is stationary and that the sun, moon, and stars are all moving around Earth. But is the sky really moving above you? Centuries ago, before there were space shuttles or even telescopes, there was no easy way to find out.

Figure 1 This photo was made by exposing the camera film for several hours. Each star appears as part of a circle, and all the stars seem to revolve around a single point.

READING STRATEGIES

Reading Tip As students read the chapter, have them construct a list of the evidence that supports the heliocentric model and includes motion of the satellites of Jupiter and the phases of Venus.

Study and Comprehension As students read the section, have them write brief summaries of the information under each heading. Remind students that summarizing involves stating briefly, in their own words, the main points and key details. In a class discussion, invite volunteers to give oral summaries of the information in the section.

Wandering Stars

When the ancient Greeks watched the stars move across the sky, they noticed that the patterns of most of the stars didn't change. Although the stars seemed to move, they stayed in the same position relative to each other. For example, the constellations kept the same shapes from night to night and from year to year.

As they observed the sky more carefully, the Greeks noticed something surprising. Five points of light seemed to wander among the stars. The Greeks called these objects *planets*, from the Greek word meaning "wandering star." The Greeks made very careful observations of the motions of the five planets they could see. You know these planets by the names the ancient Romans later gave them: Mercury, Venus, Mars, Jupiter, and Saturn.

Greek Ideas: Earth at the Center

When you look up at the sky, you can almost imagine that you are under a rotating dome with the stars pasted on it. The Greeks thought that they were inside a rotating dome they called the celestial sphere. Most Greek astronomers believed that the universe is perfect and unchangeable and that Earth is stationary in the center of the celestial sphere. Since *geo* is the Greek word for Earth, an Earth-centered explanation is known as a **geocentric** (jee oh SEN trik) system. **In a geocentric system, Earth is at the center of the revolving planets.**

In A.D. 140, the Greek astronomer Ptolemy (TAHL uh mee) explained the motion of the planets in another way. Like the earlier Greeks, Ptolemy thought that Earth is at the center of the system of planets. Ptolemy also thought that the moon, Mercury, Venus, the sun, Mars, Jupiter, and Saturn revolve around Earth.

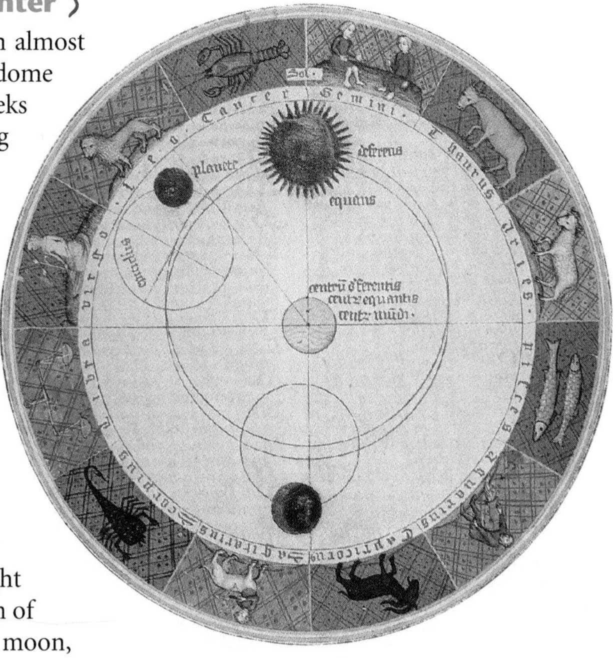

In Ptolemy's explanation, however, the planets move on little circles that move on bigger circles. Ptolemy thought that this explained why the planets seem to move at different speeds, and even backwards, among the stars. For the next 1,400 years, people believed that Ptolemy's ideas were correct.

☑ *Checkpoint* What is a geocentric system?

Figure 2 In the 1500s, an astronomy book published this illustration of Ptolemy's system. *Interpreting Diagrams* **Where is Earth located in this illustration?**

Program Resources

◆ **Teaching Resources** 2-1 Lesson Plan, p. 41; 2-1 Section Summary, p. 42
◆ **Guided Study Workbook** Section 2-1

Answers to Self-Assessment

Caption Question

Figure 2 Earth is in the center.

☑ *Checkpoint*

A geocentric system is one in which Earth is at the center of a system of revolving planets.

2 Facilitate

Wandering Stars

Building Inquiry Skills: Inferring

Guide students in evaluating what the ancient astronomers knew about stars. Ask: **Why did the Greeks only see five planets?** *(They did not have telescopes and could not see the other planets because they are too dim.)* **learning modality: verbal**

Greek Ideas: Earth at the Center

Cultural Diversity

Remind students that the Romans named the planets they knew after their gods. Tell them that other cultures gave objects in the sky names meaningful in those cultures. Ask students from other cultures to give examples of such names from their cultures. **learning modality: verbal**

Using the Visuals: Figure 1

Ask students to infer why exposing the film for several hours produced the circular effect shown in the figure. If they have difficulty, ask: **What is the single point around which the stars seem to revolve?** *(Polaris or the North Star)* Remind students that in the Northern Hemisphere, the stars seem to rotate around the North Star. Leaving the camera shutter open as this rotation occurs produces the circular effect. **learning modality: visual**

Ongoing Assessment

Drawing Have students draw and label a diagram of a geocentric system. The diagram should include the sun, Earth, and at least one other planet.

Copernicus's Idea: Sun at the Center

Building Inquiry Skills: Comparing and Contrasting

Have students diagram Copernicus's heliocentric model and then compare their diagram with the geocentric model in Figure 2. Ask: **How does Earth's motion differ in each system?** (*Geocentric—Earth is not moving; heliocentric—Earth rotates on its axis and revolves around the sun*) **How does the motion of planets differ in each system?** (*Geocentric—planets revolve around Earth; heliocentric—all planets revolve around the sun*) **learning modality: logical/mathematical**

Portfolio Students can save their diagrams in their portfolios.

Galileo's Observations

Including All Students

Invite students who need additional challenges to research the phases of Venus in an astronomy textbook or other reference book. Students can draw diagrams to show how the sun, Earth, and Venus are aligned as Venus passes through its phases. Students can present their diagrams to the class. **learning modality: visual**

Building Inquiry Skills: Modeling

Have students model the movements of the inner planets. Divide the class into groups of four. Have each group draw concentric circles of radii 3.5 m, 5.0 m, and 7.5 m. One student representing the sun will stand in the center. The other students will model the planets Venus, Earth, and Mars by walking around the circles at different speeds. The students must time their movement so that "Venus" on the inner circle takes three steps, in the same time as "Earth" on the second circle takes two steps and "Mars" on the outer circle takes one step. Make sure students observe their relative positions as they walk, especially how inner planets overtake outer planets. **learning modality: kinesthetic**

Copernicus's Idea: Sun at the Center

In the early 1500s, the Polish astronomer Nicolaus Copernicus developed another explanation for the motions of the planets. Copernicus thought that the sun is at the center of the system of planets. His sun-centered system is called a **heliocentric** (hee lee oh SEN trik) system. *Helios* is Greek for "sun." **In a heliocentric system, Earth and the other planets revolve around the sun.** Copernicus's explanation included the six planets he knew about: Mercury, Venus, Earth, Mars, Jupiter, and Saturn.

Galileo's Observations

In the 1500s and 1600s, most people still believed Ptolemy's geocentric explanation. However, the Italian astronomer Galileo Galilei, who lived nearly 100 years after Copernicus, thought that the heliocentric explanation was correct.

Recall from Chapter 1 that Galileo was the first scientist to use a telescope to look at objects in the sky. With his telescope, Galileo made two discoveries that supported the heliocentric model. First, Galileo saw four moons revolving around Jupiter. Galileo's observations of Jupiter's moons showed that not everything in the sky revolves around Earth.

Figure 3 From this observatory, Tycho Brahe made accurate observations of the planets for nearly 20 years. His data became the basis for many important discoveries.

Galileo's observations of Venus also supported Copernicus's heliocentric system. Galileo discovered that Venus goes through phases similar to those of Earth's moon. Galileo reasoned that the phases of Venus could not be explained if Earth were at the center of the system of planets. So Ptolemy's geocentric system could not be correct.

Galileo's evidence gradually convinced others that Copernicus's explanation was correct. Today, people talk about the "solar system" rather than the "Earth system." This shows that people accept Copernicus's idea that the sun is at the center.

✓ *Checkpoint* *What two discoveries made by Galileo supported the heliocentric description of the solar system?*

Brahe and Kepler

Copernicus and Galileo had correctly identified the sun as the center of the system of planets. But Copernicus, like Ptolemy, assumed that the orbits of the planets are circles.

Copernicus's ideas were based on observations made by the ancient Greeks. In the late 1500s, Tycho Brahe (TEE koh BRAH uh), a Danish astronomer, made

Background

History of Science Johannes Kepler believed the universe contained many profound mathematical patterns and relationships. One of his life-long endeavors was to identify a relationship between the mathematics of the movement of the planets around the sun and the mathematics of musical sound. Kepler compared the mathematics of many aspects of planetary motion to musical harmonies before asserting that he had discovered a clear relationship. In his book *Harmonice Mundi* (The Harmony of the World), Kepler assigned a range of sounds to each planet. Modern scientists do not accept Kepler's musical theories. However, his research may have led him to discover the relationship between the speed of a planet and its distance from the sun, a concept published in the same book.

much more accurate observations. Brahe carefully observed the positions of the planets for almost 20 years.

In 1600, a German mathematician, Johannes Kepler, went to work analyzing Brahe's data. Kepler tried to figure out the shape of the planets' orbits. At first, he assumed that the orbits are circles. When Kepler tried to figure out the exact orbit of Mars, however, no circle fit the observations.

Kepler had discovered that the orbit of each planet is an ellipse. An **ellipse** is an elongated circle, or oval shape. Kepler found that if he assumed that Mars's orbit is an ellipse, his calculations fit Brahe's observations better.

Inertia and Gravity

Kepler had discovered the correct shape of the planets' orbits. But he could not explain why the planets stay in orbit. The work of the English scientist Isaac Newton provided the answer to that puzzle. **Newton concluded that two factors—inertia and gravity—combine to keep the planets in orbit.**

Galileo had discovered that a moving object will continue to move until some force acts to stop its motion. This tendency of a moving object to continue in a straight line or a stationary object to remain in place is the object's **inertia**. The more mass an object has, the more inertia it has. As you found if you did the Discover activity, an object with greater inertia is more difficult to start or stop.

Isaac Newton picked up where Galileo had left off. Late in his life, Newton told the story of how watching an apple fall from a tree in 1665 had made him think about motion. He hypothesized that the same force that pulls the apple to the ground also pulls the moon toward Earth. This force, called gravity, attracts all

Figure 4 Newton was a man of many achievements. Among them was the invention of this telescope.

A Loopy Ellipse

You can draw an ellipse. **ACTIVITY**

1.  Carefully stick two pushpins about 10 cm apart through a sheet of white paper on top of corrugated cardboard.

2. Tie the ends of a 30-cm piece of string together. Place the string around the pushpins.

3. Keeping the string tight, move a pencil around inside the string.

4. Now place the pushpins 5 cm apart. Repeat Step 3.

Predicting How does changing the distance between the pushpins affect the ellipse's shape? What shape would you draw if you used only one pushpin?

Brahe and Kepler

Building Inquiry Skills: Inferring

To help students understand elliptical orbits, diagram a planet and its orbit on the board. Challenge students to infer why scientists record a planet's average distance from the sun. Ask: **In an elliptical orbit, what happens to the distance between the planet and the sun?** (*It changes as the planet revolves.*) Have a volunteer point out where on the diagram the planet is closest and where it is farthest from the sun. Tell students that Earth is closest to the sun in the Northern Hemisphere winter. Ask: **What effect does the distance from the sun have on Earth's temperature?** (*The distance from the sun has little noticeable effect on Earth's temperature.*) **learning modality: visual**

TRY THIS

Skills Focus predicting **ACTIVITY**
Materials *2 pushpins, white paper, corrugated cardboard, ruler, 30-cm string, pencil*
Time 15 minutes
Tips Provide students with pieces of cardboard the same size as a sheet of paper. Remind students to keep the string taut when drawing their lines.
Expected Outcome Students should predict that moving the pushpins closer together makes the ellipse more round. If they used only one pushpin, they would draw a circle.
Extend Challenge students to predict the shape of ellipses formed with pushpins 2.5 cm and 7.5 cm apart. Encourage them to test their predictions.
learning modality: kinesthetic

Media and Technology

 **Exploring Earth Science Videodisc**
Unit 1, Side 1, "For the Love of Astronomy"

Chapter 1

Answers to Self-Assessment

✓ *Checkpoint*

Jupiter's four moons revolve around the planet. Venus goes through phases similar to those of Earth's moon.

Ongoing Assessment

Writing Have students write a paragraph explaining in their own words the contributions made to the heliocentric model by Copernicus, Galileo, Kepler, and Newton.

Inertia and Gravity

Using the Visuals: Figure 5

As students examine the figure, have them trace the path the planet would take if the sun's gravity disappeared. (*The planet would continue to move in a straight path in the direction it was going when the gravity disappeared.*) **learning modality: visual**

More to Discover

Addressing Naive Conceptions

Explain to students that it is difficult to accurately represent the sizes and distances of objects in the solar system on a diagram such as Figure 6. If the sun and the planets were drawn to the same scale as the distances on the diagram, the sun would be a tiny dot about 0.10 mm in diameter and the planets would all be microscopic. On the other hand, if the distances were drawn to the same scale as the sizes of the planets, the diagram would have to be about 1.0 km wide! **learning modality: visual**

Real-Life Learning

In 1982, all of the planets were within 95° of each other as viewed from the sun. This alignment caused some sensationalist newspapers and books to predict earthquakes and global disasters. Assign students to groups of four. Have each group develop an explanation of why this kind of planetary alignment could never cause any noticeable effects on Earth. (*Gravity from the planets is far too weak.*) **cooperative learning**

Building Inquiry Skills: Graphing

To compare the distances between the planets and the sun, students can make a bar graph using the data in Figure 6. The *x*-axis should show the names of the planets and the *y*-axis the distance from the sun. Help students choose the intervals for the *y*-axis. They may want to have 1 cm equal 500 million km. **learning modality: logical/ mathematical**

Mercury 58,000,000 km
Venus 108,000,000 km
Earth 150,000,000 km
Mars 228,000,000 km
Jupiter 778,000,000 km
Saturn 1,427,000,000 km

objects toward each other. The strength of gravity depends on the masses of the objects and the distance between them.)

Newton figured out that Earth keeps pulling the moon toward it with gravity. At the same time, the moon keeps moving ahead because of its inertia. Earth curves away as the moon falls toward it, so the moon winds up in orbit around Earth.

In the same way, the planets are in orbit around the sun because the sun's gravity pulls on them while their inertia keeps them moving ahead. Therefore, the planets keep moving around the sun and end up in orbit.

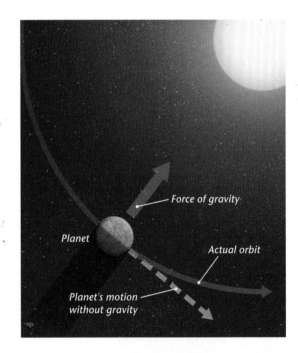

Figure 5 If there were no force of gravity, inertia would make a planet travel in a straight line. But because gravity pulls the planet toward the sun, the planet actually travels in an elliptical orbit around the sun. *Interpreting Diagrams What would happen if a planet had no inertia?*

Force of gravity
Planet
Actual orbit
Planet's motion without gravity

| Uranus | Neptune | Pluto |
| 2,871,000,000 km | 4,497,000,000 km | 5,913,000,000 km |

Figure 6 This illustration shows the average distances of the planets from the sun. The sizes of the planets are not to scale.

More to Discover

Since Newton's time, our knowledge about the solar system has increased dramatically. Newton knew of the same six planets the ancient Greeks had known—Mercury, Venus, Earth, Mars, Jupiter, and Saturn. Now astronomers know three more planets—Uranus, Neptune, and Pluto. Astronomers have also identified many other objects in the solar system, such as comets and asteroids, that you will learn about later in this chapter.

Galileo and Newton used telescopes on Earth to observe the solar system. Astronomers still use telescopes on Earth, but they have also made close-up observations of the planets from space probes sent far into the solar system. Our understanding of the solar system continues to change every day. Who knows what new discoveries will be made in your lifetime!

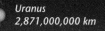

Section 1 Review

1. How is Copernicus's description of the system of planets different from Ptolemy's description?
2. How did Galileo's observations of Jupiter's moons help to show that the geocentric explanation is incorrect?
3. What shape are the orbits of the planets? How was the discovery of this orbit shape made?
4. What two factors act together to keep the planets in orbit around the sun?
5. **Thinking Critically Applying Concepts** People usually say that the sun rises in the east, moves across the sky, and sets in the west. Is this description literally correct? Explain.

> **Check Your Progress** CHAPTER PROJECT 2
> Begin by making a table that shows the distances of the planets from the sun. To help visualize the solar system, you can reduce all the distances by the same amount: for example, divide all distances by 100,000 or 1,000,000. You can use the resulting smaller numbers to design a scale model of the solar system. Record your calculations on your data sheet. Now choose a different scale and repeat your calculations. Which scale makes it easier to see the relative distances between the planets and the sun?

Answers to Self-Assessment

Caption Question

Figure 5 The planet would be pulled into the sun.

3 Assess

Section 1 Review Answers

1. Ptolemy thought that Earth was in the center of the system of planets. The other planets, the moon, and the sun all revolve around Earth. Copernicus thought that the sun was in the middle of Earth's orbit, and that the other planets revolved around the sun in circular orbits.
2. Galileo's observations of moons revolving around Jupiter showed that not everything in the sky revolved around Earth.
3. The planets' orbits are elliptical. Kepler analyzed Brahe's observations about the motion of Mars and found that the data matched an elliptical orbit.
4. Gravity and inertia act together to keep the planets in orbit.
5. No. Earth is rotating from west to east. This causes the sun to appear to move across the sky in the opposite direction.

> **Check Your Progress** CHAPTER PROJECT 2
> If students completed the Building Inquiry Skills activity on page 54, they can use that information here. They can also refer to the Addressing Naive Conceptions strategy on page 54. Suggest that students use lined paper or graph paper to keep their calculations neat and easy to follow. If students are having difficulty finding a good scale, suggest that they try 1: 10,000,000.

Performance Assessment

Organizing Information Have students create concept maps that illustrate the relationships among the following: Kepler, Ptolemy, Newton, Galileo, heliocentric, elliptical orbit, geocentric, inertia, and gravity.

SECTION 2 The Sun

Objectives

After completing the lesson, students will be able to

◆ describe how the sun produces its energy;

◆ list and describe the layers of the sun's atmosphere;

◆ identify features of the sun's surface.

Key Terms nuclear fusion, core, photosphere, chromosphere, corona, solar wind, sunspot, prominence, solar flare

1 Engage/Explore

Activating Prior Knowledge

Invite students who have gotten sunburned to tell about their experiences. Encourage all students to imagine going outside on a clear, hot day and feeling the warmth of the sun. Then ask: **What do we receive from the sun?** (*Samples: Light, heat*)

DISCOVER

Skills Focus observing
Materials *binoculars, ring stand, ruler, thin cardboard, scissors, masking tape, white paper*
Time 15 minutes
Tips If binoculars are not available, make a pinhole in a sheet of cardboard and project the sun's image through the hole onto the white paper. (If the pinhole is made very small, sometimes larger sunspots will be visible.) CAUTION: *Students must never look directly at the sun.* A small telescope can also be used to project the image. CAUTION: *The image of the sun focused to a point by a small telescope can cause burns and ignite paper.*
Think It Over Students should see a large bright circle. They may also see and draw sunspots.

SECTION 2 The Sun

DISCOVER · ACTIVITY

How Can You Safely Observe the Sun?

1. Clamp a pair of binoculars to a ring stand.

2. Cut a hole in a 20-cm by 28-cm sheet of thin cardboard so that it will fit over the binoculars, as shown in the photo. The cardboard should cover one lens, but allow light through the other lens. Tape the cardboard on securely. **CAUTION:** *Never look directly at the sun. You will hurt your eyes if you do.*

3. Use the binoculars to project an image of the sun onto a sheet of white paper. The cardboard will shade the white paper. Change the focus and move the paper back and forth until you get a sharp image.

Think It Over
Observing Draw what you see on the paper. What do you see on the surface of the sun?

GUIDE FOR READING

◆ How does the sun get its energy?

◆ What are the layers of the sun's atmosphere?

◆ What are some features of the sun's surface?

Reading Tip As you read, write a sentence defining each boldfaced term in your own words.

The sun's gravity is by far the most powerful force in the solar system—strong enough to hold all of the planets and comets in orbit! The sun's gravity is so strong because the sun's mass is very large. In fact, 99.8 percent of the mass of the solar system is in the sun.

Like Earth, the sun has an interior and an atmosphere. Unlike Earth, however, the sun does not have a solid surface. The sun is a ball of glowing gas. About three fourths of the sun's mass is hydrogen, one fourth is helium, and very small amounts are other chemical elements.

The Sun's Interior

The interior of the sun is like a giant furnace. Like furnaces in houses, the sun produces energy. But the sun does not get its energy from burning fuels such as oil. **Instead, the sun's energy comes from nuclear fusion.** In the process of **nuclear fusion,** hydrogen atoms join together to form helium. Nuclear fusion occurs only under conditions of extremely high temperature and pressure. The temperature inside the sun's **core,** or center, reaches about 15 million degrees Celsius, high enough for nuclear fusion to occur.

READING STRATEGIES

Reading Tip Remind students that one way to make sure they understand key ideas in their reading is to write the ideas in their own words. After students have written sentences defining features on the sun's surface, have them read aloud their definitions to partners. Encourage partners to discuss ways that these features can affect communications satellites.

Program Resources

◆ **Teaching Resources** 2-2 Lesson Plan, p. 45; 2-2 Section Summary, p. 46

◆ **Integrated Science Laboratory Manual,** J-2, "Measuring the Diameter of the Sun"

◆ **Guided Study Workbook** Section 2-2

The total mass of the helium produced by nuclear fusion is slightly less than the total mass of the hydrogen that goes into it. The change in mass occurs because some of the matter is converted into energy, including light and heat. The light and heat gradually move from the core of the sun to its atmosphere and escape into space. Some of this light and heat reach Earth, becoming Earth's main source of energy.

There is enough hydrogen fuel in the core of the sun to last for a total of 10 billion years. The sun is now only about 5 billion years old, so you don't have to worry about the sun "burning out" any time soon!

✓ **Checkpoint** *Where in the sun does nuclear fusion occur?*

The Sun's Atmosphere

The sun's atmosphere has three layers: the photosphere, the chromosphere, and the corona. There are no boundaries between the layers of the sun.

The Photosphere The inner layer of the sun's atmosphere is called the **photosphere** (FOH tuh sfeer). The Greek word *photo* means "light," so *photosphere* means the sphere that makes light. When you look at an image or photograph of the sun, you are looking at the photosphere.

The Chromosphere During a total solar eclipse, the moon blocks light from the photosphere. The photosphere no longer provides the glare that keeps you from seeing the sun's faint, outer layers. At the beginning and end of a total eclipse, you can see a reddish glow just around the photosphere. This glow comes from the middle layer of the sun's atmosphere, the **chromosphere.** The Greek word *chromo* means "color," so the chromosphere is the "color sphere."

The Corona In the middle of a total solar eclipse, the moon also blocks light from the chromosphere. At these times an even fainter layer of the sun becomes visible, as you can see in Figure 7. This outer layer, which looks like a white halo around the sun, is called the **corona,** which means "crown" in Latin. From Earth's surface, the corona is only visible during eclipses or from special telescopes. But astronomers can use telescopes in space to observe the corona all the time and to study how it changes.

Figure 7 During a total solar eclipse, you can see light from the corona, the outer layer of the sun's atmosphere. *Inferring Why is it easiest to photograph the sun's outer layers during a solar eclipse?*

Chapter 2 **J ◆ 57**

Media and Technology

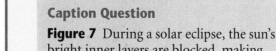

Exploring Physical Science Videodisc Unit 4, Side 2, "Wired to the Sun"

Chapter 7

Answers to Self-Assessment

Caption Question

Figure 7 During a solar eclipse, the sun's bright inner layers are blocked, making the outer layers easier to see.

✓ **Checkpoint**

Nuclear fusion occurs in the sun's core.

2 Facilitate

The Sun's Interior

Demonstration

Materials *2 large glass jars with lids, 2 plastic thermometers, black plastic, waterproof glue (hot glue works well)*
Time 45 minutes

Glue black plastic on one-half of the *inside* of the jar. Glue the plastic thermometer to the inside of the jar next to the black plastic so it can be read without opening the jar. Fill the jars with cold water, leaving 1.0 cm for expansion, and cap tightly. Take the class outside and place one jar in a shady spot and the other in direct sun propped up so that sunlight fully illuminates the inside of the jar. Read the temperature of each jar every five minutes for thirty minutes. Back in the classroom, have students graph the temperature versus time for each container. Ask: **What happened to the temperature of the jars?** (*Shady jar may have gone up or down slightly; sunny jar rose several degrees.*) **What caused the temperature to rise?** (*Energy from the sun*) **Where did this energy come from?** (*Nuclear fusion*). **learning modality: kinesthetic**

The Sun's Atmosphere

Including All Students

Show students color photos of the sun at various stages of an eclipse. Encourage students to point out the photosphere, corona, and chromosphere. **learning modality: visual**

Ongoing Assessment

Drawing Have students diagram the sun's interior and atmosphere, and then label where nuclear fusion occurs and where the greatest production of light occurs.

Features on the Sun

Including All Students

The terms used to describe the sun's features may be difficult or unfamiliar for students whose native language is not English. However, all of the terms are descriptive so students can use word skills to analyze the meaning. Have students separate the terms *sunspot* and *solar flare* into their parts. Allow students to look up the words and word parts in the dictionary. Encourage students to explain how the terms help describe the features of the sun. **limited English proficiency**

Skills Focus interpreting data

Materials *binoculars, ring stand, ruler, thin cardboard, scissors, masking tape, white paper*

Time 10 minutes per day over 10 days

Tips Warn students not to look directly at the sun because sunlight can injure their eyes. Students should identify the variables they must control to get the best data. Suggest students look for sunspots two or three times per day for ten days. Their data tables should include the number of sunspots recorded at each interval as well as the average number of sunspots per day. After the first five days, have students predict how the average number of sunspots will change over the next five days. When their observations are complete, students can draw conclusions about the accuracy of their predictions.

Extend Have students compile class results and evaluate the class average for the number of sunspots observed in a ten-day period. Invite students whose findings vary from those of other students to explain why. **learning modality: logical/mathematical**

Viewing Sunspots
ACTIVITY

You can observe changes in the number of sunspots.

1. Make a data table to record the average number of sunspots you see each day.
2. Decide on a time to look for sunspots each day.
3. View the sun in the way described in the Discover activity. **CAUTION:** *Never look directly at the sun. You will hurt your eyes if you do.*
4. Make and record your observations.

Interpreting Data How much did the average number of sunspots change from day to day?

The corona sends out a stream of electrically charged particles called **solar wind.** Normally Earth's atmosphere and magnetic field block these particles. However, near the North and South poles, the particles can enter Earth's atmosphere, where they hit gas molecules and cause them to glow. The result is rippling sheets of light in the sky called auroras.

☑ *Checkpoint* During what event could you see the sun's corona?

Features on the Sun

For hundreds of years, scientists have used telescopes to look at the sun. (To protect their eyes, they used a filter or projected the sun onto a white surface, as in the Discover activity.) The dark spots that they saw on the sun's surface became known as sunspots. The spots seemed to move across the sun's surface, which showed that the sun rotates on its axis, just as Earth does. **Features on or above the sun's surface include sunspots, prominences, and solar flares.**

Sunspots As you can see in Figure 8, sunspots look like small, dark areas on the sun's surface. But in fact, they can be as large as Earth. Sunspots are areas of gas on the sun that are cooler than the gases around them. Cooler gases don't give off as much light as hotter gases, which is why sunspots look darker than the rest of the photosphere.

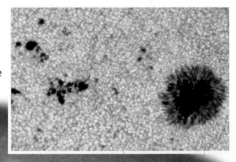

Figure 8 Sunspots are areas of gas on the sun that are cooler than the gas around them. Many of the sunspots in these photos are about as large as Earth.

Background

Facts and Figures Some scientists believe that the sunspot cycle influences weather on Earth. Among the evidence for this is the so-called Little Ice Age, which took place from about 1550 until 1850. During this time, most parts of the world experienced cooler and harsher weather.

The Little Ice Age has been associated with a period of low sunspot activity between 1645 and 1715. This period is called the Maunder minimum after the English astronomer who described it. Sunspots were first detected about 1600, but there are few recorded sightings during the Maunder minimum. Sunspots sightings resumed after 1715.

There is evidence that such times of low sunspot activity occur about every 500 years. Perhaps another Little Ice Age will begin in 2050.

The number of sunspots on the sun varies over a period of 10 or 11 years. Some scientists have hypothesized that short-term changes in climate on Earth may be related to sunspot cycles. Satellites have recently collected data that show that the amount of energy the sun produces changes slightly from year to year. Some scientists think that these increases and decreases, which may be linked to the number of sunspots, may cause changes in Earth's temperature. Scientists need to make more observations in order to test this hypothesis.

EXPLORING *the Sun*

The diameter of the sun (not including the chromosphere and the corona) is 1.4 million kilometers.

Corona
Thickness: millions of kilometers
Temperature: about 2,000,000°C

Sunspots
Areas of cooler gases in the photosphere are called sunspots.

Chromosphere
Thickness: 2,000–3,000 km
Temperature: 5,000–10,000°C

Prominence
A prominence is a huge, looping mass of gas seen above the chromosphere.

Photosphere
Thickness: 400 km
Temperature: 5,000–8,000°C
The sunlight that reaches Earth comes from the photosphere.

Core
Temperature: as hot as 15,000,000°C, hot enough to convert hydrogen into helium by nuclear fusion, releasing light and heat

Media and Technology

▥ **Transparencies** "Exploring the Sun," Transparency 7

◉ **Exploring Earth Science Videodisc**
Unit 1, Side 1, "Sunny Days"

Chapter 6

Program Resources

◆ **Teaching Resources** 2-2 Review and Reinforce, p. 47; 2-2 Enrich, p. 48

Answers to Self-Assessment

☑ *Checkpoint*
You can see the sun's corona during an eclipse.

EXPLORING
the Sun

Have students look up the meanings of the word *corona* and the prefixes *chromo-* and *photo-*. Ask: **Why is the corona called a corona?** (*It surrounds the sun like a crown.*) **Why is the core called a core?** (*Because it's at the center*) **What is the source of light that reaches Earth from the sun?** (*the photosphere*) **What is the source of energy for the light and heat produced by the sun?** (*nuclear fusion*) Explain to students that the chromosphere lies just above the photosphere and has an intense red color when seen during an eclipse.

Extend Challenge students to explain why the surface of the sun is much cooler than the center. **learning modality: visual**

Ongoing Assessment

Drawing Have students draw and label a diagram of the surface of the sun. Diagrams should include a sunspot, a flare, and a prominence. Have students include an explanation of what each solar feature is.

Section 2 Review Answers

1. Hydrogen fuel undergoes nuclear fusion and creates helium. Some of the energy from this process is released as light and heat.

2. photosphere, chromosphere, and corona

3. The solar wind is a stream of electrically charged particles sent out into space from the corona.

4. Sunspots are areas of gases on the sun that are cooler than the gases around them. Prominences are reddish loops of gas that link different parts of sunspot regions. Solar flares are explosions that occur when prominences suddenly connect.

5. Sunspots are made up of gases that are cooler than the gases around them. Because of this, they give off less light and thus appear darker.

6. The number of sunspots varies over a 10- to 11-year cycle.

7. A prominence is a loop of gas that links different parts of sunspot regions. A solar flare is an explosion that results when several prominences connect.

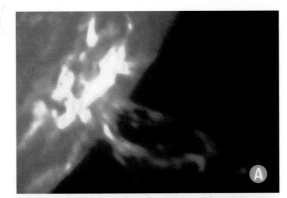

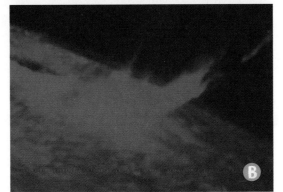

Figure 9 **A.** Prominences are huge loops of gas that connect different parts of sunspot regions. **B.** Solar flares on the sun release large amounts of energy. *Relating Cause and Effect How can solar flares affect communications on Earth?*

Prominences Sunspots usually occur in pairs or groups. Reddish loops of gas called **prominences** link different parts of sunspot regions. When a group of sunspots is near the edge of the sun as seen from Earth, these loops can stick out over the edge of the sun. If an eclipse hides the sun's photosphere, astronomers are able to see these loops. Prominences are about the same temperature as the sun's chromosphere, about 10,000 degrees Celsius.

Solar Flares Sometimes the loops in sunspot regions suddenly connect, releasing large amounts of energy. The energy heats gas on the sun to millions of degrees Celsius, causing the hydrogen gas to explode out into space. These explosions are known as **solar flares.**

Solar flares can greatly increase the solar wind from the corona, resulting in an increase in the number of particles reaching Earth's atmosphere. These solar wind particles can affect Earth's upper atmosphere, causing magnetic storms. Magnetic storms sometimes disrupt radio, telephone, and television signals. Magnetic storms can also cause electrical power problems for homes and businesses.

Section 2 Review

1. How is energy produced in the sun's core?
2. Name the layers of the sun's atmosphere.
3. What is the solar wind?
4. Describe three features found on or above the surface of the sun.
5. Why do sunspots look darker than the rest of the sun's photosphere?
6. How does the number of sunspots change over time?
7. **Thinking Critically Comparing and Contrasting** What is the difference between a prominence and a solar flare?

STORMY SUNSPOTS

Problem

How are magnetic storms on Earth related to sunspot activity?

Skills Focus

graphing, interpreting data

Materials

graph paper   pencil   straightedge

Procedure

1. Use the data in the table to make a line graph of sunspot activity between 1967 and 1997.
2. On the graph, label the *x*-axis "Year." Use a scale with 2-year intervals, from 1967 to 1997.
3. Label the *y*-axis "Sunspot Number." Use a scale of 0 through 160 in intervals of 10.
4. Graph a point for the Sunspot Number for each year.
5. Complete your graph by drawing lines to connect the points.

Sunspots

Year	Sunspot Number	Year	Sunspot Number
1967	93.8	1983	66.6
1969	105.0	1985	17.9
1971	66.6	1987	29.4
1973	38.0	1989	157.6
1975	15.5	1991	145.7
1977	27.5	1993	54.6
1979	155.4	1995	17.5
1981	140.4	1997	23.4

Analyze and Conclude

1. Based on your graph, which years had the highest Sunspot Number? The lowest Sunspot Number?
2. How often does the cycle of maximum and minimum activity repeat?
3. When was the most recent maximum sunspot activity? The most recent minimum sunspot activity?
4. Compare your sunspot graph with the magnetic storms graph. What relationship can you infer between periods of high sunspot activity and magnetic storms? Explain.
5. **Apply** During which years do you think electrical disturbances on Earth were most common?

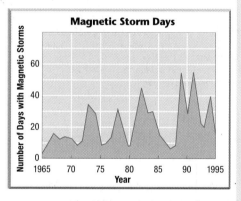

Magnetic Storm Days

More to Explore

Using the pattern of sunspot activity you found, predict the number of peaks you would expect in the next 30 years. Around which years would you expect the peaks to occur?

Stormy Sunspots

Preparing for Inquiry

Key Concept Sunspot activity and magnetic storms on Earth can be related by analyzing sunspot activity over time.

Skills Objective Students will be able to
◆ make a graph of average sunspot number versus year;
◆ compare a graph of sunspot activity to a graph of number of magnetic storms on Earth during the same period.

Time 30 minutes

Advance Planning Distribute graph paper and straightedges to the students who will do the lab.

Guiding Inquiry

Introducing the Procedure

◆ Tell students that a magnetic storm is defined as a brief disturbance in Earth's magnetic field.
◆ "Sunspot number" is a technical term that takes into account both the number of sunspot groups and the number of individual sunspots.

Troubleshooting the Experiment

◆ Do not allow students to make a bar graph.

Expected Outcome

◆ Students will draw a graph that shows three peaks and three valleys in sunspot activity from 1967–1997.
◆ The sunspot activity valleys seem to coincide with valleys in the magnetic storm days graph.

Analyze and Conclude

1. Highest: 1967–1969, 1979–1981 and 1989–1991; Lowest: 1975–1977, 1985–1987 and 1995–1997
2. Every 10–12 years
3. Maximum: 1989; Minimum: 1995
4. The three sunspot activity valleys (1975, 1985, and 1995) occur at the same time as valleys in magnetic storm days. The three sunspot activity peaks (1970, 1980, and 1990) seem to precede by one or two years a magnetic storm peak (1973, 1982, and 1992).

Program Resources

◆ **Teaching Resources** Real-World Lab blackline masters, pp. 65–66

Media and Technology

Lab Activity Videotape
Astronomy, 3

5. Electrical disturbances on Earth were probably most common from 1967–1969, 1979–1981, and 1989–1991.

Extending the Inquiry

More to Explore Students add the time it takes to get a repeat to the year of the last maximum (1991) With a repeat of 10–11 years, you expect to get peaks around 2001–2002, 2012–2013 and 2023–2024.

The Inner Planets

Objectives

After completing the lesson, students will be able to
◆ describe the main characteristics of the inner planets.

Key Terms terrestrial planet, retrograde motion, greenhouse effect

1 Engage/Explore

Activating Prior Knowledge

Show students a colored drawing of the solar system with the names of the planets covered. Ask: **Which planet is Earth?** (*The third planet from the sun*) Ask students to explain why they guessed that Earth was the third planet. (*Sample: The planet was colored blue, and Earth has water which makes it look blue from space.*) Then invite students to examine the map and point out other planets they think are most like Earth. (*Students should point out the inner planets.*)

DISCOVER

Skills Focus observing
Materials *compass, ruler*
Time 10 minutes
Tips Stress that students should make the small lines dark enough to be seen from a distance. To keep their drawings straight, suggest that they label them as *Original* and *Copied from a Distance.*
Think It Over The partner may see and draw patterns and lines that are not in the original drawing. The view from across the room is not an accurate representation of what the original drawing looked like.

SECTION 3 The Inner Planets

DISCOVER .... ACTIVITY

How Does Mars Look From Earth?

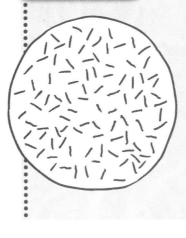

1. Work in pairs. On a sheet of paper, draw a circle 20 cm across to represent Mars. Draw about 100 small lines, each about 1 cm long, at random places inside the circle.

2. Have your partner look at your drawing of Mars from the other side of the room. Your partner should draw what he or she sees.

3. Compare your original drawing with what your partner drew. Then look at your own drawing from across the room.

Think It Over
Observing Did your partner draw any connecting lines that were not actually on your drawing? What can you conclude about the accuracy of descriptions of other planets as observed from Earth?

GUIDE FOR READING

◆ What are the main characteristics of the inner planets?

Reading Tip As you read about each planet, write down the similarities and differences between that planet and Earth.

Where could you find a planet whose surface is hot enough to melt lead? How about a planet whose atmosphere has almost entirely leaked away? And how about a planet with volcanoes higher than any on Earth? Finally, what about a planet with oceans of water brimming with fish and other life? These are descriptions of the four planets closest to the sun, known as the inner planets.

Earth and the other three inner planets—Mercury, Venus, and Mars—are more similar to each other than they are to the five outer planets. **The four inner planets are small and have rocky surfaces.** These planets are often called the **terrestrial planets,** from the Latin word *terra,* which means "Earth." Figure 10 gives a summary of information about the inner planets.

Earth

Our planet's atmosphere extends more than 100 kilometers above Earth's surface. The oxygen you need to live makes up about 20 percent of the gases in Earth's atmosphere. Almost all the rest is nitrogen gas, with small amounts of argon and other gases. Earth's atmosphere also contains water vapor and clouds of water droplets. From space, astronauts can usually see past the clouds to Earth's surface.

Most of Earth, about 70 percent, is covered with water. Perhaps the planet should be named "Water" instead of "Earth"! No other planet in our solar system has oceans like Earth's.

READING STRATEGIES

Reading Tip Suggest that students use Venn diagrams to compare and contrast each inner planet and Earth. Demonstrate how to use a Venn diagram to compare and contrast two subjects. First, have volunteers read aloud the information about Earth and Mercury in the section. Then draw a Venn diagram on the chalkboard. As students name similarities between Mercury and Earth, write these in the overlapping portion of the diagram. Then have students name differences and record these in the outer portions of the circles. Instruct students to complete additional Venn diagrams for the remaining planets.

Study and Comprehension Have students work in small groups. Each member of the group can read the material on a planet, then teach the other members of the group about that planet.

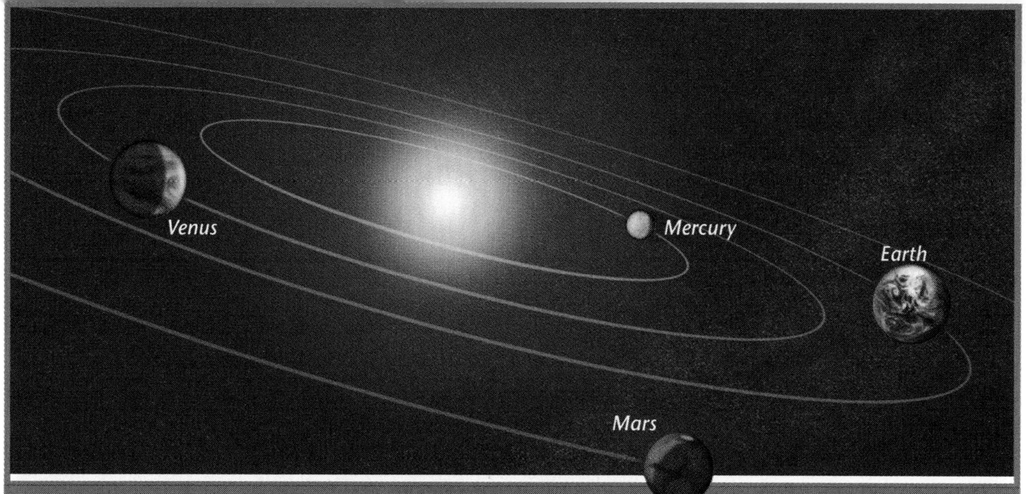

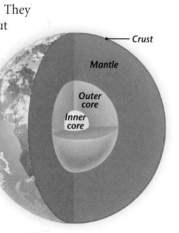

The Inner Planets

Planet	Diameter (kilometers)	Period of Rotation (Earth days)	Average Distance From the Sun (kilometers)	Period of Revolution (Earth years)	Number of Moons
Mercury	4,878	59	58,000,000	0.24	0
Venus	12,104	243	108,000,000	0.62	0
Earth	12,756	1	150,000,000	1	1
Mars	6,794	1.03	228,000,000	1.9	2

INTEGRATING EARTH SCIENCE As you can see in Figure 11, Earth has three main layers—a crust, a mantle, and a core. The crust includes the solid rocky surface. Under the crust is the mantle, a layer of hot molten rock. When volcanoes erupt, this hot material rises to the surface. Earth has a dense inner core made up mainly of iron and nickel. The outer core is liquid, but the inner core is probably solid.

Scientists have been studying Earth for many years. They use what they know about Earth to make inferences about the other planets. For example, when astronomers find volcanoes on other planets, they infer that these planets have or once had hot material inside them. As we continue to learn more about our own planet, scientists will be able to apply that new knowledge to the study of the other planets.

Figure 10 The inner planets take up only a small part of the solar system. The diameter of the entire solar system is more than 25 times the diameter of Mars's orbit.

- Crust
- Mantle
- Outer core
- Inner core

Figure 11 Earth has a solid, rocky surface. *Interpreting Diagrams* What are Earth's three main layers?

Chapter 2 **J ◆ 63**

Answers to Self-Assessment
Caption Question
Figure 11 crust, mantle, and core

2 Facilitate

Earth

Building Inquiry Skills: Interpreting Data

To help students interpret the data in Figure 10, ask: **Which planets are most similar in size?** *(Venus and Earth)* Then ask: **How many times does Mercury revolve around the sun during one Earth year?** *(About 4)* Challenge students to make generalizations about a planet's average distance from the sun and its period of revolution. *(The farther from the sun, the longer it takes to complete one period of revolution.)* **learning modality: logical/mathematical**

Integrating Earth Science

Materials *hard-boiled egg, blunt kitchen knife, paper towel*
Time 10 minutes
Tips Invite students to use hard-boiled eggs to model the layers of Earth. Have them place the eggs on paper towels, then use the knives to slice the shelled eggs crosswise. Ask students to identify what each part of the egg represents. *(Shell—crust; white—mantle; yolk—core)* Ask: **How is the model different from Earth?** *(Earth's core is liquid, but the egg yolk is solid.)* Students should take care when using kitchen knives. Make sure students do not eat the eggs. They should wash their hands after disposing of the eggs. **learning modality: kinesthetic**

Ongoing Assessment

Drawing Have students draw a cross-section of Earth and its atmosphere and label the crust, mantle, outer core, inner core, and atmosphere.

Portfolio Students can save their drawings in their portfolios.

Mercury

Building Inquiry Skills: Observing

Help students understand **ACTIVITY** why scientists have difficulty making observations of Mercury. Pair students. Have one student hold a coin about 10 cm in front of a dim desk lamp. The head side of the coin should face away from the bulb. Challenge the other student to determine the date on the coin. Caution the student not to look directly at the light bulb. Ask: **What do you observe about the coin?** *(The brightness of the bulb makes it impossible to see the date.)* Have students explain why this is similar to the problems encountered by scientists who want to observe Mercury's surface features. *(The brightness of the sun makes it hard to see the features of Mercury's surface.)* **learning modality: kinesthetic**

Using the Visuals: Figure 12

Direct students to look at the picture of the moon on page 41. Point out that Mercury and the moon look very similar. Have students describe the features shared by the moon and Mercury. *(Heavily cratered surface, little atmosphere, no liquid water, little erosion)* Ask: **What difference do you see between the surface of the moon and that of Mercury?** *(Mercury's surface has no maria.)* **learning modality: verbal**

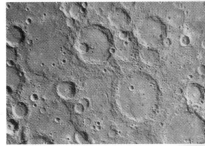

Figure 12 This photo of Mercury and the closeup view of some of its craters (inset) were taken by the *Mariner 10* space probe.

Mercury

The planet closest to the sun is Mercury. Mercury is not much larger than Earth's moon and has no moons of its own. Astronomers have been able to infer that the interior of Mercury is made up mainly of the dense metals iron and nickel.

Exploring Mercury Because Mercury is so close to the sun, people on Earth never get a good view of Mercury. Much of the knowledge that astronomers have about Mercury's surface came from a single probe, *Mariner 10*. It flew by three times in 1974 and 1975. *Mariner 10* photographed only half of Mercury's surface, so astronomers still don't know much about what the rest of Mercury is like.

Mariner 10's photographs show that, like the moon, Mercury has many flat plains and many craters on its surface. The craters on Mercury have been named for artists, writers, and musicians, including the composers Bach and Mozart.

Mercury's Atmosphere Mercury has an extremely thin atmosphere. Apparently the gases Mercury once had were heated so much that the gas particles moved very fast. Since they were moving so fast, the gas particles escaped from Mercury's weak gravity into space. However, astronomers have detected small amounts of sodium and other gases in Mercury's atmosphere.

Mercury is a planet of extremes. It is so close to the sun that during the day, the side facing the sun reaches temperatures of 430°C. Because Mercury has almost no atmosphere, at night all the heat escapes into space. The temperature drops to −170°C. Mercury thus has a greater range of temperatures than any other planet in the solar system.

842° F

−338° F

☑ *Checkpoint* Why is it difficult for astronomers to learn about Mercury?

Background

Facts and Figures Until the 1960s, astronomers thought that Mercury's day was the same length as its year. In 1965, observations by Doppler radar showed that Mercury rotates three times in every two Mercury years. Mercury has a very eccentric orbit—sometimes 46 million km from the sun, at other times 70 million km.

Sunrise on Mercury would look strange to someone from Earth. At some places on the planet, the sun would appear to rise, increase in size, then stop, reverse, and stop again before rising again and decreasing in size.

Venus

Whenever you see a bright object in the west after sunset, it is probably Venus. When Venus shines brightly like that, it is known as the "evening star," though of course it really isn't a star. Stars shine with their own light, while Venus shines because it is reflecting light from the sun, just as the other planets and moons do. At other times, you see Venus rise before the sun in the morning. It is then known as the "morning star." At still other times, Venus is too close to the sun in the sky for you to see it from Earth.

Venus is so similar in size to Earth that it is sometimes called Earth's twin. Astronomers also think that the density and internal structure of Venus are similar to Earth's. However, in many other ways, Venus is very different from Earth.

Venus's Rotation Venus takes about 7.5 Earth months to revolve around the sun. It takes about 8 months for Venus to rotate on its axis. Venus rotates so slowly that its "day" is longer than its "year." Oddly, Venus rotates from east to west, the opposite direction from most other planets and moons. This type of rotation is called **retrograde rotation,** from the Latin words for "moving backward." One hypothesis proposed by astronomers to explain this unusual rotation is that Venus was struck by a very large object billions of years ago. Such a collision could have caused the direction of its rotation to change.

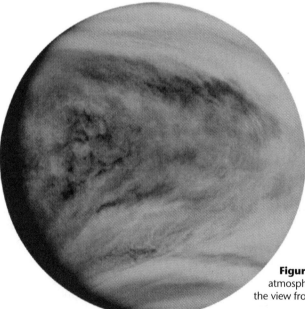

Figure 13 The thick atmosphere of Venus makes the view from space a cloudy one.

Chapter 2 **J ◆ 65**

Sharpen your Skills

Graphing ACTIVITY

Using data in Figure 10 on page 63, make a line graph of the average distance from the sun and period of revolution of Mercury, Venus, Earth, and Mars. Describe how the two variables are related. If you wish, add data on Jupiter, Saturn, Uranus, Neptune, and Pluto from Figure 19 on page 71.

Answers to Self-Assessment

✓ *Checkpoint*

Mercury is so close to the sun that it is difficult for astronomers on Earth to get a good view of it.

Venus

Demonstration

To help students visualize the unusual rotation of Venus, place one globe on a table to represent Earth. Spin the globe so that it turns from west to east. Ask: **How long does it take for Earth to spin once around its axis?** *(24 hours or 1 day)* Place another globe next to the first to represent Venus. Spin the globe very slowly so that it turns from east to west. Invite students to identify the differences between the rotations of Venus and Earth. *(Venus rotates from east to west, Earth from west to east. Venus is slower than Earth. On Venus, the sun "rises" in the west and "sets" in the east.)* **learning modality: visual**

Sharpen your Skills

Graphing

Materials *graph paper, colored pencils* ACTIVITY
Time 15 minutes
Tips Students should set up their graphs with the distances to the planets on the *x*-axis, and the period of revolution on the *y*-axis. Discuss the units. Suggest students use 1 cm = 10,000 km for units of distance and 1 cm = 0.01 year for time.
Expected Outcome Data should form a line with a positive slope. The inner and outer planets must be graphed separately because the same scale will not work for both.
Extend Ask students to predict the relationship between the diameter of a planet and its period of rotation, then create graphs to test their predictions.

Ongoing Assessment

Writing Have students describe how sunrise on Venus differs from sunrise on Earth.

Including All Students

To help students who are still mastering English understand the origin of the term *greenhouse effect,* show them a picture of a greenhouse with plants growing inside. Explain that a greenhouse lets in sunlight and prevents convection from carrying heat away. The plants inside stay warm. Pair students who are still mastering English with native speakers, and have them each create flowcharts or sketches that compare the path of light and heat energy in a greenhouse with the path of light and heat energy on Venus.

Extend Have students research possible environmental problems caused by changes in Earth's greenhouse effect. **limited English proficiency**

Music CONNECTION

Recordings of this work are widely available. Check your school or public library for a copy. Holst was trying to musically describe the *astrological* and *mythological* characteristics of these seven planets. Encourage students to listen for *astronomical* connections. **learning modality: kinesthetic**

In Your Journal Students' responses will depend on the piece they heard. They may suggest the use of specific instruments to give a feel or appearance of a planet. Students may describe the music with words such as *loud, soft, eerie, brash,* or *faraway.*

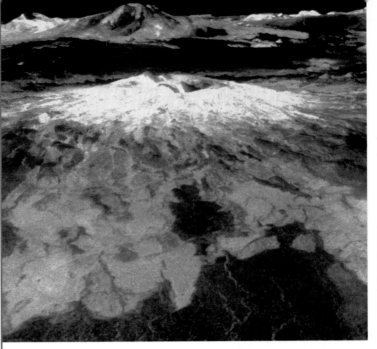

Figure 14 The *Magellan* spacecraft used radar to penetrate Venus's clouds. This three-dimensional image of a volcano on Venus was created by a computer using radar data. The height of the mountains is exaggerated to make them stand out.

Music CONNECTION

The English composer Gustav Holst, who lived from 1874 to 1934, composed a group of pieces for orchestra entitled *The Planets.* The seven pieces describe musically the planets Mars, Venus, Mercury, Jupiter, Saturn, Uranus, and Neptune.

In Your Journal

Listen to a recording of one of the pieces from *The Planets.* How did Holst use music to represent the planet? What words would you use to describe what you heard?

Venus's Atmosphere The atmosphere of Venus is so thick that every day is a cloudy one. Venus never has a sunny day. From Earth, astronomers see only a smooth cloud cover over Venus all the time.

If you could stand on the surface of Venus, you would quickly be crushed by the weight of its atmosphere. The pressure of Venus's atmosphere is 90 times greater than the pressure of Earth's atmosphere. You could not breathe on Venus because its atmosphere is mostly carbon dioxide. Also, its clouds are partly made of sulfuric acid.

Because Venus is closer to the sun than Earth, it gets more solar energy than Earth does. Ordinary light from the sun can penetrate Venus's atmosphere and hit its surface. The surface heats up and then gives off heat. Carbon dioxide traps this heat in the atmosphere. So Venus's surface becomes hotter and hotter, until it is about 460°C—hot enough to melt lead. This trapping of heat by the atmosphere is called the **greenhouse effect.**

Exploring Venus A total of 19 spacecraft have visited Venus, more than have visited any other planet. Some have even penetrated its clouds and landed on its surface. The first spacecraft to land and send back information, *Venera 7,* landed in 1970 but survived for only 23 minutes. Later spacecraft were more durable and sent back pictures and other data from Venus's surface.

Scientists have learned most of what they know about Venus's surface from data collected by the *Magellan* probe. The *Magellan*

Background

History of Science Because of Venus's extreme heat, high atmospheric pressure, and clouds of sulfuric acid, it would be almost impossible for astronauts to go there. To gather information about Venus, scientists have sent unmanned space probes. The Soviet Union was the first nation to attempt interplanetary exploration. In 1961, it launched the probe *Venera 1,* which passed within 99,000 km of Venus but did not transmit information. In 1966, the Soviets launched *Venera 3,* the first spacecraft to crash-land on another planet. In 1967, *Venera 4* parachuted a capsule of instruments to the planet's surface. *Venera 7* (1970) detected radioactive isotopes on Venus's surface. In 1975, *Venera 9* sent back the first close-up photographs of the surface of the planet.

probe reached Venus in 1990, carrying radar instruments. Radar works through clouds, so *Magellan* was able to map Venus's entire surface.

The *Magellan* views are so detailed that computers can be used to figure out what Venus would look like if you could fly just above its surface. Figure 14 shows one of these radar images. Venus is covered with rock, similar to many rocky areas on Earth. Venus has volcanoes with lava flows, many craters, and strange domes not found on other planets.

☑ *Checkpoint* *Why is the surface of Venus so hot?*

Mars

Mars is called the "red planet" because it has a slightly reddish tinge when you see it in the sky. The atmosphere of Mars is mostly carbon dioxide and has only 1 percent the pressure of Earth's atmosphere. You could walk around on Mars, but you would have to wear an airtight suit and carry your own air, like a scuba diver. Mars has clouds but they are very thin compared to the clouds on Earth.

Canals on Mars? In 1877, an Italian astronomer, Giovanni Schiaparelli (sky ah puh REL ee), announced that he had seen long, straight lines on Mars. He called them *canale*, or channels. In the 1890s and early 1900s, Percival Lowell, an American astronomer, convinced many people that these lines were canals that had been built by intelligent Martians to carry water. Astronomers now know that Lowell was mistaken. There are no canals on Mars.

Astronomers have found that some water remains on Mars in the form of ice at its north pole, as shown in Figure 15. During the winter, this polar ice cap is covered by a layer of frozen carbon dioxide. Mars' south pole has an ice cap made mostly of frozen carbon dioxide.

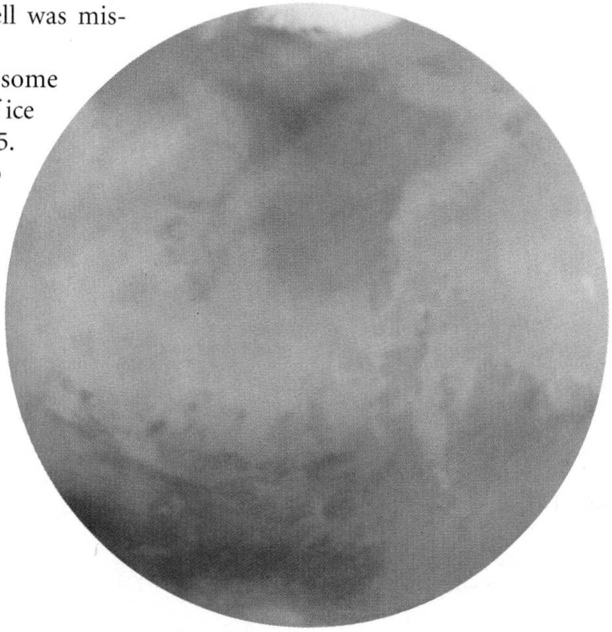

Figure 15 Because of its thin atmosphere and its distance from the sun, Mars is quite cold. Mars has ice caps at both poles.

Explain to students that radar images are formed when radio waves are bounced off a surface. Have students infer why scientists used radar to get an image of the volcano on Venus. (*They could not see the volcano because the thick atmosphere of Venus blocked the view.*) Explain that the radar-imaging technique exaggerates the heights of objects such as the volcano. Ask students: **Why might astronomers want to use an exaggerated scale when examining an image?** (*Astronomers increase the scale of an image so that they can examine details more clearly.*) Inform students that the colors in the figure are generated by the computer-imaging process. The actual volcano colors vary, and appear more like those of volcanoes on Earth. **learning modality: visual**

Mars

Addressing Naive Conceptions

Students' conceptions about the features and history of Mars may be based on science-fiction stories, television shows, and movies. As students complete their reading about Mars, have them prepare a Fact/Fiction sheet to distinguish scientific findings about Mars from science fiction. **learning modality: verbal**

Answers to Self-Assessment

☑ *Checkpoint*

The surface of Venus is so hot because carbon dioxide traps heat inside the atmosphere. This is called the greenhouse effect.

Ongoing Assessment

Skills Check Instruct students to make a Venn diagram comparing the features of Venus's atmosphere with the features of Earth's atmosphere.

Skills Focus inferring
Materials tape, paper, goggles
Time 15 minutes
Tips Perform this activity in a large open area. Make sure that there are no obstacles on which students might trip or hit their heads.
Answers Simple directions such as "Turn left" or "Take four steps forward" probably worked best. Students would have had to move slowly. This activity is similar to the way NASA engineers moved *Sojourner*. The rover could not move by itself but had to be given directions by remote control. The controller had to be careful not to have *Sojourner* run into anything, and the rover had to move very slowly.
Extend Have students infer difficulties NASA encountered when trying to get the rover to perform tasks on Mars.
learning modality: kinesthetic

Building Inquiry Skills: Observing

Materials sand, rectangular baking pans, large beaker, bucket for sand disposal
Time 15 minutes

 Place large buckets in strategic locations around the room for sand disposal. Warn students to keep the sand out of the sinks. Have pairs of students build slopes with moist sand in one end of a rectangular metal baking pan. The sand should slope from just below the rim on one end to about the middle of the pan. Have students pour a slow, steady stream of water onto the top of the slope and observe what happens as the water runs down the slope. Have students continue pouring until there is about 1 cm of water in the pan. Ask: **How did the flowing water change the surface of the sand?** *(It formed channels.)* Ask students to infer why scientists believe water once flowed on Mars. *(Channels on Mars look similar to channels formed by flowing water on Earth.)* **learning modality: visual**

Remote Control

How hard is it to explore another planet by remote control?

1. Tape a piece of paper over the front of a pair of goggles. Have your partner put them on.
2. Walk behind your partner and give him or her directions to move to another part of the room. **CAUTION:** *Do not give directions that would cause your partner to walk into a wall or corner, trip on an obstacle, or hit anything.*
3. Trade places and repeat Steps 1 and 2.

Inferring Which verbal directions worked best? How quickly could you move? How is this activity similar to the way NASA engineers moved *Sojourner* on Mars in 1997? How fast do you think the rover could move?

Figure 16 The surface of Mars is rugged and rocky. The object at the bottom of the photo is the *Mars Pathfinder* lander. You can see the remote-control rover *Sojourner* in the middle of the photo.

Seasons on Mars Because the axis of Mars is tilted, Mars has seasons just as Earth does. As the seasons change on the dusty surface of Mars, wind storms arise and blow the dust around. Since the dust is blown off some regions, these regions look darker. A hundred years ago, some people thought these regions looked darker because plants were growing there. Astronomers now realize that it is just that wind storms blow dust off the surface.

Exploring Mars The United States has sent many spacecraft to Mars. The first ones, in the 1960s, seemed to show that Mars is barren and covered with craters like the moon. Later spacecraft showed that regions of Mars have giant volcanoes. Astronomers see signs that hot material flowed down the volcanoes in the past, but they don't think the volcanoes are active now.

In 1976, two NASA spacecraft, *Viking 1* and *Viking 2*, landed on Mars. They sent back close-up pictures from Mars's surface. The pictures showed that the rocks look red because they are covered with a rusty dust. Other parts of the *Viking* spacecraft went into orbit around Mars, sending back detailed pictures.

In 1997, *Mars Pathfinder* landed on Mars. As Figure 16 shows, close-up photographs from *Mars Pathfinder* show no oceans or even puddles of water. Photographs taken from space do show evidence that water flowed on Mars millions of years ago.

Background

Facts and Figures In 1879, Giovanni Schiaparelli discovered another feature of Mars, a large crater he called *Nix Olympica*. Photographs from *Mariner 9* (1971–1972) showed that this crater was the caldera of possibly the largest volcano in the entire solar system, *Olympus Mons*. This volcano is one of several huge volcanoes on a plateau called *Tharsis*. Olympus Mons has ten times the volume of Mauna Kea in Hawaii, the largest volcano on Earth, and at 27 km, is three times as high as Mount Everest. The caldera of Olympus Mons is 85 km across, and the entire volcano covers a circular area 550 km across.

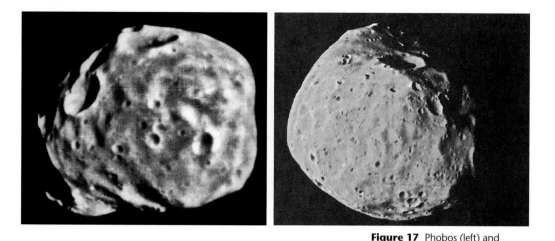

Figure 17 Phobos (left) and Deimos (right) are Mars's two small, crater-covered moons.

Mars Pathfinder carried a microwave-sized remote-control rover, called *Sojourner,* that investigated rocks on Mars. Also in 1997, another probe, *Mars Global Surveyor,* arrived in orbit around Mars, where it began mapping and photographing all of the planet's surface in detail.

Mars's Moons Mars has two very small moons. Phobos, the larger moon, is only 27 kilometers in diameter, about the distance a car can travel on the highway in 15 minutes. Deimos is even smaller, only 15 kilometers in diameter. Close-up views from space show that, like Earth's moon, Phobos and Deimos are covered with craters.

Section 3 Review

1. What features do all of the inner planets have in common?
2. What is Mercury's atmosphere like? Explain.
3. Why can astronomers see the surface of Mars clearly, but not the surface of Venus?
4. How have astronomers been able to study the surface of Venus?
5. What evidence do astronomers have that water once flowed on Mars?
6. **Thinking Critically Relating Cause and Effect** Venus is much farther from the sun than is Mercury. Yet temperatures on Venus are as high as those on the sunny side of Mercury. Explain why.

Check Your Progress
CHAPTER PROJECT 2

Now you will design a model that shows the relative diameters of the planets. Try several different scales to find one for which the smallest planet is clearly visible but the sun would still fit into your classroom. Convert the sun's and planets' diameters to scaled-down diameters and record your results on your data sheet. Compare your scaled-down diameters to objects you are familiar with, such as coins. Include your comparisons in your data sheet.

Program Resources

◆ **Teaching Resources** 2-3 Review and Reinforce, p. 51; 2-3 Enrich, p. 52

3 Assess

Section 3 Review Answers
1. They are all small and rocky.
2. Mercury has almost no atmosphere. The gases its atmosphere once had were heated so much by the sun that they escaped from Mercury's weak gravity into space.
3. The thin atmosphere of Mars is easy to see through; the very thick atmosphere of Venus is not.
4. Astronomers have been able to study the surface of Venus using unmanned spacecraft and by looking at radar images taken by the *Magellan* probe.
5. Astronomers have found that some water remains on Mars in the form of ice at its north pole, and patterns in photographs taken from *Mars Pathfinder* show evidence that water once flowed.
6. Venus's thick atmosphere traps heat due to the greenhouse effect.

Check Your Progress
CHAPTER PROJECT 2

If students have trouble finding a scale that works, suggest they try 1 cm = 10,000 km. At this scale, Mercury would be about the size of a pea, and the sun would be about the size of an easy chair.

Performance Assessment

Skills Check Have students create models of the four inner planets using art supplies and classroom items. Models should include some distinguishing characteristics of each planet. **Portfolio** Students can save their models in their portfolios.

The Outer Planets

Objectives

After completing the lesson, students will be able to
◆ describe the main characteristics of the gas giant planets;
◆ compare Pluto with the other planets.

Key Term gas giant

 **Engage/Explore**

Activating Prior Knowledge

Divide the class into groups of five. Give each student in a group an index card with the name of one outer planet written on it. Have students write three things they think they know about their planets. When they have finished, students can share their cards with the group. Collect the cards and use them to build a list of naive conceptions.

DISCOVER

Skills Focus classifying **ACTIVITY**
Materials *quarter, metric ruler, lined paper, butcher paper or poster board, compass, pushpin, and string*
Time 15 minutes
Tips A quarter has a diameter of 24 mm. Jupiter and Saturn will be too large to draw with a compass, so use a pin and string for them. CAUTION: *Compasses have sharp points and can cause injury. Warn students to be careful and watch for inappropriate behaviors.* For the best comparison, have students locate the center of each circle in the same place. Students will need large paper, such as poster boards or butcher paper, to fit the larger circles onto one sheet.
Expected Outcome Students' circles should have these diameters: Earth, 24 mm; Jupiter, 264 mm; Saturn, 226 mm; Uranus, 96 mm; Neptune, 94 mm; Pluto, 4 mm.
Think It Over Jupiter, Saturn, Uranus, Neptune, Earth, Pluto; Jupiter; Pluto

---

DISCOVER .... ACTIVITY

How Large Are the Outer Planets?

Planet Diameters	
Planet	**Diameter**
Earth	1
Jupiter	11
Saturn	9.4
Uranus	4.0
Neptune	3.9
Pluto	0.17

The table shows the diameters of the outer planets compared to Earth. For example, Jupiter's diameter is 11 times Earth's diameter.

1. Measure the diameter of a quarter in millimeters. This represents Earth's diameter. Trace the quarter to represent Earth.

2. If Earth were the size of a quarter, calculate how large Jupiter would be. Now draw a circle to represent Jupiter.

3. Repeat Step 2 for each of the other outer planets.

Think It Over

Classifying List the planets in order from largest to smallest. What is the largest outer planet? Which outer planet is much smaller than Earth?

GUIDE FOR READING

◆ What are the main characteristics of the gas giant planets?

◆ How is Pluto different from the other outer planets?

Reading Tip Before you read, preview the photos and captions in this section. Then write down any questions you have. Look for answers as you read.

M ost of what astronomers know about the outer planets has come from visits by NASA space probes. *Voyager 1* and *Voyager 2* reached Jupiter in 1979 and sent back close-up views of the planet. *Voyager 1* went on to visit Saturn in 1980. *Voyager 2* also visited Saturn, but then moved on to explore Uranus and Neptune. In 1995, the spacecraft *Galileo* reached Jupiter and dropped a probe into Jupiter's atmosphere.

Structure of the Gas Giants

Compared to Earth, some planets are huge. The largest planet, Jupiter, has a diameter that is 11 times Earth's diameter. Jupiter's mass is more than 300 times Earth's mass. If you could put Earth next to Jupiter, Earth would look like a tiny Chihuahua next to an enormous Great Dane. If Earth were the height of an average student, Jupiter would be as tall as a six-story building.

Jupiter and the other planets farthest from the sun, as seen in Figure 19, are called the outer planets. The first four outer planets—Jupiter, Saturn, Uranus, and Neptune—are much larger than Earth, and do not have solid surfaces. Because these four planets are all so large, they are also called the **gas giants**. The fifth outer planet, Pluto, is small and rocky like the terrestrial planets.

Figure 18 If the tiny Chihuahua were Earth's size, the Great Dane would be about half Jupiter's size.

READING STRATEGIES

Reading Tip Explain to students that previewing the photos and captions will help them understand what they are about to read. Write the questions below on the board. Suggest students answer the questions as they preview each image and its caption.
◆ How does the picture relate to the caption?

◆ How does the caption help me understand the picture?
◆ What do I already know about the information in the picture and caption?
◆ What else do I want to learn about the subject of this picture?

Compare/Contrast Table Have students make a compare/contrast table to show similarities and differences among the outer planets.

The Outer Planets

Planet	Diameter (kilometers)	Period of Rotation (Earth days)	Average Distance From the Sun (kilometers)	Period of Revolution (Earth years)	Number of Moons
Jupiter	142,800	0.41	778,000,000	12	18
Saturn	120,540	0.43	1,427,000,000	29	18
Uranus	51,200	0.72	2,871,000,000	84	20
Neptune	49,500	0.67	4,497,000,000	165	8
Pluto	2,200	6.4	5,913,000,000	248	1

Atmospheres Because the gas giants have so much mass, they exert a much stronger gravitational force than the terrestrial planets. The strong gravity keeps the giant planets' gases from escaping, so they have deep atmospheres. The composition of their atmospheres is similar to the gases in the sun. They are, on average, about 75 percent hydrogen, 24 percent helium, and 1 percent other elements.

None of the giant planets has a solid surface. If you could parachute into Jupiter's atmosphere, you would sink into denser and denser gas. You would be crushed by the enormous pressure long before you got to the center, or core, of the planet.

Solid Cores Astronomers think that each of the giant planets has a partly solid core made of rock, ice, frozen carbon dioxide, and other compounds. Each of these cores may have several times as much mass as Earth. But they are buried so deep inside the planets that it has been hard to find out much about them.

☑ *Checkpoint* Why do the gas giants have large atmospheres?

Figure 19 The outer planets are much farther apart than the inner planets. At this scale, the inner planets are so small and close to the sun that they cannot be shown. *Observing Which outer planet is closest to the sun?*

---

2 Facilitate

Structure of the Gas Giants

Using the Visuals: Figure 19
Have students use their finger to trace the orbits of each planet in the figure. Ask: **Which planet has an orbit that crosses the orbit of another?** *(Pluto crosses the orbit of Neptune.)* Then draw students' attention to the data in the table. Allow them time to evaluate the distances of the planets from the sun. Ask: **Which planet is about twice as far from the sun as Jupiter?** *(Saturn)* **Which planet is about six times as far from the sun as Jupiter?** *(Neptune)*

Astronomers using sophisticated new technology and software have recently identified a number of additional small moons in orbit around Jupiter, Saturn, and Uranus. In order to be officially recognized, additional observations are required to establish orbits for these moons. **learning modality: logical/mathematical**

Building Inquiry Skills: Applying Concepts
Invite students to imagine that they are sending a space probe to examine a gas giant. Encourage them to apply what they know about the planet's structure to describe what the probe would encounter as it approached the visible surface. *(There is no real solid surface, the atmosphere just gets thicker and thicker. Eventually, the combination of heat and pressure would probably cause the probe to fail.)* Ask: **Could the probe penetrate all the way to a solid surface? Explain.** *(Probably not. The solid core is buried deep inside the planet.)* **learning modality: verbal**

Program Resources

◆ **Teaching Resources** 2-4 Lesson Plan, p. 53; 2-4 Section Summary, p. 54
◆ **Guided Study Workbook** Section 2-4

Answers to Self-Assessment

Caption Question
Figure 19 Jupiter

☑ *Checkpoint*
The gas giants have so much mass that they exert a strong gravitational force that keeps the planets' gases from escaping.

Ongoing Assessment

Writing Have students list features that characterize gas giants. *(Large size; far from the sun; partly solid frozen core; dense atmosphere made up mostly of hydrogen and helium)*

Building Inquiry Skills: Making Models

Materials *clear plastic 1-L bottle with lid, water, pepper, funnel or spoon*

Time 10 minutes

If students have completed *Weather and Climate*, point out the resemblance between the Great Red Spot and a hurricane on Earth. Allow students to model the motion of the Great Red Spot. Pair students. Have each pair fill a clear, plastic bottle half full with water. Using a funnel or a spoon, pour in a spoonful of pepper. Seal the bottle and swirl the water forcefully. Ask: **What happens to the pepper grains?** *(They spin in a large swirl.)* Have students compare the appearance of the spinning pepper to the photographs of the Great Red Spot. *(Both look like giant swirls.)* Challenge students to infer what forces are causing the Giant Red Spot to swirl. Ask: **What kind of data would you need to collect to test your inferences?** *(Sample: Differences in pressure in Jupiter's atmosphere cause the Giant Red Spot. Data that show the pressure of the atmosphere around the Giant Red Spot would be needed to test this inference.)*

learning modality: kinesthetic

Jupiter is the most massive planet. In fact, Jupiter is more than 300 times as massive as Earth.

Jupiter's Atmosphere Like all of the gas giant planets, Jupiter has a thick atmosphere made up mainly of hydrogen and helium. Jupiter's atmosphere contains many colorful bands and swirls of thick clouds. An especially interesting feature in Jupiter's atmosphere is its Great Red Spot, a giant area of swirling clouds many times bigger than Earth. The Great Red Spot, shown in Figure 20, appears to be an ongoing storm similar to a hurricane on Earth.

Jupiter's Moons Recall that the astronomer Galileo discovered four of Jupiter's moons. These moons are named Io (EYE oh), Europa, Ganymede, and Callisto. These four moons are Jupiter's largest moons. Io, Ganymede, and Callisto are all larger than Earth's own moon. Since Galileo's time, astronomers have discovered more than a dozen additional moons revolving around Jupiter.

The *Voyager* and *Galileo* probes sent back images that showed detailed views of many of Jupiter's moons. Jupiter's moons are very different from one another, as you can see in Figure 21.

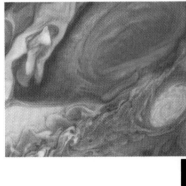
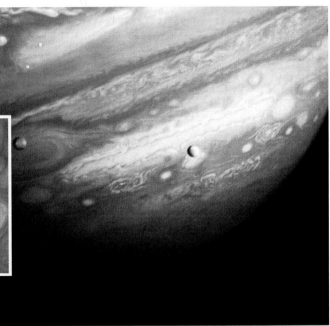

Figure 20 The larger photo of Jupiter was taken by the *Voyager 1* spacecraft. The small objects in front of Jupiter are two of Jupiter's moons, Io (left) and Europa (right). The Great Red Spot, shown in the inset, is a giant storm much larger in size than Earth.

Background

Facts and Figures

◆ Jupiter has a three-ring system that was discovered by *Voyager 1*. The main ring is about 7,000 km wide and contains the orbits of two small moons. The main ring merges into the halo, a broad ring of material about 20,000 km thick. Outside the main ring is a very broad, faint ring called the gossamer ring.

◆ In 2 B.C., Jupiter passed behind Venus as viewed from Earth. Since the planets all have slightly different orbital planes, this "occultation" of one planet by another is extremely rare. Astronomers use such events to gain additional information about our solar system.

Figure 21 The astronomer Galileo discovered Jupiter's four largest moons. **A.** Io's surface is covered with large, active volcanoes. **B.** Callisto's surface is icy and covered with craters. **C.** Ganymede is the largest of Jupiter's moons. **D.** Europa's icy crust may have liquid water underneath.
Inferring Why was Galileo able to see only Jupiter's largest moons?

Io is covered with volcanoes. Over a dozen huge volcanoes are erupting all the time, so Io's surface changes from year to year because of the flows of hot material. The sulfur in the flows gives a variety of colors to Io's surface. From space, Io looks like a giant pizza. Europa has an icy crust that may have liquid water underneath. You will learn more about Europa in Section 6.

Ganymede is the largest of Jupiter's moons and has about twice the mass of Earth's moon. Ganymede's surface is icy and partly covered with craters. Other parts of the surface show giant grooves in the ice. Callisto also has an icy surface. It is so heavily cratered that no part of its surface is free of craters.

☑ *Checkpoint* *What are Jupiter's four largest moons?*

Saturn

The second-largest planet in the solar system is Saturn. Saturn is slightly smaller than Jupiter, but including its beautiful rings it has a greater overall diameter. The *Voyager* probes showed that Saturn, like Jupiter, has a thick atmosphere made up mainly of hydrogen and helium. Saturn's atmosphere also contains clouds and storms, but they are less dramatic than those on Jupiter. Saturn is the only planet that is less dense than water.

Saturn's Rings When Galileo first looked at Saturn with a telescope, he could see that something was sticking out on the sides, but he didn't know what it was. A few decades later, another astronomer using a better telescope discovered that Saturn had rings around it. Astronomers later found that these rings are made of chunks of ice and rock, each traveling in its own orbit around Saturn.

TRY THIS

Model Saturn

Here's how you can build a scale model of Saturn. **ACTIVITY**

1. Use a plastic foam sphere 8 cm in diameter to represent Saturn.

2. ✂ Use an overhead transparency to represent Saturn's rings. Cut a circle 18 cm in diameter out of the transparency. Cut a hole 9 cm in diameter out of the center of the circle.

3. Stick five toothpicks into Saturn, spaced equally around its equator. Put the transparency on the toothpicks and tape it to them. Sprinkle baking soda on the transparency.

4. Use a peppercorn to represent Titan. Place the peppercorn 72 cm away from Saturn on the same plane as the rings.

Making Models What do the particles of baking soda represent?

Saturn

TRY THIS

Skills Focus making models **ACTIVITY**

Materials *8-cm plastic foam sphere, clear plastic sheet, ruler, scissors, compass, 5 toothpicks, tape, baking soda, peppercorn, glue (optional)*

Time 20 minutes

Tips You may want to cut circles from the center of the transparencies yourself so that students do not need to use sharp-nosed scissors.

Expected Outcome Students should understand that the particles of baking soda represent the chunks of ice and rock that make up Saturn's rings.

Extend Challenge students to use their model to demonstrate why the rings of Saturn are occasionally invisible from Earth. **learning modality: kinesthetic**

Answers to Self-Assessment

Caption Question

Figure 21 The other moons are too small and dim to have been visible through Galileo's telescope.

☑ *Checkpoint*

Io, Callisto, Ganymede, Europa

Ongoing Assessment

Oral Presentation Have students describe what they would see if they stood on the surfaces of Jupiter's four largest moons.

Saturn, continued

Using the Visuals: Figure 23

Have students write sentences describing the distinctive appearance of each of the moons shown in the figure. They should include any features that are visible, such as unusual color or large craters and note similarities to other objects in the solar system.

Portfolio Students can save their sentences in their portfolios.
learning modality: visual

Building Inquiry Skills: Comparing and Contrasting

Students can make a table showing the similarities and differences between Saturn and Jupiter. The table should include size, density, appearance, composition, and any other features students wish to include. **learning modality: logical/mathematical**

Visual Arts Connection

The particles in Saturn's rings create an image of a solid surface when viewed from a distance. Artists who paint in the *pointillist* style use tiny dots to create a similar visual effect. One famous painting in this style has over 3,400,000 dots! Computer graphics images are built up in the same way, with hundreds of thousands of tiny colored dots forming the image. Obtain art reference books with examples of pointillist paintings to show to students. Challenge them to create pointillist-style drawings of one of the outer planets.

Portfolio Students can save their drawings in their portfolios.

Figure 22 Saturn's rings are made up of ice chunks and rocks of many different sizes. The smaller photo shows that there are actually many small rings. The colors in this photo have been added by a computer. *Observing* Why might it be hard to see Saturn's rings when their edges are facing Earth?

From Earth, it looks as though Saturn has only a few rings, and that they are divided from each other by narrow, dark regions. The *Voyager* spacecraft discovered that each of these obvious rings is divided into dozens of smaller rings. In all, Saturn has hundreds of rings.

Saturn's rings are broad and thin, like a compact disc. Sometimes the rings are tipped so that observers see them at an angle. Occasionally, they are on edge, and then, because they are so thin, astronomers can't see them at all.

In the last few decades, rings have been discovered around the other three gas giants as well. But the rings around Jupiter, Uranus, and Neptune are not as spectacular as Saturn's.

Saturn's Moons Saturn's largest moon, Titan, is larger than Earth's own moon. Titan was discovered in 1665 but was known only as a point of light until the *Voyagers* went by. The probes showed that Titan has an atmosphere so thick that little light can get through it. Astronomers studying Hubble Space Telescope images can barely see Titan's surface.

Four other moons of Saturn are each over 1,000 kilometers in diameter. They are named Tethys (TEE this), Iapetus (eye AP uh tus), Dione, and Rhea. *Voyager* images show craters and canyons on these moons.

☑ **Checkpoint** What are Saturn's rings made of?

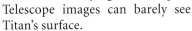

Figure 23 This image of Saturn and six of its moons combines photos taken by *Voyager 1* and *Voyager 2*.

Background

History of Science Like her brother William, Caroline Herschel (1750–1848) was born in Hanover in what is now Germany. William developed an interest in astronomy, even grinding mirrors for his own telescopes. At night, Caroline took notes on William's observations. During the day, she kept house, helped William grind and polish mirrors, and made the difficult computations connected with his observations.

Caroline also made her own observations. In 1786, she became the first woman to discover a comet. After William married in 1788, Caroline continued her studies, discovering seven more comets. William died in 1822, and Caroline returned to Hanover, where she completed the cataloguing of 2,500 nebulae and many star clusters. She died in 1848, two months short of her 98th birthday.

Uranus

Although the gas giant Uranus (YOOR uh nus) is about four times the diameter of Earth, it is still much smaller than Jupiter and Saturn. Uranus is twice as far from the sun as Saturn, so it is much colder. Uranus looks bluish because of traces of methane in its atmosphere.

Discovery of Uranus In 1781, Uranus became the first new planet discovered since ancient times. Astronomer William Herschel, in England, found an object in the sky that did not look like a star. At first he thought it might be a comet. But other astronomers soon calculated its orbit and realized that it was a planet beyond Saturn. The discovery made Herschel famous and started an era of solar system exploration.

Exploring Uranus In 1986, about 200 years after Herschel's discovery, *Voyager 2* arrived at Uranus and sent back our only close-up views of that giant planet. Images from *Voyager 2* show only a few clouds on Uranus's surface, but even these few allowed astronomers to calculate that Uranus rotates in about 17 hours.

Strangely, Uranus's axis is tilted at an angle of about 90° from the vertical, as shown in Figure 24. Viewed from Earth, Uranus is rotating from top to bottom instead of from side to side, the way most of the other planets do. Astronomers think that billions of years ago Uranus was hit by an object that knocked it on its side.

Uranus's Moons Photographs from *Voyager 2* showed that Uranus's five largest moons have icy, cratered surfaces. The craters show that the moons have been hit by rocks from space. Uranus's moons also have lava flows on their surfaces, suggesting that material has erupted from inside each moon. *Voyager 2* images revealed ten moons that had never been seen before. In 1999, astronomers discovered three more moons, for a total of 20.

Figure 24 A. This composite image of *Voyager 2* photos includes Uranus and five of its 20 moons. **B.** Unlike most other planets, Uranus rotates on its side.

Language Arts
CONNECTION

The ancient Romans named the planets after the gods they worshipped. Mercury was the fast, winged messenger of the gods. Venus was the goddess of beauty and Mars was the god of war. Jupiter was the king of the Roman gods. Saturn was the Roman god of agriculture.

The planets discovered in the last 200 years have also been named after ancient gods. Uranus was the Greek god who was the husband of Gaea, Earth. Neptune was the Roman god of the sea. Pluto was the Roman god of the underworld.

In Your Journal

Look in a reference book to find out more about one of the gods for which a planet has been named. Make a poster showing that god and describing his or her character.

Answers to Self-Assessment

Caption Question

Figure 22 The rings are so thin that when their edges face Earth they are nearly invisible.

☑ *Checkpoint*

Ice chunks and rocks

Using the Visuals: Figure 24
Some students may think that the axis of rotation of Uranus always points to the sun. Have students lay a pencil over the axis of rotation, then trace the orbit of Uranus by moving the pencil. The pencil should always point to the left edge of the paper.

Language Arts
CONNECTION

Explain to students that the planets were supposed to share characteristics of the gods after which they were named. Provide reference books for students. Allow them to work in groups to find out more about the gods the planets were named for. They can try to think of a reason why each planet was given the name it has, both by the Romans and by modern astronomers. (*Sample: Mercury, the fastest moving planet, was named for the swiftest of the gods. Mars, with its distinctive reddish color, was named for the god of war.*)

Extend Have students rename the planets after famous characters from literature or popular culture. Ask them to explain their choices.

In Your Journal Students can consult mythology books and other reference books to read about ancient gods. If students wish to explore the names of bodies other than planets, allow them to research the names of moons of different planets. **learning modality: verbal**

Ongoing Assessment

Writing Have students create two fact sheets about Uranus. The first should include facts known about the planet before the *Voyager* images. The second should include facts learned since the *Voyager* images.

Neptune

Building Inquiry Skills: Relating Cause and Effect

Materials *small marble,* *large marble, medium-sized bowl, piece of spandex large enough to cover the bowl, large rubber band*

Time 10 minutes

Tips Invite students to predict how a large object's gravity could affect the orbit of a planet. To check their predictions, have students fasten a piece of spandex over the bowl and hold it in place with the large rubber band. The surface of the spandex should be smooth. Next roll the small marble across the surface several times and observe and record its motion. *(It rolls straight.)* Now place the large marble in the center so that the surface will be depressed in the center. Make sure it is still smooth. Have students roll the small marble in various paths across the spandex and observe its path. *(The small marble will be deflected by the curve in the surface of the fabric. The closer it comes to the large marble, the more it will be deflected.)* Ask students to compare the model to what happens in the space around a massive object like Neptune. *(The large marble models a mass like Neptune. The curve in the surface of the spandex models gravity. The small marble models other objects whose path is deflected by Neptune.)* **learning modality: kinesthetic**

Pluto and Charon

Building Inquiry Skills: Classifying

Pluto is unlike any other planet because it is much smaller than the gas giants and it is less dense than the inner planets. It is ten times larger than an asteroid, and only one other asteroid is known to have a satellite. So what is it? Challenge students to write a paragraph explaining why Pluto should be classified as a planet, an asteroid, or as some other object.

 Students can save their paragraphs in their portfolios.

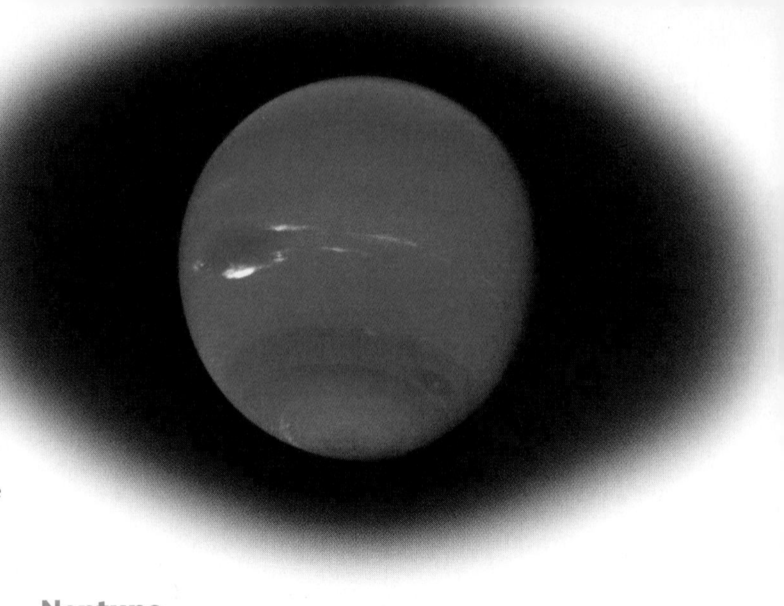

Figure 25 The Great Dark Spot was a giant storm in Neptune's atmosphere. The storm is now gone.

Figure 26 Neptune's largest moon, Triton, is covered with ridges and craters.

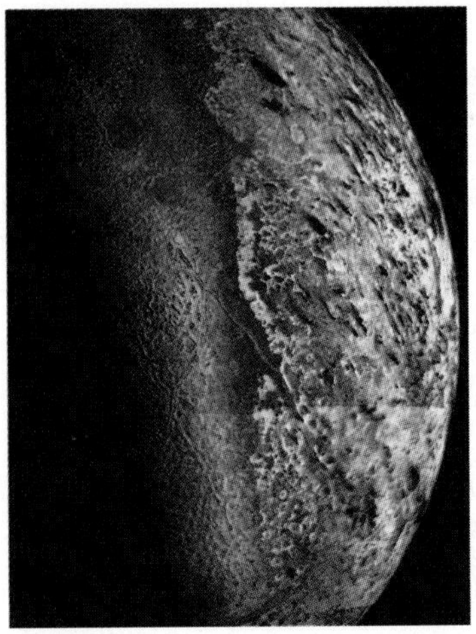

Neptune

Neptune is even farther from the sun than Uranus—in fact, it is 30 times Earth's distance from the sun. Unlike Uranus's nearly featureless blue atmosphere, Neptune's atmosphere contains visible clouds.

Discovery of Neptune The planet Neptune was discovered as a result of a mathematical prediction. Uranus was not quite following the orbit astronomers predicted for it. Astronomers hypothesized that there must be another, unseen planet whose gravity was affecting Uranus's orbit. By 1846, mathematicians in both England and France had calculated the orbit of this new planet. A few months later, an observer in Germany saw an unknown object in the sky. It was the new planet, now called Neptune.

Exploring Neptune In 1989 *Voyager 2* flew by Neptune, where it photographed a Great Dark Spot, as shown in Figure 25, about the size of Earth. Like the Great Red Spot on Jupiter, the Great Dark Spot probably was a giant storm. But the storm didn't last long. Images from the Hubble Space Telescope taken five years later showed that the Great Dark Spot was gone. Other, smaller spots and regions of clouds on Neptune seem to come and go.

Neptune's Moons Astronomers have discovered eight moons revolving around Neptune. Neptune's largest moon is Triton. The *Voyager* photos show that the region near Triton's south pole is covered with a cap of ice, and that dark material erupts from underneath.

☑ *Checkpoint Before they could see Neptune, what evidence led scientists to conclude that it existed?*

Background

History of Science Clyde Tombaugh was only 24 when he discovered Pluto. As a boy he had been intrigued by the view of the heavens he saw through an uncle's telescope. After he finished high school, Tombaugh built his own telescope. When he sent sketches of his observations of Jupiter and Mars to the Lowell Observatory, they offered him a job—finding Pluto.

Astronomers had predicted the existence of Pluto based on calculations that indicated a distant planet was disturbing the orbits of Uranus and Neptune. They know now that Pluto's small mass could not have caused this disturbance, but they were looking for another planet, and Tombaugh found it!

Tombaugh received a scholarship to the University of Kansas, but he continued to work at the Lowell Observatory until 1946.

Pluto and Charon

Pluto and its single moon Charon are very different from the gas giants. **Pluto and Charon have solid surfaces and masses much less than that of Earth.** In fact, Pluto is less than two thirds the size of Earth's moon. Since Charon is more than half the size of Pluto, astronomers often consider them to be a double planet instead of a planet and a moon.

Pluto and Charon are so far from the sun that they revolve around the sun only once every 248 Earth years. Because Pluto and Charon are so small and far away, astronomers have been unable to learn much about them.

Discovery of Pluto and Charon The American astronomer Clyde Tombaugh discovered Pluto in 1930. He had been searching for a large object he thought might be affecting Neptune's orbit. Tombaugh spent 10 months looking at hundreds of thousands of images before he found Pluto. Charon was not discovered until 1978, by the astronomer James Christy. Christy was studying photographs of Pluto when he noticed that Pluto seemed to have a "bump." The bump turned out to be Charon.

Is Pluto Really a Planet? Pluto is so small that many astronomers do not think it should be called a planet at all. Pluto may be merely the largest of thousands of objects revolving around the sun out beyond Neptune. If astronomers had found these other objects before they found Pluto, they might not have called Pluto a planet.

Figure 27 The space between Pluto and Charon couldn't be clearly seen from Earth until 1999, when Pluto and Charon were observed with new telescopes. This photo, taken with the Hubble Space Telescope, clearly shows them as two objects. *Inferring Why do astronomers often call Pluto and Charon a double planet?*

Section 4 Review

1. How are the gas giants similar to each other? How are they different?
2. How is Pluto different from the gas giants?
3. What is the most prominent feature of Jupiter's surface? What causes this feature?
4. Why do astronomers think Uranus may have been hit by another object billions of years ago?
5. **Thinking Critically Predicting** Do you think astronomers have found all of the moons of the outer planets? Explain.

> **Check Your Progress** CHAPTER PROJECT 2
> Once you have models that show size and distance separately, design another scale model of the solar system. This time, use the same scale for both size and distance. If your chalkboard is the sun, which planets would be in your classroom? Where would the other planets be with respect to your classroom, school grounds, and town?
> Discuss with classmates any problems that would come up in building a model using the same scale for both size and distance. Revise your model as needed.

Chapter 2 **J ◆ 77**

Answers to Self-Assessment

Caption Question

Figure 27 Pluto and Charon are close in size and close together.

☑ *Checkpoint*

Uranus was not following the orbit that scientists predicted. Scientists believed that the gravity of a large object, probably a planet, was affecting Uranus's orbit.

3 Assess

Section 4 Review Answers

1. They are all much larger than Earth, and do not have solid surfaces. They differ in size, number of moons, presence of rings, the tilt of their axes, and the presence of storms in their atmospheres.
2. Pluto is smaller and denser than the gas giants.
3. The Great Red Spot is Jupiter's most prominent feature. It is probably caused by a hurricane-like storm in the atmosphere.
4. Uranus's axis is tilted 90°. This could have been caused by a collision with another object.
5. No. Many of the moons were found only with the help of the *Voyager* photographs. Future probes will probably find other moons that *Voyager* may have missed.

> **Check Your Progress** CHAPTER PROJECT 2
> By this time, students should have a model showing relative size and a model showing relative distance. The larger the model, the more successful it will be in accurately representing the sizes of the planets. It is difficult to find a suitable scale that will clearly show both sizes and distances between the planets. For example, if the distance to Pluto is made equal to 100 m, then the size of Pluto would be 0.03 mm! Jupiter would be the size of a BB. If the size of Pluto is made 1.00 mm, then the distance to Pluto would be 2.6 km!

Performance Assessment

Drawing Have students draw diagrams of the outer planets that show their relative sizes, order, and at least one distinguishing characteristic of each planet.

Portfolio Students can save their diagrams in their portfolios.

Speeding Around the Sun

Preparing for Inquiry

Key Concept Since the pull of gravity is stronger, planets closer to the sun must move faster in order to maintain a stable orbit. The length of time it takes a planet to go around the sun is related to the distance of the planet from the sun.

Skills Objectives Students will be able to:

◆ formulate hypotheses concerning the revolution of a planet around the sun related to its distance from the sun.

◆ test their hypotheses to determine if they are supported by the available data.

◆ determine whether their hypotheses should be accepted or rejected based on the results of their tests.

Time 45 minutes

Advance Planning If you have not yet taught the skill of developing a hypothesis, see page 138 of the Skills Handbook. Perform this activity on your own first to become familiar with any problems students may experience in keeping the stopper swinging at various distances from the plastic tube. Use the materials to assemble a sling and test it for safety. Make sure that there is enough open space for groups to work without hitting each other.

Alternative Methods If you are concerned about students hitting one another, carry out the physical aspects of the lab as a demonstration from which students can develop the skill of formulating a hypothesis. In place of the stopper, a tennis ball with rubber bands around it or any other soft object of suitable weight and density that can be safely tied to the end of the string can be used. In place of the plastic tube, a pen tube with smooth ends may be used. Keep these for following years. To ensure that the string will not come out of the tube, tie a washer that does not fit through the tube to the string.

SPEEDING AROUND THE SUN

In this lab, you will make and test a hypothesis about how a planet's distance from the sun is related to its period of revolution.

Problem

How does a planet's distance from the sun affect its period of revolution?

Materials

string, 1.5 m   one-hole rubber stopper
plastic tube, 6 cm   stopwatch
meter stick
weight or several washers

Procedure

1. What do you think is the relationship between a planet's distance from the sun and its period of revolution? Write your hypothesis in the form of an "If . . . then . . ." statement.

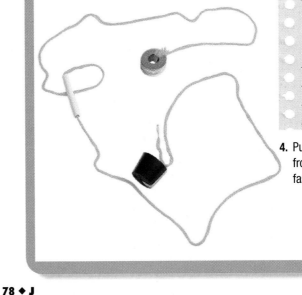

2. To test your hypothesis, you need to make a model planet.

   a. Thread the string through the rubber stopper hole. Tie the end of the string to the main part of the string. Pull tightly to make sure that the knot will not become untied.

   b. Thread the other end of the string through the plastic tube and tie a weight to that end. Have your teacher check both knots.

   c. Hold the plastic tube in your hand above your head. Swing the stopper around above your head. Practice keeping the stopper moving at a constant speed. The circle represents the planet's orbit. **CAUTION:** *Stand away from other students. Make sure the swinging stopper will not hit students or objects. Do not let go of the string.*

3. Before you try different distances for your model planet, copy the data table into your notebook.

DATA TABLE

Distance (cm)	Period of Revolution			
	Trial 1	Trial 2	Trial 3	Average
20				
40				
60				

4. Pull the string so the stopper is 20 cm away from the plastic tube. Swing the stopper just fast enough to keep the stopper moving.

Guiding Inquiry

Invitation Discuss the difference between a hypothesis and a scientific fact. A hypothesis is a possible explanation for a set of observations or answer to a scientific question.

Introducing the Procedure

◆ Have students think of the inward pull of the string as gravity.

◆ The activity should give students a "feel" for the effects of gravity and the increased speed as the orbit gets smaller.

Troubleshooting the Experiment

◆ Students may have to practice keeping the stopper moving at a constant speed. They may try to keep the stopper moving with the same frequency. Tell them to keep the stopper moving just fast enough to keep it up.

Expected Outcome

◆ Students will see that it takes longer for a single revolution when the string is longer.

◆ Students may have to reformulate their hypotheses from Step 8.

5. Have your partner time how long it takes for the stopper to make 10 revolutions. Divide by 10 to find the period of revolution. Record this number as Trial 1.

6. Repeat Steps 4–5 two more times. Record your results as Trials 2 and 3. Add the results of the three trials together and divide by three to find the average period of revolution.

7. If you pull the stopper out to 40 cm, do you think the period of revolution will increase or decrease? To find out, pull the stopper out to 40 cm and repeat Steps 4–6.

8. Based on your results in Step 7, do you want to revise your hypothesis? Make any needed changes. Then pull the stopper out to 60 cm and repeat Steps 4–6.

Analyze and Conclude

1. Which object in your model represented the sun? Which represented the planet?

2. What force did the pull on the string represent?

3. When you pulled the stopper out to make the orbit larger, did the string then represent a stronger or weaker force of gravity? Why?

4. What happened to the period of revolution when you made the orbit larger in Steps 7 and 8?

5. Did your observations support your hypothesis? Summarize your conclusions based on your observations.

6. Which planets take less time to revolve around the sun—those closer to the sun or those farther away? Use the model to support your answer.

7. **Think About It** What information did you consider when you made your hypothesis? How did having some experimental data help you modify your hypothesis?

Design an Experiment

Write a hypothesis relating the mass of a planet to its period of revolution. Then, using a stopper with a different mass, modify the activity to test your hypothesis. Before you swing the stopper, have your teacher check your knots.

◆ Inform students that, as distance from the sun increases, the gravitational pull of the sun on a planet decreases. In addition, the circumference of the orbit increases as distance from the sun increases. This means that the planet is traveling more slowly over a greater distance.

Analyze and Conclude

1. The plastic tube represented the sun. The rubber stopper represented the planet.
2. The pull on the string represented the force of gravity.
3. When the orbit was larger, the string represents a weaker force of gravity since the planet is further away.
4. As the orbit became larger, the period of revolution became longer.
5. Sample: The period increased, so the observations support the hypothesis.
6. Planets closer to the sun should take less time to revolve around the sun. When the string was short, the period of revolution was short.
7. Sample: String length determines orbit size, which determines the distance the stopper must travel in one orbit. We predict orbits of greater size will take longer to complete. The data supported the hypothesis.

Extending the Inquiry

Design an Experiment By adding additional rubber stoppers, the mass of the swinging object is increased. By repeating the swing of the increased mass in the same orbit, students will find that planets have the same period at the same distance. They may also notice that the inward pull of the string has to be greater with more stoppers. The force of gravity between the sun and a planet is related to the mass of the planet. The inertia of a planet is also related to its mass. Thus, the effect of increasing the mass is to increase both the pull of the sun's gravity and the ability of the planet to withstand that pull through inertia. The resulting acceleration on the planet is the same, regardless of mass.

Safety

Any time there is a swinging stopper, make sure it is in an open space free to swing clear of all students and objects. Make sure that the object on the opposite end of the string from the stopper cannot be pulled through the pen tube. Check the strength of the string to make sure that it will not break. Tell students to wear eye protection throughout the lab. Review the safety guidelines in Appendix A.

Sample Data Table

Distance (cm)	Trial 1 (s)	Trial 2 (s)	Trial 3 (s)	Average (s)
20	0.4	0.5	0.4	0.43
40	0.6	0.6	0.7	0.63
60	0.8	0.8	0.8	0.80

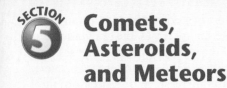

Comets, Asteroids, and Meteors

Objectives

After completing the lesson, students will be able to
◆ describe the characteristics of comets and asteroids;
◆ describe the formation of meteoroids.

Key Terms comet, asteroid, asteroid belt, meteoroid, meteor, meteorite

1 Engage/Explore

Activating Prior Knowledge

Ask students if they have ever seen a shooting star. Invite them to describe what a shooting star looks like. Ask them to speculate about what it is. After the discussion, tell students that in this section, they will investigate the nature of comets, asteroids, and shooting stars, which are actually meteors.

DISCOVER

Skills Focus inferring
Materials *modeling clay, pencil, 3 10-cm lengths of string, small fan*
Time 10 minutes
Tips You may wish to have more than one fan available and allow two or three students to test their models at the same time.
Expected Outcome The strings point away from the fan, behind the ball of clay.
Think It Over Moving the ball does not change the direction in which the strings point. A comet's tail always points away from the sun.

SECTION
5 Comets, Asteroids, and Meteors

DISCOVER .... ACTIVITY

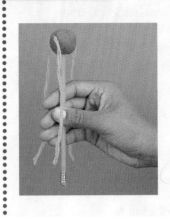

Which Way Do Comet Tails Point?

1. Form a small ball out of modeling clay to represent a comet.
2. Using a pencil point, push three 10-cm lengths of string into the ball. The strings represent the comet's tail. Stick the ball onto the pencil point, as shown in the photo.
3. Hold the ball about 1 m in front of a fan. The air from the fan represents the solar wind. Move the ball toward the fan, away from the fan, and from side to side.
CAUTION: *Keep your fingers away from the fan blades.*

Think It Over
Inferring How does moving the ball affect the direction in which the strings point? What determines which way the tail of a comet points?

GUIDE FOR READING

◆ What are the characteristics of comets and asteroids?
◆ Where do meteoroids come from?

Reading Tip As you read, make an outline of this section using the headings as the main topics.

Imagine watching a cosmic collision! That's exactly what happened in July 1994. Eugene and Carolyn Shoemaker and David Levy discovered a new comet in 1993 that had previously broken into pieces near Jupiter. In 1994, the fragments returned and crashed into Jupiter. On Earth, astronomers were fascinated to see the huge explosions—some were as large as Earth!

As this story shows, the sun, planets, and moons aren't the only objects in the solar system. There are also millions of smaller objects, most of which are classified as comets and asteroids.

Comets

One of the most glorious things you can see in the night sky is a comet. A bright comet may be visible only for days or weeks or months, but is well worth seeing. In April 1997, for example, Comet Hale-Bopp and its bright dust tail were clearly visible even without a telescope.

You can think of a **comet** as a "dirty snowball" about the size of an Earth mountain. **Comets are chunks of ice and dust whose orbits are usually very long, narrow ellipses.** Because their orbits are so

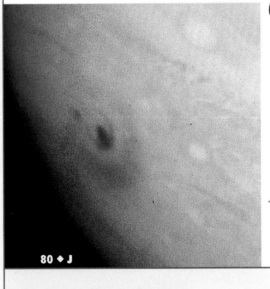

◀ A dark ring on Jupiter caused by comet Shoemaker-Levy 9

READING STRATEGIES

Reading Tip Write the following outline guide on the board and review each item with students. Then have students outline the section as they read.
I. First Main Idea
  A. First supporting idea or fact
    1. detail or example
    2. detail or example
  B. Second supporting idea or fact
II. Second Main Idea (outline will continue)

Study and Comprehension Provide each student with three note cards, and have them write *comet*, *asteroid*, and *meteor* on the cards, one term per card. As students read the section, have them list the characteristics of the object on the opposite side of each card. Then have partners take turns using their sets of note cards as flashcards for testing each other's knowledge of comets, asteroids, and meteors.

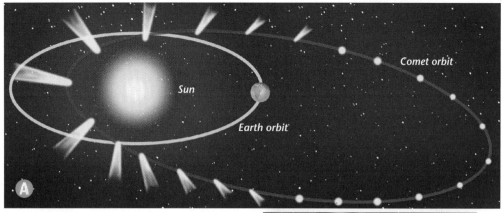

elliptical, few of them pass near Earth. They can usually then be seen only briefly. When a comet gets close enough to the sun, the energy in the sunlight turns the ice into gas, releasing dust. The gas and dust form an outer layer called the coma. Figure 28 shows the inner layer of the comet, which is then called the nucleus. The brightest part of a comet, the comet's head, is made up of the nucleus and coma.

Remember that the sun's corona produces a stream of particles called the solar wind. Solar wind pushes the gas from a comet away from the sun. Gas and dust form the comet's tail. The tail looks like hair; in fact, the name *comet* means "long-haired star" in Greek.

A comet's tail can be hundreds of millions of kilometers long and stretch across most of the sky. The material is stretched out very thinly, however, so there isn't much mass in a comet tail.

In 1705, Edmond Halley, an English astronomer, calculated the orbits of 24 comets that people had observed over hundreds of years. Halley realized that several of the comets seemed to have the same orbit and suggested that they were actually the same comet. Halley calculated that this comet appeared about every 76 years, and predicted that it would reappear in 1758. When this prediction came true, the comet was named Halley's Comet. In 1986, the last time Halley's Comet appeared, the European Space Agency's *Giotto* spacecraft flew within a few hundred kilometers of it.

☑ *Checkpoint* (How did Halley's Comet get its name?)

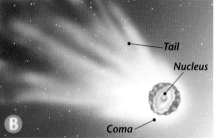

Figure 28 **A.** Most comets revolve around the sun in very long, narrow orbits. **B.** The main parts of a comet are the nucleus, the coma, and the tail. *Observing What shape is a comet's orbit?*

Program Resources

◆ **Teaching Resources** 2-5 Lesson Plan, p. 57; 2-5 Section Summary, p. 58
◆ **Guided Study Workbook** Section 2-5

Answers to Self-Assessment

Caption Question

Figure 28 The shape of a comet's orbit is a long, narrow ellipse.

☑ *Checkpoint*

Edmond Halley identified a comet, and calculated that it appeared every 76 years. He predicted the comet would reappear in 1758. When Halley's prediction came true, the comet was named after him.

2 Facilitate

Comets

Using the Visuals: Figure 28

Ask students how the orbit of a comet is different from the orbit of a planet. (*The orbits of most comets are much longer and narrower.*) **learning modality: visual**

Building Inquiry Skills: Inferring

As students explore the structure of a comet, have them make inferences about observing comets from Earth. Ask: **Which part of the comet do we see? Why?** (*The coma and tail; they are the brightest parts of the comet.*) **Why would it be difficult to view the nucleus?** (*It is very small and obscured by the coma.*) **learning modality: verbal**

Building Inquiry Skills: Predicting

Ask students to predict whether they are likely to ever have the opportunity to see Halley's comet. (*Probably, for most students*) Encourage students to determine approximately how old they will be at that time. (*Most will be in their 70s.*) **learning modality: logical/ mathematical**

ACTIVITY

Ongoing Assessment

Writing Have students explain how the coma and tail of a comet are formed.

J ◆ 81

Asteroids

Have students locate the Yucatan peninsula on a world map. Ask: **Since a giant asteroid hit this area, why haven't scientists found the object that made the crater?** *(It probably exploded into dust on impact.)* Tell students that asteroids and other objects from space that land on Earth usually explode into dust or vapor. Ask: **What may have happened to the dust from the asteroid that hit the Yucatan?** *(Sample: It fell into the ocean, settled on the ocean floor, was buried by layers of sediment, and eventually turned back into rock.)* **learning modality: verbal**

Meteors

Building Inquiry Skills: Hypothesizing

Materials *plaster of Paris, water, disposable plastic trays, assortment of round objects with different sizes and masses, petroleum jelly*

Time 40 minutes

Since objects in the classroom don't explode on impact, it is only possible to model *some* of the aspects of crater formation. Assign students to groups. Have each group choose one variable to test, such as height, mass, or size of object, and develop a hypothesis relating crater size to the variable chosen. Coat the marbles with petroleum jelly. Prepare liquid plaster of Paris. Have students fill a clean polystyrene tray with the liquid. Wait a few minutes until the material begins to set, then quickly drop the marbles, controlling all except the manipulated variable. When the plaster of Paris sets completely, remove the marbles and examine the craters. Ask: **How did the variable you chose affect the size of the crater it made?** *(Answers will vary, but crater size should increase with height and mass.)* **learning modality: kinesthetic**

Figure 29 The asteroid belt (left) lies between Mars and Jupiter. Asteroids come in many sizes and shapes, as shown in this artist's depiction (center). NASA's *Galileo* mission photographed the asteroid Gaspra (right) .

Asteroids

Between 1801 and 1807, astronomers discovered four small objects between the orbits of Mars and Jupiter. They named the objects Ceres, Pallas, Juno, and Vesta. Over the next 80 years, astronomers found 300 more. These objects, called **asteroids,** are too small and too numerous to be considered full-fledged planets. **Most asteroids revolve around the sun between the orbits of Mars and Jupiter.** This region of the solar system, shown in Figure 29, is known as the **asteroid belt.**

Astronomers have discovered more than 10,000 asteroids, and more are found every month. Ceres, Pallas, Juno, and Vesta are among the dozen that are over 250 kilometers across.

INTEGRATING EARTH SCIENCE Some asteroids come near the orbit of Earth. Someday, one of these near-Earth asteroids could hit Earth. When a large asteroid hit Earth 65 million years ago, it exploded, making a crater 200 kilometers in diameter near the Yucatán Peninsula of Mexico. The explosion almost certainly raised trillions of tons of dust into the atmosphere, blocking the light from the sun for months. Debris from the explosion probably started huge fires that destroyed much of Earth's forests and grass. Scientists hypothesize that as a result many species of organisms, including the dinosaurs, became extinct.

Meteors

Imagine being outside in the country on a clear night, looking up at the sky. Suddenly, you see a streak of light flashing across the sky. Within seconds, you see another streak. For an hour or so, you see a streak at least once a minute. You are watching a meteor shower. Meteor showers happen regularly, several times a year.

Background

History of Science Consider these facts about the first asteroid to be discovered, Ceres.

◆ Ceres was discovered twice, the first time by Giuseppe Piazzi, on January 1, 1801, in Palermo, Sicily. Piazzi named the asteroid *Ceres* after the Roman goddess of grain (who was also the patron saint of Sicily). Because Piazzi was ill, he only observed the asteroid for about one month, and it moved into the daytime sky. The German astronomer Franz von Zach rediscovered Ceres on January 1, 1802.

◆ Ceres is the largest known asteroid.

◆ When Piazzi named the asteroid he had discovered, he began the asteroid-naming convention astronomers still use today—asteroids are named *by* their discoverers, unlike comets, which are named *for* their discoverers.

Even when there is no meteor shower, you frequently can see meteors if you are far from city lights and the sky is free of clouds. On average, a meteor streaks overhead every 10 minutes.

A **meteoroid** is a chunk of rock or dust in space. **Meteoroids usually come from comets or asteroids.** When a comet breaks up, it forms a cloud of dust that continues to move through the solar system. When Earth passes through one of these dust clouds, bits of dust enter Earth's atmosphere.

When a meteoroid enters Earth's atmosphere, friction makes it burn up and produce the streak of light you see in the sky—a **meteor.** If the meteoroid is large enough, it may not burn up completely. Meteoroids that pass through the atmosphere and hit Earth's surface are called **meteorites.** The craters on the moon and on other objects in the solar system were caused by meteoroids.

Meteorites fall all over Earth. Most of them look just like stones, so nobody notices them. A few meteorites are made almost entirely of iron and nickel, and so are unusually heavy for their size. This makes them more likely to be identified as meteorites than as Earth rocks.

Figure 30 A. Meteor Crater in Arizona is the best-known meteorite crater on Earth. It was formed when a meteorite hit Earth about 40,000 years ago. **B.** Meteoroids make streaks of light, like the one above, as they burn up in the atmosphere.

Section 5 Review

1. What is a comet made of?
2. Where are most asteroids found?
3. What are the main sources of meteoroids?
4. What is the difference between a meteor and a meteorite?
5. **Thinking Critically Predicting** Describe what might happen if an asteroid the size of the one that hit Earth 65 million years ago hit Earth today.

Science at Home

Meteor showers occur regularly on specific dates. (The Perseids meteor shower, for example, occurs every August 12.) Look in the newspaper or almanac for information about the next meteor shower. With adult family members, go outside on that night and look for meteors. Explain to your family what causes the glow.

Program Resources

● **Science Explorer Series** *Earth's Changing Surface,* Chapter 4
◆ **Teaching Resources** 2-5 Review and Reinforce, p. 59; 2-5 Enrich, p. 60

3 Assess

Section 5 Review Answers
1. Chunks of ice and dust
2. In the asteroid belt that lies between Jupiter and Mars
3. Most meteoroids come from comets or asteroids.
4. A meteor is a meteoroid that enters Earth's atmosphere and burns up. A meteorite is a meteoroid that passes through Earth's atmosphere and hits Earth's surface.
5. Effects would vary, depending on whether the object hit on land or water. In either case, the collision would raise huge clouds of dust, blocking light from the sun. Many species of living things could become extinct as a result of the blocked sunlight.

Science at Home

Since they will be outdoors after dark, caution students they should only view a meteor shower with an adult. Meteor showers are more easily seen outside cities, in areas where bright lights do not block the glow from the meteors. Students should explain that the glow is caused by friction caused by Earth's atmosphere heating the rock as it falls.

Performance Assessment

Oral Presentation Have students narrate the life story of an asteroid that orbits close to Earth and eventually hits the ground.

SECTION 6 Is There Life Beyond Earth?

Objectives

After completing the lesson, students will be able to
- identify the conditions needed for living things to exist on Earth;
- state why Mars and Europa are thought to be good places to look for signs of life.

Key Term extraterrestrial life

1 Engage/Explore

Activating Prior Knowledge

Show students a potted plant and a goldfish in a bowl. Invite students to suggest what is the same about these two. (*Both are alive.*) Ask: **How do we know these things are alive?** (*They grow, reproduce, excrete wastes.*) **What do these things both need to stay alive?** (*Water, space, energy*)

DISCOVER

Skills Focus forming operational definitions
Materials *yeast, warm water, bowl, thermometer, spoon, sugar, stopwatch or clock*
Time 15 minutes
Tips You may wish to buy yeast in bulk rather than packets. A packet of yeast contains about one tablespoon. Provide a source of water at the correct temperature. Encourage students to record as many observations as they can.
Expected Outcome Before adding water, students will observe that the yeast is dry, brown, grainy, and not changing. After adding water, students should observe that the yeast is making bubbles and has a distinct odor.
Think It Over The observations that yeast is dry, brown, grainy, and immobile suggest that yeast is not alive. The observations that the yeast is bubbling, has a smell, and appears to be growing suggest that yeast is alive. You can tell that something is alive if it eats, breathes, or grows.

SECTION 6 Is There Life Beyond Earth?

DISCOVER

Is Yeast Alive or Not?

1. Open a package of yeast and pour it into a bowl.
2. Look at the yeast carefully. Make a list of your observations.
3. Fill the bowl about halfway with warm water (about 20°C). Add a spoonful of sugar. Stir the mixture with the spoon. Wait five minutes.
4. Now look at the yeast again and make a list of your observations.

Think It Over
Forming Operational Definitions Which of your observations seem to suggest that yeast is not alive? Which observations suggest that yeast is alive? How can you tell if something is alive?

GUIDE FOR READING

- What conditions do living things need to exist on Earth?
- Why do scientists think Mars and Europa are good places to look for signs of life?

Reading Tip As you read, write down evidence to support this statement: Life may exist in other parts of the solar system.

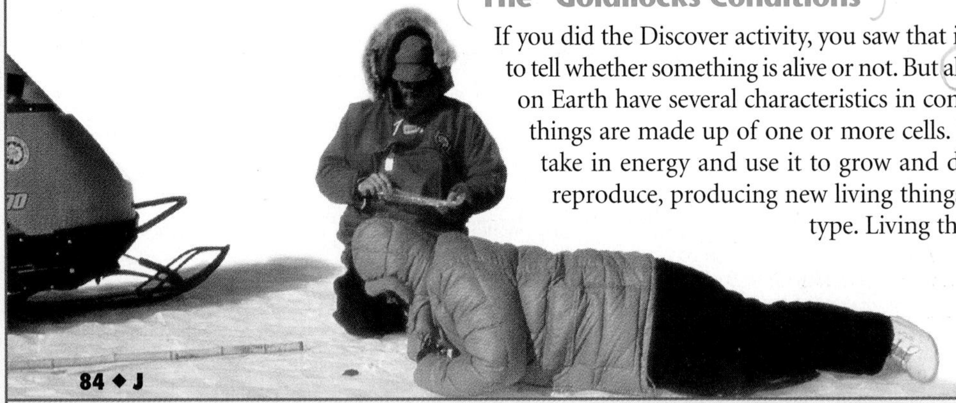

Figure 31 Dr. Ursula Marvin (lying down) studies meteorites such as this one in Antarctica.

Most of Antarctica is covered with snow and ice. You would not expect to see rocks lying on top of the whiteness. But surprisingly, in some places people have found rocks lying on the surface. When scientists examined the rocks, they found that the rocks are meteorites. A few of the meteorites came from Mars. Astronomers think that meteoroids hitting the surface of Mars must have blasted chunks of rock into space. The rocks eventually entered Earth's atmosphere and landed in Antarctica.

Recently a team of scientists announced that a meteorite from Mars found in Antarctica shows tiny shapes that look like fossils—the remains of ancient life preserved in rock. Many scientists doubt that the shapes really are fossils. But if they are, it would be a sign that life forms similar to bacteria once existed on Mars. Life other than that on Earth would be called **extraterrestrial life.**

The "Goldilocks Conditions"

If you did the Discover activity, you saw that it can be hard to tell whether something is alive or not. But all living things on Earth have several characteristics in common. Living things are made up of one or more cells. Living things take in energy and use it to grow and develop. They reproduce, producing new living things of the same type. Living things also give off waste.

READING STRATEGIES

Reading Tip Before students read, explain that looking for evidence to support a statement is a good way to become involved with the ideas in a section. Remind students that they are looking for evidence from the section only. After the activity, encourage students to discuss other evidence they have heard or read that supports theories of life in other parts of the solar system.

Program Resources

- **Teaching Resources** 2-6 Lesson Plan, p. 61; 2-6 Section Summary, p. 62
- **Guided Study Workbook** Section 2-6

A yeast cell, for example, is a living thing. Each yeast organism has one cell. Yeast cells take in sugar for energy. They reproduce and make new yeast cells. And yeast cells produce carbon dioxide as waste. A yeast cell, then, fulfills all the requirements for a living thing.

Nobody knows whether life exists anywhere other than Earth. Scientists often talk about the conditions needed by "life as we know it." **Earth has liquid water and a suitable temperature range and atmosphere for living things to survive.** Other planets do not have such favorable conditions, which scientists sometimes call the "Goldilocks conditions." That is, the temperature is not too hot and not too cold. It is just right. If Earth were hotter, water would always be a gas—water vapor. If Earth were colder, water would always be solid ice. On Earth, water exists as a liquid as well as a solid and a gas.

Are these the conditions necessary for life? Or are they just the conditions that Earth's living things happen to need? Scientists have only one example of life to study: life on Earth. Unless scientists find life somewhere else, there will be no way to answer these questions.

✓ *Checkpoint* *What are some characteristics of all living things?*

Life on Earth

In recent years, astounding discoveries have been made deep under the ocean. Sunlight never penetrates there. But deep-diving submarines have discovered giant tube worms and other animals that live at very high pressure in the dark. Single-celled forms of life have been discovered that are different from plants, animals, or bacteria. These newly discovered life forms get their energy not from sunlight, but from chemicals. Other scientists have found tiny life forms in caves and deep inside solid rocks. Still other scientists have found life surviving in hot springs that had been thought to be too hot to support life.

The range of conditions in which life can exist is much greater than scientists once thought. Perhaps life forms exist that do not even need the "Goldilocks conditions"!

Figure 32 These colonies of microorganisms were discovered deep in a cave in Mexico. *Inferring How does studying unusual organisms like these help scientists predict what extraterrestrial life might be like?*

Communicating

You are writing a letter to a friend who lives on another planet. Your friend has never been to Earth and has no idea what the planet is like. Explain in your letter why the conditions on Earth make it the ideal place for living things.

2 *Facilitate*

The "Goldilocks Conditions"

Cultural Diversity

When the *Voyager* spacecraft were launched, each had a time capsule that carried a message from Earth. The messages included languages, music, sounds, and images from many different cultures. As a class project, find out what messages were sent aboard the spacecraft. Then have students list the things that they would send to reflect their own culture. **learning modality: verbal**

Sharpen your *Skills*

Communicating

Time 15 minutes
Tips Have pairs of students critique each other's letters. Then have students write a final draft of their letters.
Expected Outcome Letters should include that Earth has liquid water and a suitable temperature range and atmosphere for living things.
Extend Challenge students to present the information in a chart listing the three Goldilocks Conditions and how Earth satisfies these conditions.

Life on Earth

Addressing Naive Conceptions

Some students may think that the search for extraterrestrial life is a search for only intelligent life forms. Ask: **Why would scientists be excited about discovering single-celled forms of life on other planets?** (*Single-celled life forms could suggest that multi-celled organisms may also exist on other planets.*) **learning modality: verbal**

Ongoing Assessment

Drawing Have students create a diagram showing characteristics of living things.

Media and Technology

🔘 **Exploring Life Science Videodisc**
Unit 1, Side 2,
"Evolution of Cells"

Chapter 2

Answers to Self-Assessment

Caption Question

Figure 32 Scientists learn more about the wide range of conditions in which life on other planets might exist.

✓ *Checkpoint*

Living things are made up of one or more cells, take in energy and use it to grow and develop, reproduce, and give off waste.

Life on Mars?

Building Inquiry Skills: Drawing Conclusions

Ask students: **What hypothesis were scientists testing when they sent the *Viking* spacecraft to Mars?** *(One hypothesis was that Mars may once have had life.)* Then ask: **What kinds of samples did the *Viking* examine?** *(Air and soil samples)* Next have students determine how these samples were useful to scientists. *(Scientists found no evidence of life on Mars.)* **learning modality: logical/mathematical**

Building Inquiry Skills: Making Judgments

Allow teams of students to debate the existence of life on Mars. Have each team prepare by making a list of all their arguments for one side of the debate. Then have pro and con teams present their arguments to each other and discuss the evidence on both sides. **cooperative learning**

Life on Europa?

Including All Students

Encourage students who need additional challenges to speculate on what kinds of life forms could exist beneath Europa's icy crust. Students should find out what living things survive under Earth's Arctic ice. Then have students suggest a possible test that could be done to find out whether similar kinds of life forms exist on Europa. **learning modality: logical/mathematical**

Language Arts Connection

Encourage students to read science-fiction short stories about life on other planets. Instruct them to try to distinguish fact from fiction. Encourage students to share stories with the class, and discuss the likelihood that they could ever take place. **learning modality: verbal**

Life on Mars?

Recall that Mars is the planet most similar to Earth. That makes Mars the most obvious place to look for living things similar to those on Earth.

The *Viking* Missions In 1970, a spacecraft found regions on the surface of Mars that look like stream beds with criss-crossing paths of water. These shapes, shown in Figure 33, were almost certainly formed by flowing water. **Since life as we know it requires water, scientists hypothesize that Mars may have once had the conditions needed for life to exist.**

Twin *Viking* spacecraft reached Mars in 1976. Each had one part that landed on Mars's surface and another part that stayed in orbit, taking pictures of most of the surface. Each of the *Viking* landers carried a compact biology laboratory meant to search for life forms.

The biology laboratories on the landers tested the Martian air and soil for signs of life. Each laboratory was designed to see if there were life forms that used oxygen and gave off carbon dioxide, as many living things on Earth do. A robot scoop brought some soil from Mars's surface into the lab and added water to see if the sample gave off oxygen. None of these tests showed any evidence of life.

✓ *Checkpoint* What evidence shows that there may once have been running water on Mars?

Meteorites From Mars Interest in life on Mars was increased by the report in 1996 about the meteorite from Mars that may contain fossils. The scientists' report started a huge debate. What were the tubelike things in the meteorite? Many scientists have suggested that the tiny shapes found in the meteorite do not prove that life forms once existed on Mars. Perhaps the shapes came from natural processes on Mars and are just lumps of hardened clay. Perhaps the shapes came from snow that got into cracks in the meteorite after it landed on Earth. Were the shapes

Figure 33 These patterns on the surface of Mars are probably evidence that liquid water once flowed on Mars. *Applying Concepts Why does this evidence make it more likely that there may once have been life on Mars?*

Background

Facts and Figures The tests performed by the scientific labs on the *Viking* landers gave no clear evidence of life on Mars. This conclusion, however, came after much debate, because the tests results were not negative. The tests were designed to detect life by exposing soil samples to controlled conditions, then detecting chemicals that would normally be produced by life processes. The tests not only detected these chemicals, but also detected them in much larger quantities than any life in the barren soil could possibly have produced. Obviously, something else was happening inside the test containers.

Scientists now hypothesize that the Martian soil contains chemicals similar to hydrogen peroxide that reacted with water and generated the positive test results. As a result, the *Viking* landers told us little about possible life on Mars.

too deep inside the rocks to be from Earth? Perhaps the shapes are too small to be the remains of life forms. They are only one-hundredth the size of any other known life forms.

The most effective way to answer these questions is to send more probes to Mars. Future Mars missions should be able to bring samples of rocks and soil back to Earth for detailed analysis. Scientists may not yet have evidence of life on Mars, but hope is growing that we can soon solve the mystery.

Life on Europa?

Many scientists think that Europa, one of Jupiter's moons, may have the conditions necessary for life to develop. Photos from *Voyager* and *Galileo* showed that Europa has a very smooth, icy crust with giant cracks in it.

Close-up views from *Galileo* show that Europa's ice has broken up and re-formed, resulting in twisted, house-sized blocks of ice. Similar patterns occur in the ice crust over Earth's Arctic Ocean. Could this mean that there is a liquid ocean under Europa's ice? The water in the ocean could possibly be kept liquid by heat coming from inside Europa. **If there is liquid water on Europa, there might also be life.**

How can scientists study conditions under Europa's ice sheet? Such studies are many years off. People will have to wait for the next generation of space probes to search for liquid water on Europa.

Figure 34 Europa is covered with a layer of ice similar to the ice covering Earth's Arctic Ocean. There may be liquid water under the ice.

Section 6 Review

1. What conditions does life on Earth need to survive?
2. Why do astronomers think there could be life on Europa?
3. How did the *Viking* missions search for life on Mars?
4. **Thinking Critically Applying Concepts** Do you think there could be life as we know it on Venus? Explain. (*Hint*: Review page 66.)

Science at Home

Imagine that scientists have found intelligent extraterrestrial life. With family members, make up a message to send to the extraterrestrials. Remember that they will not understand English, so you should use only symbols and drawings in your message.

Section 6 Review Answers

1. Liquid water, a suitable temperature range and atmosphere, and sunlight or other source of energy

2. Europa is covered by a layer of ice like Earth's Arctic Ocean, and there may be liquid water underneath the ice.

3. Both *Viking* landers had biology laboratories. Each laboratory examined the air and soil for signs of oxygen being used up and carbon dioxide being produced.

4. No, because life as we know it cannot exist at 460°C, the surface temperature of Venus.

Science at Home

Encourage students to consider what information about Earth and its inhabitants would be most important for extraterrestrials to know. Suggest that students ask each family member to contribute one piece of the message.

Portfolio Students can save their messages in their portfolios.

Program Resources

◆ **Teaching Resources** 2-6 Review and Reinforce, p. 63; 2-6 Enrich, p. 64

Answers to Self-Assessment

Caption Question

Figure 33 Since life as we know it requires water, evidence of liquid water flowing on Mars makes it more likely that there may once have been life there.

☑ *Checkpoint*

Regions on the surface of Mars that look like stream beds with crisscrossing paths of water

Performance Assessment

Writing Have students explain which of the planets and their moons in our solar system would be good places to search for signs of life and which would not.

Space Exploration— Is It Worth the Cost?

Purpose

To discuss the value of space exploration

Panel Discussion

Time 1 day to prepare; 1 hour for panel discussion

Have students discuss space exploration in groups of three or four. Allow them access to books, magazine articles, or the Internet to find information on the potential benefits of space exploration.

Once students have had time to discuss the issues in groups, bring them back together and lead a panel discussion on the pros and cons of space exploration. Have each group act as one panel member, representing one point of view and taking turns presenting points in the discussion.

Extend Ask students to come up with several questions concerning space exploration that they could ask their family or community members in order to gain other insights into the space program and its potential benefits. For example, students may not realize how inspiring Armstrong's trip to the moon was when it took place unless they talk to someone who was an adult in the 1960s.

You Decide

Have students complete the first two steps on page 88 before the panel discussion begins as a way to prepare themselves for taking part. After the discussion is concluded, students can complete Step 3 on page 88, using what they learned in the discussion to find solutions to the problem. Students may set priorities for Congress's budget in many different ways. Many will put feeding the poor or researching diseases near the top of the list and space exploration near the bottom.

Space Exploration—Is It Worth the Cost?

Imagine that your spacecraft has just landed on Mars after a two-month journey from Earth. You've spent years planning for this moment. Canyons, craters, and distant plains stretch out before you. You check your spacesuit and prepare to step out onto the rocky red surface of Mars.

Is such a trip likely? Would it be worthwhile? How much is space flight really worth to human society? Scientists and politicians have already started to debate such questions. Space exploration can help us learn more about the universe. But exploration is risky and expensive. Sending people into space costs billions of dollars and risks human lives. How can we balance the costs and benefits of space exploration?

The Issues

Should Humans Travel Into Space? Many Americans think that Neil Armstrong's walk on the moon in 1969 was one of the great moments in history. Also, learning how to keep people alive in space has led to improvements in everyday life. Safer equipment for firefighters, easier ways to package frozen food, and effective heart monitors have all come out of space program research.

What Are the Alternatives? Space exploration can involve a project to put a person on Mars. It also can involve a more limited use of scientific instruments near Earth, such as the Hubble Space Telescope. Instead of sending people, we could send space probes like *Mars Pathfinder* to other planets.

Is Human Space Exploration Worth the Cost? Scientists who favor human travel into space say that only people can collect certain kinds of information. And using simpler space vehicles that are cheaper to build can also save money. But no one knows if research in space really provides information quicker than research that can be done on Earth. Many critics of space research think that other needs are more important. One United States senator said, "Every time you put money into the space station, there is a dime that won't be available for our children's education or for medical research."

You Decide

1. **Identify the Problem**
   In your own words, list the costs and benefits of space exploration.

2. **Analyze the Options**
   Make a chart of three different approaches to space exploration: sending humans to another planet, doing only Earth-based research, and one other option. What are the benefits and drawbacks of each approach?

3. **Find a Solution**
   Imagine that you are a member of Congress who has to vote on a new budget. There is a fixed amount of money to spend, so you have to decide which needs are most important. Make a list of your top ten priorities. Explain your decisions.

Background

NASA has included a detailed justification of space exploration on their Web site. NASA argues that the basic knowledge about the universe gained through space exploration gives us a better understanding of Earth. Space exploration has allowed applications in satellite communication. Many technological breakthroughs have come as a result of the space program. The space program supports many jobs and is thus good for the economy. The exploration of space serves as an inspiration to mankind to explore the unknown and push back boundaries. Additional information is available at **www.nasa.gov/** and **www.nss.org/**.

SECTION 1 — Observing the Solar System

Key Ideas

◆ Ptolemy thought that Earth is at the center of the system of planets.

◆ Copernicus thought that the sun is at the center of the planets. Galileo's observations supported Copernicus's theory.

◆ Kepler discovered that the orbits of the planets are ellipses.

◆ Newton concluded that two factors—inertia and gravity—combine to keep the planets in orbit.

Key Terms

geocentric   ellipse
heliocentric   inertia

SECTION 2 — The Sun

Key Ideas

◆ The sun's energy comes from nuclear fusion.

◆ The sun's atmosphere has three layers: the photosphere, the chromosphere, and the corona.

◆ Features on or above the sun's surface include sunspots, prominences, and solar flares.

Key Terms

nuclear fusion   solar wind
core   sunspot
photosphere   prominence
chromosphere   solar flare
corona

SECTION 3 — The Inner Planets

Key Idea

◆ The four inner planets—Mercury, Venus, Earth, and Mars—are small and have rocky surfaces. They are often called the terrestrial planets.

Key Terms

terrestrial planets
retrograde rotation
greenhouse effect

SECTION 4 — The Outer Planets

Key Ideas

◆ Four outer planets—Jupiter, Saturn, Uranus, and Neptune—are much larger than Earth.

◆ Pluto and Charon have solid surfaces and masses much less than that of Earth.

Key Term

gas giant

SECTION 5 — Comets, Asteroids, and Meteors

Key Ideas

◆ Comets are chunks of ice and dust that usually have long, elliptical orbits.

◆ Most asteroids revolve around the sun between the orbits of Mars and Jupiter.

Key Terms

comet   asteroid belt   meteor
asteroid   meteoroid   meteorite

SECTION 6 — Is There Life Beyond Earth?

INTEGRATING LIFE SCIENCE

Key Ideas

◆ Earth has liquid water and a suitable temperature range and atmosphere for living things to survive.

◆ Since life as we know it requires water, scientists hypothesize that Mars may have once had the conditions for life to exist.

Key Term

extraterrestrial life

Organizing Information

Compare/Contrast Table On a separate piece of paper, make a table comparing and contrasting the geocentric and heliocentric systems. Include information on the following: object at the center of the system; objects that move around the center; who the system was first proposed by; and whom supported the system. (For more on compare/contrast tables, see the Skills Handbook.)

Chapter 2 **J ◆ 89**

Organizing Information

Compare/Contrast Table

	Geocentric System	Heliocentric System
Object at center	Earth	sun
Objects that move around center	planets and sun	Earth and other planets
Proposed by	ancient Greek astronomers	Copernicus
Supporters	Ptolemy	Galileo and others

Media and Technology

▪ **Interactive Student Tutorial CD-ROM** J-2

▪ **Computer Test Bank** *Astronomy,* Chapter 2 Test

Program Resources

◆ **Teaching Resources** Chapter 2 Project Scoring Rubric, p. 40; Chapter 2 Performance Assessment, pp. 121-123; Chapter 2 Test, pp. 124-127

Reviewing Content
Multiple Choice
1. d 2. d 3. c 4. a 5. c

True or False
6. ellipse 7. true 8. true 9. Jupiter
10. true

Checking Concepts

11. Galileo's observations of Venus' phases could not be explained by the geocentric system. His observations of the motions of Jupiter's moons showed that not everything in the sky revolves around Earth.

12. Newton concluded that gravity and inertia keep the planets in the orbits that Kepler found by looking at Brahe's observations.

13. It is usually impossible to see the sun's corona because its faint light is overwhelmed by the bright light of the photosphere and chromosphere.

14. Dark-looking areas of gas on the sun that are cooler than the gases around them

15. Mercury is so hot that the gases in the atmosphere escaped from Mercury's weak gravity.

16. One hypothesis is that Venus was struck by a large object billions of years ago and this collision caused Venus' direction of rotation to change.

17. The terrestrial planets are relatively small and rocky. The gas giants are much larger and lack a solid surface.

18. These astronomers think Pluto should not be a planet because it is so small. They think it may just be the largest of thousands of objects revolving around the sun beyond Neptune.

19. Solar wind pushes the gases in a comet's tail away from the sun.

20. No. Life on Earth can exist without sunlight, in caves, and in solid rock. Scientists could look for evidence of life in these places.

21. Students should include descriptions of the terrestrial planet and the gas giant that they visit. High marks should be given for accurate, clearly written descriptions.

Reviewing Content

For more review of key concepts, see the Interactive Student Tutorial CD-ROM.

Multiple Choice
Choose the letter of the answer that best completes each statement.

1. Copernicus thought that the solar system was
   a. celestial.
   b. elliptical.
   c. geocentric.
   d. heliocentric.
2. The part of the sun where nuclear fusion occurs is the
   a. photosphere.   b. chromosphere.
   c. corona.   d. core.
3. Planets with atmospheres composed mostly of carbon dioxide include
   a. Earth and Mercury.
   b. Venus and Mercury.
   c. Venus and Mars.
   d. Mercury and Mars.
4. The Great Red Spot is a huge storm on
   a. Jupiter.   b. Neptune.
   c. Saturn.   d. Pluto.
5. Most asteroids orbit the sun
   a. between the sun and Mercury.
   b. between Earth and Mars.
   c. between Mars and Jupiter.
   d. between Neptune and Pluto.

True or False
If the statement is true, write true. If it is false, change the underlined word or words to make the statement true.

6. The shape of the orbit of each planet is a <u>circle</u>.
7. Sunspots are regions of <u>cooler</u> gases on the sun.
8. The atmosphere of Venus has <u>higher</u> pressure than the atmosphere of Earth.
9. Aside from the sun, <u>Saturn</u> is the largest source of gravity in the solar system.
10. Conditions favorable to life as we know it are sometimes called the <u>Goldilocks conditions</u>.

Checking Concepts

11. How did Galileo's observations support the heliocentric system?

12. How did Newton's work on orbits add to the work Kepler had done?

13. Why is it usually impossible to see the sun's corona?

14. What are sunspots?

15. Why does Mercury have only a thin atmosphere?

16. How do astronomers explain that Venus rotates in the opposite direction from most planets and moons?

17. What are the major characteristics of the terrestrial planets? How do they differ from the gas giants?

18. Why do some astronomers think that Pluto should not be called a planet?

19. Why does a comet's tail always stream away from the sun?

20. Do living things have to live on the surface of a planet or moon? Where else on a planet or moon could scientists look for evidence of life?

21. Writing to Learn Imagine you are an astronaut on a mission to explore the solar system. Write a trip journal telling the story of your trip from Earth to another terrestrial planet and to a gas giant. Include a description of each planet.

Thinking Critically

22. Relating Cause and Effect How would Earth move if the sun (including its gravity) suddenly disappeared? Explain your answer.

23. Applying Concepts Explain why Venus is hotter than it would be without its atmosphere.

24. Comparing and Contrasting Compare and contrast meteoroids, meteors, and meteorites.

25. Making Generalizations Why would the discovery of liquid water on another planet be important?

Thinking Critically

22. Because of inertia, Earth would continue to move in a straight path in the direction it was going when the sun disappeared.

23. Venus's atmosphere creates a greenhouse effect that traps heat energy from the sun.

24. A meteoroid is a chunk of rock or dust in space. If a meteoroid enters Earth's atmosphere and burns up, a streak of light called a meteor is seen. If a meteoroid hits Earth's surface, it is called a meteorite.

25. Since water is essential to life on Earth, the presence of water on another planet increases the possibility that life may be found there.

Applying Skills

Use the diagram of an imaginary, newly discovered planetary system around Star X to answer Questions 26–28. The periods of revolution of planets A, B, and C are 75 Earth days, 200 Earth days, and 300 Earth days.

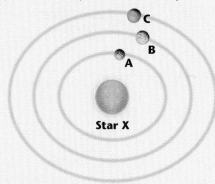

26. Interpreting Data Which planet in this new planetary system revolves around Star X in the shortest amount of time?

27. Making Models In 150 days, how far will each planet have revolved around Star X? Copy the diagram and sketch the positions of the three planets to find out. How far will each planet have revolved around Star X in 400 days? Sketch their positions.

28. Drawing Conclusions Can planet C ever be closer to planet A than to planet B? Study your drawings to figure this out.

Project Wrap Up Now you are ready to present your solar system. Explain how you were able to work with large distances. Display your data tables showing how you did the calculations and how you checked them for accuracy. Compare the distances in your models to distances inside and outside your classroom.

Reflect and Record In your journal, explain what you would change in your model of the solar system. What would you do to improve the model? How effectively did you use computers or calculators to get the data?

Test Preparation

Use these questions to prepare for standardized tests.

Study the table. Then answer Questions 29–32.

Planet	Period of Rotation (Earth days)	Period of Revolution (Earth years)	Average Distance From the Sun (million kilometers)
Mars	1.03	1.9	228
Jupiter	0.41	12	778
Saturn	0.43	29	1,427
Uranus	0.72	84	2,871
Neptune	0.67	165	4,497

29. Which of these planet's orbits is farthest from Earth's orbit?
a. Mars
b. Jupiter
c. Uranus
d. Neptune

30. Which planet has a "day" that is most similar in length to a day on Earth?
a. Mars
b. Jupiter
c. Uranus
d. Neptune

31. Light takes about 8 minutes and 20 seconds to travel from the sun to the Earth, 150 million kilometers away. About how long does it take light to travel from the sun to Jupiter?
a. 10 minutes
b. 25 minutes
c. 43 minutes
d. 112 minutes

32. Which one of the following conclusions about planets is supported by the information in the table?
a. As distance from the sun increases, period of rotation increases.
b. As distance from the sun increases, period of revolution increases.
c. As distance from the sun increases, period of revolution decreases.
d. There is no relationship between distance from the sun and period of revolution.

Program Resources

◆ **Inquiry Skills Activity Book** Provides teaching and review of all inquiry skills
◆ **Standardized Test Preparation Book** Provides standardized test practice
◆ **Reading in the Content Area** Provides strategies to improve science reading skills
◆ **Teacher's ELL Handbook** Provides multiple strategies for English language learners

---

Applying Skills

26. Planet A which takes only 75 days
27. Planet A will have revolved around star X twice. Planet B will have completed three quarters of one revolution. Planet C will have completed only one half of one revolution. In 400 days, planet A will have completed five revolutions and be one third through a sixth; planet B will have completed two revolutions; and planet C will have completed one revolution and be one third through a second.
28. Yes. Planet A and C could be on one side of the star and B on the other. After 300 days, planet A and C are where they began, on the same side of star X, but planet B is on the opposite side of the star.

Project Wrap Up Students should explain that they scaled all distances by a constant amount to make them manageable. They could have checked their numbers by multiplying the scaled numbers by the reciprocal of their scaling factor to see if they obtained the correct planet sizes. Students should have a good understanding that the sun is very large, that planets vary considerably in size, and that space is mostly "empty space."

Reflect and Record Students might change the scale and present the model in a very large area in order to make the smallest planets visible. Students will reflect that it was not possible to find a scale that was good for comparing the sizes of the planets and the sun with one that was good for showing the distances between the planets and the sun. Since students are dealing with very large numbers with many zeros, they should have found calculators useful in avoiding arithmetic errors.

Test Preparation

29. d **30.** a **31.** c **32.** b

CHAPTER 3 Stars, Galaxies, and the Universe

Sections	Time	Student Edition Activities	Other Activities	
CHAPTER PROJECT 3 **Star Stories** p. J93	Ongoing (2 weeks)	Check Your Progress, pp. J100, J116, J124 Project Wrap Up, p. J127	TE	Chapter 3 Project Notes, pp. J92–93
1 **INTEGRATING PHYSICS** **Tools of Modern Astronomy** pp. J94–102 ◆ 3.1.1 Describe the electromagnetic spectrum. ◆ 3.1.2 Identify the main purpose of a telescope. ◆ 3.1.3 Describe how astronomers use spectrographs.	4–5 periods/ 2–$2\frac{1}{2}$ blocks	**Discover** Are Those Stars Really a Group?, p. J94 **Try This** Locating Radio Waves, p. J96 **Sharpen Your Skills** Inferring, p. J100 **Real-World Lab: How It Works** Make Your Own Telescope, p. J101	TE TE ISLM	Building Inquiry Skills: Observing, p. J95 Inquiry Challenge, p. J99 J-3, "Chemical Composition and the Spectrum"
2 **Characteristics of Stars** pp. J103–111 ◆ 3.2.1 Describe how astronomers measure distances to nearby stars. ◆ 3.2.2 Explain how stars are classified.	4–5 periods/ $2\frac{1}{2}$ blocks	**Discover** How Does Your Thumb Move?, p. J103 **Try This** Star Bright, p. J108 **Skills Lab: Measuring** How Far Is That Star?, pp. J110–111	TE TE	Building Inquiry Skills: Making Models, pp. J104, J106 Inquiry Challenge, p. J104
3 **Lives of Stars** pp. J112–116 ◆ 3.3.1 Describe how a star is formed. ◆ 3.3.2 Identify what determines how long a star will last. ◆ 3.3.3 Explain what happens to a star when it runs out of fuel.	$2\frac{1}{2}$ periods/ 1–2 blocks	**Discover** What Determines How Long Stars Live?, p. J112 **Sharpen Your Skills** Predicting, p. J114	TE TE	Building Inquiry Skills: Problem Solving, p. J113 Demonstration, p. J114
4 **Star Systems and Galaxies** pp. J117–120 ◆ 3.4.1 Describe a star system. ◆ 3.4.2 Identify and describe three types of galaxies.	2 periods/ 1 block	**Discover** Why Does the Milky Way Look Hazy?, p. J117 **Try This** A Spiral Galaxy, p. J119	TE	Inquiry Challenge, p. J118
5 **History of the Universe** pp. J121–124 ◆ 3.5.1 Explain the big bang theory of how the universe was formed. ◆ 3.5.2 Describe how the solar system was formed.	2 periods/ 1 block	**Discover** How Does the Universe Expand?, p. J121	TE	Building Inquiry Skills: Communicating, p. J124
Study Guide/Assessment pp. J125–127	1 period/ $\frac{1}{2}$ block		ISAB	Provides teaching and review of all inquiry skills

For Standard or Block Schedule The Resource Pro® CD-ROM gives you maximum flexibility for planning your instruction for any type of schedule. Resource Pro® contains Planning Express®, an advanced scheduling program, as well as the entire contents of the Teaching Resources and the Computer Test Bank.

Key: **SE** Student Edition
PLM Probeware Lab Manual
ISAB Inquiry Skills Activity Book

CHAPTER PLANNING GUIDE

Program Resources	Assessment Strategies	Media and Technology
TR Chapter 3 Project Teacher Notes, pp. J70–71 **TR** Chapter 3 Project Overview and Worksheets, pp. J72–75	**TE** Check Your Progress, pp. J100, J116, J124 **TE** Performance Assessment: Chapter 3 Project Wrap Up, p. J127 **TR** Chapter 3 Project Scoring Rubric, p. J76	Science Explorer Internet Site Audio CDs and Audiotapes, English-Spanish Section Summaries Transparencies 17, "Star Chart: Autumn Sky"; 18, "Star Chart: Winter Sky"; 19, "Star Chart: Spring Sky"; 20, "Star Chart: Summer Sky"
TR 3-1 Lesson Plan, p. J77 **TR** 3-1 Section Summary, p. J78 **TR** 3-1 Review and Reinforce, p. J79 **TR** 3-1 Enrich, p. J80 **TR** Real-World Lab blackline masters, pp. J97–98 **SES** Book O, *Sound and Light,* Chapter 3, Chapter 4	**SE** Section 1 Review, p. J100 **SE** Analyze and Conclude, p. J101 **TE** Ongoing Assessment, pp. J95, J97, J99 **TE** Performance Assessment, p. J100	Lab Activity Videotape, *Astronomy,* 5 Exploring Physical Science Videodisc, Unit 1 Side 1, "Looking and Listening to the Stars"; Exploring Life Science Videodisc, Unit 1 Side 1, "Tools of the Trade" Transparencies 10, "The Electromagnetic Spectrum"; 11, "Refracting and Reflecting Telescopes"
TR 3-2 Lesson Plan, p. J81 **TR** 3-2 Section Summary, p. J82 **TR** 3-2 Review and Reinforce, p. J83 **TR** 3-2 Enrich, p. J84 **TR** Skills Lab blackline masters, pp. J99–101	**SE** Section 2 Review, p. J109 **SE** Analyze and Conclude, p. J111 **TE** Ongoing Assessment, pp. J105, J107 **TE** Performance Assessment, p. J109	Lab Activity Videotape, *Astronomy,* 6 Exploring Earth Science Videodisc, Unit 1 Side 1, "Star Light, Star Bright" Transparencies 12, "Parallax"; 13, "Hertzsprung-Russell Diagram"
TR 3-3 Lesson Plan, p. J85 **TR** 3-3 Section Summary, p. J86 **TR** 3-3 Review and Reinforce, p. J87 **TR** 3-3 Enrich, p. J88	**SE** Section 3 Review, p. J116 **TE** Ongoing Assessment, pp. J113, J115 **TE** Performance Assessment, p. J116	Exploring Earth Science Videodisc, Unit 1 Side 1, "Stories From the Stars" Transparency 14, "Exploring the Lives of Stars"
TR 3-4 Lesson Plan, p. J89 **TR** 3-4 Section Summary, p. J90 **TR** 3-4 Review and Reinforce, p. J91 **TR** 3-4 Enrich, p. J92 **SES** Book A, *From Bacteria to Plants,* Chapter 1	**SE** Section 4 Review, p. J120 **TE** Performance Assessment, p. J120	Exploring Earth Science Videodisc, Unit 1 Side 1, "For the Love of Astronomy" Transparency 15, "The Milky Way Galaxy"
TR 3-5 Lesson Plan, p. J93 **TR** 3-5 Section Summary, p. J94 **TR** 3-5 Review and Reinforce, p. J95 **TR** 3-5 Enrich, p. J96	**SE** Section 5 Review, p. J124 **TE** Ongoing Assessment, p. J123 **TE** Performance Assessment, p. J124	Transparency 16, "Formation of the Solar System"
GSW Provides worksheets to promote student comprehension of content **RCA** Provides strategies to improve science reading skills **ELL** Provides multiple strategies for English language learners	**SE** Study Guide/Assessment, pp. J125–127 **TR** Performance Assessment, pp. J128–130 **TR** Chapter 3 Test, pp. J131–134 **TR** Book Test, pp. J135–138 **CTB** *Astronomy,* Chapter 3 Test **STP** Provides standardized test practice	Computer Test Bank, *Astronomy,* Chapter 3 Test Interactive Student Tutorial CD-ROM, J-3

TE Teacher's Edition
RCA Reading in the Content Area
GSW Guided Study Workbook

TR Teaching Resources
ISLM Integrated Science Laboratory Manual
ELL Teacher's ELL Handbook

CTB Computer Test Bank
STP Standardized Test Preparation Book
SES Science Explorer Series Text

Meeting the National Science Education Standards and AAAS Benchmarks

National Science Education Standards	Benchmarks for Science Literacy	Unifying Themes

Science as Inquiry (Content Standard A)

◆ **Use mathematics in all aspects of scientific inquiry.** Astronomers use parallax to determine the distance to nearby stars. *(Section 2, Skills Lab)* Astronomers also use the mathematical techniques of graphing to classify stars. *(Section 2)*

Physical Science (Content Standard B)

◆ **Properties and changes of properties in matter** Matter can emit and receive radiation of many different wavelengths. *(Section 1)*

Earth and Space Science (Content Standard D)

◆ **Earth in the solar system** The solar system formed about 5 billion years ago from a cloud of gas and dust. *(Section 5)*

Science and Technology (Content Standard E)

◆ **Abilities of technological design** In order to better understand telescopes as a tool of astronomy, students construct a simple telescope. *(Real-World Lab)*

Science in Personal and Social Perspectives (Content Standard F)

◆ **History of Science** The tools of astronomy have changed dramatically since Galileo first looked at the sky with his telescope. *(Section 1)*

1C The Scientific Enterprise The development of modern telescopes parallels the growth of science and technology. *(Section 1)*

2C Mathematical Inquiry Astronomers use parallax to determine the distance to nearby stars. *(Section 2, Skills Lab)* Astronomers also use the mathematical techniques of graphing to classify stars. *(Section 2)*

3A Technology and Science Astronomy has advanced our understanding of the universe with scientific tools such as telescopes and spectrographs. *(Section 1, Science and History)*

4A The Universe Nearby stars seem to form patterns in the sky called constellations. Most stars are part of systems of stars, ranging from double stars to clusters of thousands of stars. Most of the stars we can see are part of the Milky Way Galaxy. The universe contains billions of other galaxies. *(Section 4)*

4E Energy Transformations Forms of energy present in the universe are discussed. *(Sections 1, 3, 4, 5)*

11A Systems Most stars are part of double, triple, or even larger star systems. The Milky Way Galaxy is part of an even larger system, the universe. The solar system formed about 5 billion years ago from a cloud of gas and dust. *(Sections 4, 5)*

◆ **Energy** The electromagnetic spectrum includes all forms of radiated energy. Energy is transferred between objects in the universe by means of radiation. Energy is released from a star as a result of nuclear fusion. *(Sections 1, 3)*

◆ **Evolution** The life cycle of a star is determined by its initial mass. *(Section 3)*

◆ **Patterns of Change** Stars go through life cycles that begin with the formation of a protostar. A star's life history depends on its mass. The universe is continually expanding and changing. *(Sections 3, 5)*

◆ **Scale and Structure** Stars are classified according to size, color, temperature, and brightness. Stars are parts of larger systems of stars. Galaxies are part of the universe. *(Sections 2, 4)*

◆ **Unity and Diversity** Despite differences in size, all stars follow the same basic laws of physics. *(Sections 2, 3)*

◆ **Systems and Interactions** Most stars are part of double, triple, or even larger star systems. The Milky Way Galaxy is part of an even larger system, the universe. The solar system formed about 5 billion years ago from a cloud of gas and dust. *(Sections 4, 5)*

◆ **Modeling** Students model the construction and operation of telescopes by constructing a small telescope. *(Real-World Lab)*

Take It to the Net

 **Interactive text at www.phschool.com**

Science Explorer comes alive with iText.

- **Complete student text** is accessible from any computer with a browser.

- **Animations, simulations, and videos** enhance student understanding and retention of concepts.

- **Self-tests and online study tools** assess student understanding.

- **Teacher management tools** help you make the most of this valuable resource.

 *STAY CURRENT with* **SCIENCE NEWS®**

Find out the latest research and information about astronomy at: **www.phschool.com**

Go to **www.phschool.com** and click on the Science icon. Then click on Science Explorer under PH@school.

ACTIVITY	Time (minutes)	Materials — Quantities for one work group	Skills
Section 1			
Discover, p. 94	30	**Consumable** thread; heavy cardboard, 50 x 50 cm; tape **Nonconsumable** 1-cm plastic foam balls	Observing
Try This, p. 96	30	**Consumable** aluminum foil, clear tape, duct tape **Nonconsumable** umbrella, small radio	Inferring
Sharpen Your Skills, p. 100	10	**Consumable** No special materials are required.	Inferring
Real-World Lab, p. 101	80	**Consumable** foam holder for eyepiece (optional), transparent tape **Nonconsumable** 2 paper towel tubes of slightly different diameters, plastic objective lens, plastic eyepiece lens, meter stick	Making Models, Observing, Drawing Conclusions
Section 2			
Discover, p. 103	5	**Consumable** No special materials are required.	Observing
Try This, p. 108	20	**Nonconsumable** 3 flashlights, two with equal wattage, one brighter than the others	Making Models
Skills Lab, pp. 110–111	50	**Consumable** masking tape, paper, copier paper box (without the lid) **Nonconsumable** paper clips; pen; black and red pencils; metric ruler; meter stick; calculator; lamp with shade, with 100-watt light bulb; flat rectangular table, about 1 m wide	Measuring
Section 3			
Discover, p. 112	10	**Consumable** No special materials are required.	Inferring
Sharpen Your Skills, p. 114	10	**Consumable** No special materials are required.	Predicting
Section 4			
Discover, p. 117	15	**Consumable** paper, tape **Nonconsumable** pencil	Making Models
Try This, p. 119	20	**Nonconsumable** pipe cleaners	Observing
Section 5			
Discover, p. 121	10	**Consumable** balloon **Nonconsumable** felt-tip marker	Inferring

A list of all materials required for the Student Edition activities can be found beginning on page T15. You can obtain information about ordering materials by calling 1-800-848-9500 or by accessing the Science Explorer Internet site at: **www.phschool.com**

In this chapter, students will be introduced to characteristics of stars and techniques astronomers use to study the universe. This project will give students an opportunity to develop their skills as astronomers while giving them insight into the power of the night sky in the mythology of different cultures.

Purpose In this project, students will research stories that various cultures have told about constellations. They will create their own name for the star pattern they see in the constellation they choose and write a story to support it. Students will also use star charts to locate constellations in the night sky.

Skills Focus Students will be able to
◆ interpret star charts and observe and identify constellations;
◆ research the myth of one constellation;
◆ write an original star myth and communicate the myth to the class.

Project Time Line Students will need one or two clear nights at the beginning of the project in order to observe constellations using the star charts. Allow three or four weeks total for the project. During the first week or two, students should do research. They should spend one week on a first draft and another for editing and production of the final project. Before beginning the project, see Chapter 3 Project Teacher Notes on pages 70–71 in Teaching Resources for more details on carrying out the project. Also distribute the Chapter 3 Project Overview and Worksheets and Scoring Rubric on pages 72–76 in Teaching Resources.

Possible Materials The project requires research sources such as encyclopedias, books on mythology, and the Internet. Students should use the star charts in Appendix B to help them identify the constellations. To supplement library resources, Worksheet 1 in the Chapter 3 Teaching Resources summarizes the myths of several cultures that apply to some major constellations. Worksheet 2 will help students write their stories. Students may need art materials to make posters for their final presentations.

WEB ACTIVITY www.phschool.com

Integrating Physics 🜨

SECTION 1 **Tools of Modern Astronomy**

Discover **Are Those Stars Really a Group?**
Try This **Locating Radio Waves**
Sharpen Your Skills **Inferring**
Real-World Lab **Make Your Own Telescope**

SECTION 2 **Characteristics of Stars**

Discover **How Does Your Thumb Move?**
Try This **Star Bright**
Skills Lab **How Far Is That Star?**

SECTION 3 **Lives of Stars**

Discover **What Determines How Long Stars Live?**
Sharpen Your Skills **Predicting**

92 ◆ J

Media and Technology

🎧 **Audio CDs** and **Audiotapes**
English-Spanish Section Summaries

📖 **Transparencies** "Star Chart: Autumn Sky," "Star Chart: Winter Sky," "Star Chart: Spring Sky," "Star Chart: Summer Sky," Transparencies 17–20

Star Stories

In the spring of 1997, you could easily see comet Hale-Bopp, shown here, without any special equipment. But many of the objects astronomers study just look to you like tiny pinpoints of light—that is, if you can see them at all. However, astronomers have found many ways to learn about these "pinpoints."

In this chapter, you will discover how astronomers study the universe and what they have learned about the stars. In your project, you will find out how people in the past created stories to explain the patterns they saw in the sky. You'll learn how the names of constellations reflect the cultures of the people who named them.

Your Goal To recognize major constellations, learn the stories behind their names, and create your own star myth.

To complete the project you will
♦ learn the star patterns of at least three major constellations
♦ research the myths that gave one constellation its name
♦ write a new star myth

Get Started Begin your project by previewing page 94 to learn what a constellation is. With a group of your classmates, make a list of constellations you have heard about. Then look at the star charts in Appendix B. From the chart for the current season, choose three or four constellations to explore further.

Check Your Progress You'll be working on this project as you study this chapter. To keep your project on track, look for Check Your Progress boxes at the following points.

Section 1 Review, page 100: Locate constellations and research one.

Section 3 Review, page 116: Draw a new picture for the star pattern in your constellation and give it a name.

Section 5 Review, page 124: Write a story about your constellation.

Wrap Up At the end of the chapter (page 127), you will present your constellation along with a story that explains its name.

These telescopes on top of Mauna Kea, a mountain in Hawaii, are used to study distant stars and galaxies.

SECTION 4 Star Systems and Galaxies

Discover Why Does the Milky Way Look Hazy?
Try This A Spiral Galaxy

SECTION 5 History of the Universe

Discover How Does the Universe Expand?

J ♦ 93

Program Resources

♦ **Teaching Resources** Chapter 3 Project Teacher's Notes, pp. 70–71; Chapter 3 Project Overview and Worksheets, pp. 72–75; Chapter 3 Project Scoring Rubric, p. 76

WEB ACTIVITY www.phschool.com

You will find an Internet activity, chapter self-tests for students, and links to other chapter topics at this site.

Launching the Project To introduce the project, choose one star myth and share it with the class. Ask students to name and describe constellations they already know. Ask: **Do you know how those constellations were named?** (*Students may know stories from Greek or Roman mythology. Some students may know Native American myths.*) Allow time for students to read the description of the project in their text and the Chapter Project Overview on pages 72–73 in Teaching Resources. Before students make their nighttime observations, discuss the star chart for the season in Appendix B. Help students choose two or three easy-to-find constellations as their goals for observation. Pass out copies of the Chapter 3 Project Worksheets on pages 74–75 in Teaching Resources for students to review.

Performance Assessment

The Chapter 3 Project Scoring Rubric on page 16 of Teaching Resources will help you evaluate how well students complete the Chapter 3 Project. You may wish to share the scoring rubric with your students so they are clear about what will be expected of them.

Students will be assessed on
♦ how familiar they are with the star patterns of their chosen constellations;
♦ how thoroughly they research the myths involving their chosen constellations;
♦ how clear and well-written the final draft of their star myth is, along with how well their presentation presents the new name and story for their star pattern.

SECTION 1 Tools of Modern Astronomy

Objectives

After completing the lesson, students will be able to

◆ describe the electromagnetic spectrum;

◆ identify the main purpose of a telescope;

◆ describe how astronomers use spectrographs.

Key Terms constellation, visible light, electromagnetic radiation, wavelength, spectrum, refracting telescope, convex lens, reflecting telescope, radio telescope, observatory, spectrograph

1 Engage/Explore

Activating Prior Knowledge

Encourage students to describe the stars they have seen in the night sky. Ask: **Do some nights seem starrier than others? Does the night sky look different early in the evening than it does late at night? Is it easier to see stars from some places than from others?** Ask students to speculate whether there are more stars at some times than others, or whether there are conditions that make stars difficult to see.

DISCOVER

Skills Focus observing
Materials *scissors; ten 1-cm plastic foam balls; thread; heavy cardboard, 50 × 50 cm; tape*
Time 30 minutes
Tips Wrap the tape completely around the balls to attach the strings securely.
Think It Over Students should note that they cannot tell which balls are farther away and which are closer. Students should conclude that they cannot tell how close the stars in a constellation are to each other.

SECTION 1 Tools of Modern Astronomy

DISCOVER ··· ACTIVITY

Are Those Stars Really a Group?

1. Cut ten pieces of thread to different lengths between 5 cm and 25 cm. Tape a 1-cm plastic foam ball to the end of each piece of thread.

2. Obtain a piece of cardboard about 50 cm by 50 cm. Tape the free ends of the thread pieces to various points on the cardboard.

3. Turn the cardboard over so the balls hang down. While your partner holds the cardboard horizontally, look at the balls from the side.

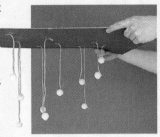

4. Imagine that the balls are stars in a constellation. With one eye closed, sketch the pattern the balls make.

Think It Over
Observing Can you tell which balls are farther away and which are closer? Do you think you can tell how close to each other the stars in a constellation are?

GUIDE FOR READING

◆ What is the electromagnetic spectrum?

◆ What is the main purpose of a telescope?

◆ Why do astronomers use spectrographs?

Reading Tip Before you read, rewrite the main headings of the section as *how, why,* or *what* questions.

Before the Civil War, thousands of enslaved African Americans fled north to freedom. Traveling in secret by night, they looked to the stars for direction. They told each other to "follow the drinking gourd"—the star pattern that points to the North Star. Most Americans today call this pattern the Big Dipper.

Patterns of stars in the sky are called **constellations.** Stars in a constellation can look as if they are close together, even though they are at very different distances from Earth. For example, the star at the end of the handle in the Big Dipper is about twice as far from Earth as most of the other stars in the Big Dipper. So the stars in a constellation are not, in fact, all close together. Constellations are just patterns formed by stars that happen to be in the same direction in the sky.

Big Dipper ▶

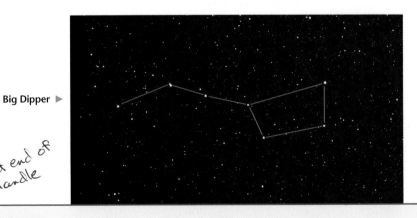

Alkaid – star at end of handle

READING STRATEGIES

Reading Tip Remind students to leave space to write answers to the questions as they read. They can then use their notes as they study. Suggest that students generate additional questions as they read the section. Remind them to begin their questions with the words *what, why,* and *how.*

Vocabulary Have students jot down the boldface terms in the section, then write definitions for each term in their own words. Partners can quiz each other on the terms.

Concept Mapping Have students make a concept map with *spectrographs* in the top circle. Then have them read and add links to other circles that describe the type of information about stars that astronomers can learn from spectrographs.

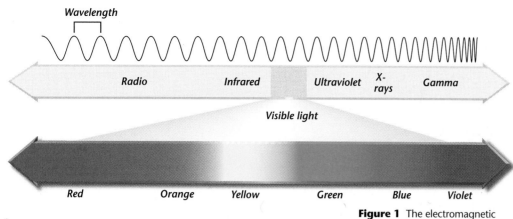

Figure 1 The electromagnetic spectrum ranges from long-wavelength radio waves through short-wavelength gamma rays. *Interpreting Diagrams Are infrared waves longer or shorter than ultraviolet waves?*

Electromagnetic Radiation

The stars in constellations appear as tiny points of light. In fact, stars are huge spheres of hot glowing gas, like the sun. By using telescopes to study the light from stars, astronomers have learned a great deal about stars and other objects in the sky.

Types of Electromagnetic Radiation

Scientists call the light you see with your eyes **visible light.** Light is a form of **electromagnetic radiation** (ih lek troh mag NET ik), or energy that can travel directly through space in the form of waves.

Visible light is only one type of electromagnetic radiation. Many objects give off radiation that you can't see. For example, the glowing coils of an electric heater give off infrared radiation, which you feel as heat. Radio waves carry signals to radios and televisions.

The Electromagnetic Spectrum

As you can see in Figure 1, the distance between the crest of one wave and the crest of the next wave is called the **wavelength.** Visible light has very short wavelengths, less than one millionth of a meter. Some electromagnetic waves have even shorter wavelengths. Other waves are much longer, even several meters long.

If you shine white light through a prism, the light spreads out to make a range of different colors with different wavelengths, called a **spectrum.** The spectrum of visible light is composed of the colors red, orange, yellow, green, blue, and violet. **The electromagnetic spectrum includes radio waves, infrared radiation, visible light, ultraviolet radiation, X-rays, and gamma rays.** All these different kinds of electromagnetic waves make up the electromagnetic spectrum, shown in Figure 1.

✓ *Checkpoint Give two examples of electromagnetic waves that you might use or experience every day.*

Electromagnetic Radiation

Using the Visuals: Figure 1

Ask: **Which part of the electromagnetic spectrum can you see?** *(Visible light)* **Which parts are not visible?** *(Everything else)* **What makes red light different from blue light?** *(Its wavelength)* **Which has a longer wavelength?** *(Red light)* **learning modality: visual**

Building Inquiry Skills: Observing

Materials *white light source, fluorescent light, posterboard with a slit 2 cm × 2 mm, prism, colored pencils, white paper, tape*
Time 30 minutes
Tips Have students work in groups of three or four to position the slit over the white light source and then tape the posterboard to the light source. Darken the room and tell students to shine light from the slit through the prism and onto a sheet of paper. Students can use colored pencils to record their observations. Discuss the effect of the prism on white light. *(The prism separated the white light into a continuous spectrum.)*
Extend Have students repeat the activity using a fluorescent light source. Ask students what happens to this light when it passes through the prism. *(The fluorescent light was separated into a continuous spectrum with bright lines)*
cooperative learning

Program Resources

◆ **Teaching Resources** 3-1 Lesson Plan, p. 77; 3-1 Section Summary, p. 78
◆ **Guided Study Workbook** Section 3-1

Media and Technology

📺 **Transparencies** "The Electromagnetic Spectrum," Transparency 10

Answers to Self-Assessment

Caption Question

Figure 1 Infrared waves are longer than ultraviolet waves.

✓ *Checkpoint*

Students may mention visible light or radio waves. Possible answers also include being exposed to ultraviolet waves in sunlight or having an X-ray taken of a broken bone.

Ongoing Assessment

Writing Have students compile a list of familiar sources of various types of radiation.

📁 *Portfolio* Students can save their lists in their portfolios.

Telescopes

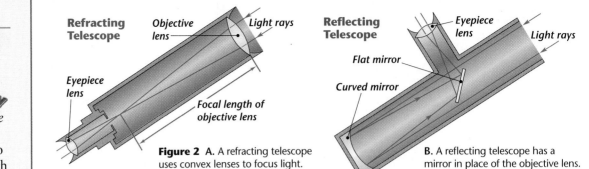

Figure 2 A. A refracting telescope uses convex lenses to focus light.

B. A reflecting telescope has a mirror in place of the objective lens.

TRY THIS

Skills Focus inferring

Materials *umbrella, small radio, aluminum foil, masking tape*

Time 30 minutes

Tips Have students use masking tape to attach the foil to the umbrella and attach the radio to the handle. To save time, you may wish to line the umbrellas with foil before the activity.

Expected Outcome Reception is best with the handle held parallel to the floor. The best position of the radio is at the focal point of the umbrella; this will depend on its curvature.

Inferring Students should explain that the handle points to the station. The waves are reflected by the foil and directed to a focal point on the handle.

Extend Challenge students to select another radio station and predict where the reception will be best. **learning modality: logical/mathematical**

Including All Students

Assemble students in pairs, making sure that students who are having difficulty distinguishing refracting and reflecting telescopes are paired with students who have a better understanding. One student in each pair will play the role of Galileo. The other student will pretend to be Isaac Newton. Each Galileo will sketch a refracting telescope while each Newton will sketch his reflecting telescope. Then have each "scientist" explain how his or her telescope works to the other. Encourage Newton and Galileo to debate the advantages and disadvantages of each design. **limited English proficiency**

Portfolio Students can save their sketches in their portfolios.

TRY THIS

Locating Radio Waves

You can use an umbrella to focus radio waves.

1. Line the inside of an umbrella with aluminum foil.
2. Turn on a small radio and tune it to a station.
3. Move the radio up and down along the umbrella handle. Find the position where the station is clearest. Radio waves reflecting off the foil focus at this point. Tape the radio to the handle.

4. Hold the umbrella at different angles. At which angle is the station the clearest?

Inferring In which direction do you think the radio station is located? Explain.

Telescopes

Objects in space give off all types of electromagnetic radiation. Many telescopes produce images using visible light. But much of modern astronomy is based on detection of other types of electromagnetic radiation. **Most telescopes collect and focus different types of electromagnetic radiation, including visible light.**

Visible Light Telescopes In 1609, Galileo used a refracting telescope to look at objects in the sky. A **refracting telescope** uses convex lenses to gather a large amount of light and focus it onto a small area. A **convex lens** is a piece of transparent glass, curved so that the middle is thicker than the edges.

Galileo's telescope, like the refracting telescope in Figure 2, used two lenses—an eyepiece lens and an objective lens. When light passes through the objective lens, the lens focuses the light at a certain distance away from the lens. This distance is called the focal length of the lens. Different lenses have different focal lengths. The larger the objective lens, the more light it can collect, making it easier for astronomers to see faint objects.

Isaac Newton built the first **reflecting telescope** in 1668. It used a mirror instead of an objective lens. Like the lenses in a refracting telescope, the mirror in a reflecting telescope focuses a large amount of light onto a small area. The larger the mirror, the more light the telescope can collect. The largest visible light telescopes are now all reflecting telescopes.

Radio Telescopes Devices used to detect radio waves from objects in space are called **radio telescopes**. Most radio telescopes have curved, reflecting surfaces—up to 305 meters in diameter. These surfaces focus radio waves the way the mirror in a reflecting telescope focuses light waves. The surfaces of radio telescopes concentrate the faint radio waves from outer space onto small antennas like those on radios. As with visible light telescopes, the larger a radio telescope is, the more radio waves it can collect.

Background

Facts and Figures Infrared telescopes are similar to visible light telescopes. However, infrared radiation is easily blocked by water vapor in the atmosphere, so infrared telescopes are placed in observatories high on mountain tops or on satellites. The United Kingdom Infrared Telescope is located at Mauna Kea Observatory in Hawaii.

The Infrared Astronomy Satellite (IRAS), launched in 1983, made a complete survey of the sky at infrared wavelengths and revealed a large number of dense dust clouds in the Milky Way.

Another infrared telescope is on the Kuiper Airborne Observatory. This specially fitted C-141 transport jet flies at an altitude of 12,500 meters. The infrared telescope on the observatory discovered the rings of Uranus.

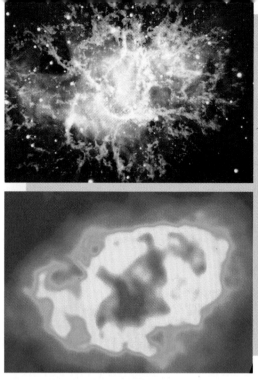

Figure 3 The Crab Nebula is the remains of a star that exploded about 1,000 years ago. The top image was photographed using visible light. The lower image was made using radio waves.

Other Telescopes Some telescopes detect infrared radiation, which has longer wavelengths than visible light. There are also telescopes that detect the shortest wavelengths—ultraviolet radiation, X-rays, and gamma rays.

☑ *Checkpoint* *What are two types of visible light telescopes?*

Observatories

A building that contains one or more telescopes is called an **observatory.** Most large observatories are located on mountaintops. Why have astronomers built the largest visible light telescopes on the tops of mountains? Earth's atmosphere makes objects in space look blurry. The sky on some mountaintops is clearer and is not brightened much by city lights.

The best observatory site on Earth is probably the top of Mauna Kea, an ancient volcano on the island of Hawaii. Mauna Kea is so tall—4,200 meters above sea level—that it is above 40 percent of Earth's atmosphere. The sky there is very dark at night, and many nights are free of clouds.

To collect data from visible light telescopes on Earth, astronomers must stay awake all night. Radio telescopes, however, can be used 24 hours a day and do not have to be on mountaintops.

Program Resources

Science Explorer Series Book O
"Sound and Light," Chapter 3

Media and Technology

Transparencies "Refracting and Reflecting Telescopes," Transparency 11

Answers to Self-Assessment

☑ *Checkpoint*

Refracting telescopes and reflecting telescopes are two types of visible light telescopes.

Using the Visuals: Figure 3

After students compare the images shown in the photos, ask: **Do both images give the same information about the Crab Nebula?** (*No, the top image shows the visible light that the Crab Nebula radiates. The image using radio waves shows some of the lower-energy radiation that the nebula radiates.*) **How have radio telescopes enabled astronomers to expand their exploration of space?** (*Radio telescopes can give information that cannot be observed visually.*) **learning modality: visual**

Observatories

Addressing Naive Conceptions

Ask students: **Why do astronomers have to stay awake all night to use visible light telescopes? Do astronomers who use radio telescopes have to stay awake all night?** Make sure students understand that the stars are in the sky during the day, but they are not visible because our eyes are not able to distinguish them against the brightness of the sun. Visible light from the sun does not interfere with radio waves. Encourage students to come up with examples of similar phenomena. (*Sample: In bright sun it can be hard to tell if a car's lights are on, a flashlight's beam cannot be seen in daylight. Sunlight does not interfere with radio or television reception.*) **learning modality: verbal**

Ongoing Assessment

Oral Presentation Organize the students into four teams and have each team appoint a spokesperson. Challenge each team to compare and contrast radio telescopes and visible light telescopes. Have each spokesperson present the findings of his or her team.

SCIENCE & History

Invite student volunteers to read aloud to the class the annotations to the time line. Have a world map available for students to use to locate the various telescopes. Help students visualize how large the telescopes are by comparing them to something students know. Ask students to calculate the sizes of the telescopes in terms of the size of familiar objects, such as the length of a school bus. *(For example, the diameter of the Arecibo Radio Telescope is about the length of three football fields.)*

In Your Journal Students can find out more about the telescopes in the feature by doing a library computer search using the keyword *telescope* or the name of a particular telescope. Once students have prepared their publicity brochures, encourage them to present them to the class. **learning modality: verbal**

Satellites

Integrating Technology

Ask students: **What are some advantages of placing telescopes in space instead of on Earth?** *(Space telescopes can detect wavelengths that are largely blocked by Earth's atmosphere.)* Inform students that when the Hubble Space Telescope mission ends in 2010, NASA will operate the Next Generation Space Telescope (NGST), scheduled to launch in 2007. NGST will be farther from Earth than the Hubble, and its mirror will be twice as large. Mention that a telescope's distance from Earth can sometimes be a source of difficulty, as when Hubble's optics had to be repaired. **learning modality: verbal**

Satellites

INTEGRATING TECHNOLOGY Most ultraviolet radiation, X-rays, and gamma rays are blocked by Earth's atmosphere. To detect these wavelengths, astronomers have placed telescopes on satellites.

The Hubble Space Telescope is a reflecting telescope with a mirror 2.4 meters in diameter. Because it is above the atmosphere, it makes images in visible light that are about seven times more detailed than the best images from telescopes on Earth. The Hubble Space Telescope can also collect ultraviolet and infrared radiation. The Chandra X-ray Observatory, similar in size to Hubble, makes images in the X-ray portion of the spectrum.

SCIENCE & History

Development of Modern Telescopes

During the last century, astronomers have built larger telescopes, which can collect more light and other types of radiation. Today's astronomers use tools that could not have been imagined 100 years ago.

1897
Yerkes Telescope

The 1-meter-diameter telescope at Yerkes Observatory in Wisconsin is the largest refracting telescope ever built. Because its main lens is so large, the Yerkes telescope can collect more light than any other refracting telescope.

1900	1920	1940

1931
Beginning of Radio Astronomy

Karl Jansky, an American engineer, was trying to find the source of static that was interfering with radio communications. Using a large antenna, he discovered that the static was coming from objects in space giving off radio waves. Jansky's accidental discovery led to the beginning of radio astronomy.

98 ◆ J

Background

Facts and Figures The word *telescope* comes from the Greek words *tele,* meaning "from afar," and *skopos,* meaning "viewer." All telescopes gather waves from the electromagnetic spectrum and magnify them. Larger optical telescopes can be used to gather more light and view more distant objects than smaller telescopes. However, gravity can distort large mirrors, and thus their images. Sectioned optical telescopes, such as the Keck telescopes in Hawaii, were developed in response to this problem. Today, a computer can be used to fine-tune the shape of a mirror.

The first radio telescope was built in 1937 by Grote Reber, an American astronomer and radio engineer. The telescope looked more like a radio antenna than an optical telescope.

Spectrographs

Most large telescopes today have spectrographs. A **spectrograph** (SPEK truh graf) breaks the light from an object into colors and photographs the resulting spectrum. **Astronomers use spectrographs to get information about stars, including their chemical compositions and temperatures.**

Chemical Compositions Chemical elements in a star's atmosphere absorb light from the star. Each element absorbs light at different wavelengths, and each absorbed wavelength is shown as a dark line on a spectrum. Just as each person has a unique set of fingerprints, each element has a unique set of lines. By comparing

In Your Journal

Research one of these telescopes or another large telescope. Create a publicity brochure in which you describe the telescope's features, when and where it was built, and what types of research it is used for.

1963

Arecibo Radio Telescope

This radio telescope in Puerto Rico was built in a natural bowl in the ground. It is 305 meters in diameter, more than three times the size of the next-largest radio telescope.

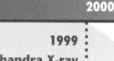

1990

Hubble Space Telescope

The Hubble Space Telescope can see objects in space more clearly than any other telescope. Astronauts have visited the telescope several times to repair or replace equipment.

1960	1980	2000

1980

Very Large Array

The Very Large Array is a set of 27 radio telescopes in New Mexico. The telescopes can be moved close together or far apart. The telescopes are linked, so they can be used as if they were one giant telescope 25 kilometers in diameter.

1999

Chandra X-ray Observatory

The hottest objects in space give off X-rays. NASA launched the Chandra X-ray Observatory into orbit to make detailed images in that part of the spectrum. Chandra X-ray images match Hubble visible-light images in detail.

Chapter 3   **J ◆ 99**

Program Resources

- **Science Explorer Series** *Sound and Light*, Chapter 4
- ◆ **Integrated Science Laboratory Manual** J-3, "Chemical Composition and the Spectrum"

Media and Technology

- **Exploring Life Science Videodisc** Unit 1, Side 1, "Tools of the Trade"
  Chapter 8
- **Exploring Physical Science Videodisc** Unit 1, Side 1, "Looking and Listening to the Stars"
  Chapter 4

Spectrographs

Inquiry Challenge

Materials *projector, prism, red, green, and blue cellophane*

Time 15 minutes

Tips Darken the room and shine the light from the projector through the prism so that the spectrum is visible on a white surface. Use a double thickness of cellophane to reduce the chance of light leaks. Encourage students to predict what will happen when a double thickness of red cellophane is held between the prism and the spectrum. *(Only the red part of the spectrum remains visible.)* Ask: **Why did the other colors disappear?** *(The cellophane allowed only the red light to pass through.)* Repeat this process with a double thickness of green cellophane and then with a double thickness of blue cellophane. Then ask students to predict what will happen when red and blue cellophane are both held between the prism and the spectrum. *(No light will pass through.)* Ask: **Why did no light pass through the cellophane?** *(If the blue cellophane is held closer to the prism, the blue light passes through and is then blocked by the red cellophane. If the red cellophane is held closer to the prism, the red light passes through and is then blocked by the blue cellophane.)* Try other color combinations, and challenge students to draw a general conclusion. **learning modality: visual**

Ongoing Assessment

Skills Check Have students explain how astronomers determine the chemical composition of a star. *(Astronomers use a spectrograph to break the light from the star into colors, and to photograph the spectrum. Based on the colors in the spectrum, astronomers can determine the elements in the star's atmosphere.)*

Sharpen your *Skills*

Inferring

Time 10 minutes

Tips Encourage students to compare the element spectrums to the star spectrums one at a time instead of all at once.

Answers Star A: hydrogen and helium; B: helium and calcium; C: hydrogen and sodium

Extend Challenge students to draw the spectrum for a star that has strong lines for hydrogen and calcium.

3 Assess

Section 1 Review Answers

1. Radio waves, infrared, visible light, ultraviolet, X-rays, and gamma rays
2. Telescopes collect and focus electromagnetic radiation.
3. Astronomers can determine the chemical composition and the temperature of the star.
4. The stars are in the same direction in the sky, but they may be far apart.
5. HST images are clearer because there is no interference from Earth's atmosphere.

. . . .

Check Your Progress CHAPTER PROJECT 3

Have students discuss the constellations they found, along with accompanying multicultural myths.

. . . .

Sharpen your Skills

Inferring **ACTIVITY**

The lines on the spectrums below are from three different stars. Each of these star spectrums is made up of an overlap of spectrums from the individual elements shown in Figure 4. In star A, which elements have the strongest lines? Which are the strongest in star B? In star C?

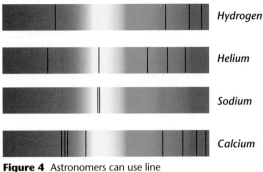

Figure 4 Astronomers can use line spectrums to find the temperatures of stars.

a star's spectrum with the known spectrums of different elements, such as those shown in Figure 4, astronomers can infer which elements are found in a star.

Temperatures Most stars have a chemical composition similar to the sun, about 73% hydrogen, 25% helium, and 2% other elements. The amount of energy each of these elements absorbs depends on the temperature of the star. Because of this, stars at different temperatures produce different line spectrums. By comparing a star's spectrum with the known spectrums of elements at different temperatures, astronomers can infer how hot the star is. Hydrogen, for example, produces very strong spectral lines when it is at about 10,000 degrees Celsius. If astronomers do not see a strong hydrogen line on a spectrum, this does not mean there is no hydrogen in the star. It just means that the star is much cooler or hotter than 10,000 degrees Celsius.

Section 1 Review

1. What are the main types of electromagnetic waves, from longest wavelength to shortest? *p.95*
2. For what purpose are most telescopes designed? *p.96*
3. What can astronomers tell from looking at a star's spectrum? *p.99*
4. How are the stars in a constellation related to each other in space? *p.94*
5. **Thinking Critically Applying Concepts** Why are images from the Hubble Space Telescope clearer than images from telescopes on Earth? *p.98*

. . . .

Check Your Progress CHAPTER PROJECT 3

Using the star charts in Appendix B, try to locate constellations in the night sky. (*Hint:* Remember that you may be looking at a constellation upside down. Also, light conditions may affect how many stars you can see.) Sketch the constellations you can locate and compare them with the ones your classmates saw. Now choose one constellation and research the myths or legends that gave it its name. Find as many stories as you can about your constellation and make notes about them.

Performance Assessment

Writing Have student "astronomers" write paragraphs describing tools and procedures they would use to study a new star, along with what information they would collect.

Background

History of Science Annie Jump Cannon, the first woman to be elected an officer of the American Astronomical Society, was born in Delaware in 1863. As an assistant at the Harvard Observatory, she became known for her exceptional ability to study and classify the spectral types of hundreds of stars per hour. Before her death in 1941, she completed a catalog that classified hundreds of thousands of stars.

Program Resources

◆ **Teaching Resources** 3-1 Review and Reinforce, p. 79; 3-1 Enrich, p. 80

Make Your Own Telescope

In this lab you will learn how to construct and use a simple refracting telescope. You can then try out your telescope.

Problem

How can you build a telescope?

Skill Focus

making models, observing, drawing conclusions

Materials

2 paper towel tubes of slightly different
  diameters
plastic objective lens
plastic eyepiece lens
foam holder for eyepiece (optional)
transparent tape
meter stick

Procedure

1. Fit one of the paper towel tubes inside the other. Make sure you can move the tubes but that they will not slide on their own.

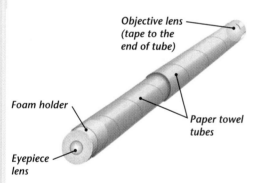

Objective lens
(tape to the
end of tube)

Foam holder

Paper towel
tubes

Eyepiece
lens

2. Place the large objective lens flat against the end of the outer tube. Tape the lens in place.

3. Insert the small eyepiece lens into the opening in the foam holder.
4. Place the foam eyepiece lens holder into the inner tube at the end of the telescope opposite to the objective lens.
5. Tape a meter stick to the wall. Look through the eyepiece at the meter stick from 5 m away. Slide the tubes in and out to focus your telescope so that you can clearly read the numbers on the meter stick. Draw your telescope. On the drawing, mark the tube position that allows you to read the numbers most clearly.
6. Use your telescope to look at other objects at different distances, both in your classroom and through the window. For each object you view, draw your telescope, marking the tube position at which you see the object most clearly. **CAUTION:** *Do not look at the sun. You will damage your eyes.*

Analyze and Conclude

1. Why do you need two tubes?
2. If you focus on a nearby object and then focus on something farther away, do you have to move the tubes together or apart?
3. How does this telescope compare to the telescopes astronomers use?
4. **Apply** How could you improve on the design of your telescope? What effects would different lenses or tubes have?

More to Explore

With an adult, go outside in the evening a few days after the first-quarter phase and observe the moon. Draw a circle with all the features you see. Label the maria (lowlands) and highlands.

Make Your Own Telescope

Preparing for Inquiry

Key Concept Students will construct and use a simple refracting telescope.
Skills Objectives Students will be able to
◆ make a refracting telescope;
◆ use the telescope to observe objects;
◆ draw conclusions about how telescopes work.
Time 80 minutes
Advance Planning Use kits or collect paper towel tubes for the telescopes. Tubes from different brands can be used for the inner and outer tubes. Various combinations of lenses are possible. For example, a 43-mm diameter 400-mm focal length objective lens paired with a 25-mm focal length eyepiece would produce a magnification of 16 times.

Guiding Inquiry

Invitation Ask: **Who invented the telescope?** *(Many students will answer Galileo.)* Actually, we don't know who invented the telescope; it may have been Hans Lippershey, a Dutch lens maker.

Introducing the Procedure
Show students the text drawing to give them an idea of what they are building.

Troubleshooting the Experiment
◆ Suggest students rest their telescopes on a stable surface.
◆ Make sure lenses are perpendicular to tube walls and parallel to each other.

Expected Outcome
Objects will be magnified and inverted when viewed through the telescopes.

Analyze and Conclude
1. To focus on objects at different distances
2. Together
3. Astronomers' telescopes are wider and therefore collect more light.
4. A wider tube and wider lenses would collect more light.

Program Resources

◆ **Teaching Resources** Real-World Lab blackline masters, pp. 97–98

Media and Technology

Lab Activity Videotape
Astronomy, 5

Extending the Inquiry

More to Explore Students' observations will depend on their eyes and how still they hold the telescope.

Safety

Caution students not to drop the lenses. Adult supervision is needed for More to Explore.

SCIENCE AND SOCIETY

Light Pollution

Purpose

To provide students with an opportunity to weigh the benefits of outdoor lighting against the problem of light pollution.

Panel Discussion

Time 40 minutes

◆ Divide the class into small groups to discuss whether there is a problem with light pollution in your city. Brainstorm a list of the advantages and disadvantages of outdoor lighting. Invite volunteers to act as panel members to weigh the issues, then discuss ways to reduce light pollution without making unacceptable compromises. For example, students may believe that light used for advertising is unnecessary or street lights should be shielded.

◆ After the panel discussion, leave time for a wrap-up to find whether any students have changed their opinions about light pollution based on the information given by panel members.

Extend Organize the class into two groups. Ask one group to identify an area of town where there appears to be too many lights. Have the other group identify an area of town that needs more lights. Challenge each group to design a plan for lighting their area that does not lead to light pollution. Groups can write letters to town officials in which they present their plans and ask whether the lighting could be modified.

You Decide

◆ Students can complete the first two steps to raise issues and possible solutions for class discussion. After the panel discussion, students can complete the last step, using what they learned to design solutions.

Portfolio Students can save their letters in their portfolios.

SCIENCE AND SOCIETY

Light Pollution

Imagine you are in a dark theater watching a movie when the lights come on. You can still see the movie, but it seems dull and faded. For the same reason, you may not see very many stars if you live in or near a city. Light from street lights and advertising signs masks much of the starlight. Artificial light that makes it difficult to see the night sky clearly is known as light pollution.

Astronomers build modern observatories far from cities and outdoor lights. But light pollution is still a problem for older observatories and for amateur astronomers like the one in this photo. If light pollution increases, how will you see glittering stars in the night sky, the broad Milky Way, meteor showers, or an occasional passing comet?

The Issues

How Important Are Outdoor Lights?
Artificial lighting is one of the great advantages of the modern age. Street lights make it easier to drive safely, reducing accidents. Night lighting allows businesses to stay open later. In addition, lighting helps people feel safer in their homes and on the streets.

What Can Be Done? Street lights are the biggest cause of light pollution. However, some types of street lights cause more light pollution than others. The three types of street light bulbs are mercury vapor bulbs, high-pressure sodium bulbs, and low-pressure sodium bulbs. Low-pressure sodium lights cause the least problem for astronomers because they shine in only a very narrow range of wavelengths. A simple filter on a telescope can eliminate this light from the telescope's view. In addition, street lights of all types can be shielded so they don't shine upward. They can also be pointed only where the light is needed.

Would Reducing Light Pollution Save Money? Mercury vapor lights are the most common type of street light. High-pressure sodium and low-pressure sodium lights use less electricity, however.

Modifying street lights to reduce light pollution would initially cost a lot of money. However, reducing unneeded light and using light bulbs that require less electricity would also reduce energy usage, which could save money.

You Decide

1. Identify the Problem
In your own words, explain the problem of light pollution.

2. Analyze the Options
List possible solutions. What procedures are involved in each solution? List the advantages and disadvantages of each solution.

3. Find a Solution
Find out what types of street lights your town or city has. Are the lights shielded? Write a letter to your city council proposing a solution to light pollution in your city or town.

Background

In an increasing number of cities, light pollution is regulated by law. Tucson, Arizona passed a light ordinance in 1972 that has significantly reduced light pollution. Other cities are now following Tucson's example. In Los Angeles, thousands of street lights have been replaced with shielded lights that do not project any light up toward the sky. In addition to street lights, lighting for billboards, flags, and church steeples often projects upward. In Atlanta, Georgia, a 1994 law requires that all new billboards have top-mounted lights that point down instead of shining up at the sign. Although there are now at least 100 light-control laws in effect worldwide, development of new suburbs and highways continues to add to the problem. Up to 2,500 stars should be visible in the United States in summer. From most towns, only a few hundred can be seen.

DISCOVER

How Does Your Thumb Move?

1. Stand facing a wall, at least an arm's length away. Stretch your arm out with your thumb up and your fingers curled.

2. Close your right eye and look at your thumb with your left eye. Line your thumb up with something on the wall.

3. Now close your left eye and open your right eye. How does your thumb appear to move along the wall?

4. Bring your thumb closer to your eye, about half the distance as before. Repeat Steps 2 and 3.

Think It Over

Observing How does your thumb appear to move in Step 4 compared to Step 3? How are these observations related to how far away your thumb is at each step? How could you use this method to estimate distances?

Imagine you could travel to the stars at the speed of light. To travel from Earth to the sun would take about 8 minutes, not very long for such a long trip! Yet the next nearest star, Proxima Centauri, is much farther away—a trip to Proxima Centauri would take 4.2 years!

Most stars are much farther away than Proxima Centauri. Our sun and Proxima Centauri are only two of the stars that make up the Milky Way. The Milky Way is a giant flat structure, called a **galaxy,** that contains hundreds of billions of stars. At the speed of light, it would take you 25,000 years to travel the 250 million billion kilometers to the center of our galaxy. If you left our galaxy and traveled at the speed of light for about 2 million years, you would eventually reach another galaxy, the Andromeda Galaxy.

There are billions of galaxies in the **universe,** which astronomers define as all of space and everything in it. Since galaxies are so far apart, most of the universe is empty space. If our galaxy were the size of a dime, the Andromeda Galaxy would be about half a meter away. The rest of the universe, as far as astronomers can see, would extend for about 2 kilometers in all directions.

GUIDE FOR READING

◆ How do astronomers measure distances to nearby stars?

◆ How are stars classified?

Reading Tip As you read, make a list of the characteristics of stars. Write a sentence describing each characteristic.

Chapter 3 **J ◆ 103**

READING STRATEGIES

Reading Tip As students read and list the characteristics of stars, have them write a sentence describing each characteristic in their own words. As they review their notes, have them write a sentence for each characteristic describing its relationship to the other characteristics. *(Sample: The brightness of a star depends on size and temperature. Large cool stars are very bright, and small hot stars are very bright.)*

Program Resources

◆ **Teaching Resources** 3-2 Lesson Plan, p. 81; 3-2 Section Summary, p. 82
◆ **Guided Study Workbook** Section 3-2

Objectives

After completing the lesson, students will be able to
◆ describe how astronomers measure distances to nearby stars;
◆ explain how stars are classified.

Key Terms galaxy, universe, light-year, parallax, giant star, apparent magnitude, absolute magnitude, Hertzsprung-Russell diagram, main sequence

1 Engage/Explore

Activating Prior Knowledge

Ask students if they have ever visited a planetarium. Invite students who have to describe their experiences. Display a star chart showing the night sky for the current season. Ask: **How do the star chart and the night sky compare?** *(Sample: You can't see all the stars shown in the chart when you look at the night sky.)* Invite students to discuss how they could use star charts to locate objects in the sky.

DISCOVER

Skills Focus observing
Time 5 minutes
Tips Encourage students to focus on their thumb, not the wall. Also, guide them to choose a location so that they are not staring directly into the sun or other source of light.
Think It Over The thumb seems to move more in Step 4, when it is closer to the student. You could use this method to estimate distances by comparing how much an object appears to move against a background. This is an example of greater parallax shift for shorter distances.

2 Facilitate

Distances to Stars

Building Inquiry Skills: Making Models

To help students remember that a light-year measures distance, not time, have them calculate the distance light travels in one minute, one hour, and one day. Make sure students use units correctly in their calculations. Invite students to use paper, rulers, and colored markers to make scale drawings comparing the calculated distances. Ask: **Does light travel farther in one hour than in one minute?** *(yes)* **learning modality: logical/mathematical**

Measuring Distances to Stars

Inquiry Challenge

Materials *protractors, two cardboard shoe boxes, measuring tape*

Time 30 minutes

To measure the distance to an object using triangulation, have students tape a protractor to each box with the straight side of the protractor adjacent and parallel to a short side of the box. Position the boxes at least 2.0 m apart with the sides parallel, and face the boxes toward a vertical object in the distance, such as a tree. Have students sight over the protractor, with their eye lined up at the center of the base of the protractor. Then move a sharp pencil point down along the curved edge of the protractor until the pencil point appears to be lined up with the distant object. Hold the pencil at this spot and read the number of degrees. Measure the distances between the two protractors and make a scaled drawing of the triangle. From the drawing, students can measure the scaled distance to the tree and calculate the actual distance. **learning modality: kinesthetic**

Figure 5 You and your friend are sitting behind a woman with a large hat.
Applying Concepts Why is your view of the screen different from your friend's view?

Your view

Your friend's view

Distances to Stars

Distances on Earth are often measured in kilometers. However, as you have seen, distances to stars are so large that the kilometer is not a very practical unit. Instead of kilometers, astronomers use a unit called the light-year. In space, light travels at a speed of 300,000 kilometers per second. A **light-year** is the distance that light travels in one year, or about 9.5 million million kilometers. Note that the light-year is a unit of distance, not time.

To help you understand what a light-year is, consider an everyday example. If you bicycle at 10 kilometers per hour, it would take you 1 hour to go to a mall 10 kilometers away. You could say that the mall is "1 bicycle-hour" away.

It takes light about 4.2 years to reach Earth from Proxima Centauri, so Proxima Centauri is 4.2 light-years, or 40 million million kilometers, away.

☑ *Checkpoint* How many kilometers are in three light-years?

Measuring Distances to Stars

Standing on Earth looking up at the sky, it seems as if there is no way to tell how far away the stars are. However, astronomers have found a way to measure those distances. **Astronomers often use parallax to measure distances to nearby stars.**

Parallax is the apparent change in position of an object when you look at it from different places. For example, imagine that you and a friend have gone to a movie. After you sit down, a woman with a large hat sits down in front of you. Because you and your friend are sitting in different positions, the woman's hat blocks different parts of the screen. If you are sitting on her left, the woman's hat appears to be in front of the dinosaur. But to your friend, who is sitting on her right, she appears to be in front of the bird.

Have the woman and her hat moved? No. But because of your relative positions, she appears to have moved. This apparent movement is parallax.

Astronomers use parallax to measure the distances to nearby stars. They look at a star when Earth is on one side of the sun. Then they

---

Background

Facts and Figures Although the distances to stars and galaxies are often measured in light-years, professional astronomers use a unit of measurement called a *parsec*. The parsec is related to parallax—a star at a distance of one parsec from Earth has a parallax of one second of arc (1/3600 of a degree). One parsec equals 3.26 light-years.

Astronomers measure distances to stars in the Milky Way in kiloparsecs (1 kiloparsec = 1,000 parsecs). For example, the sun is 8.5 kiloparsecs from the center of the Milky Way. To measure distances to other galaxies or clusters of galaxies, astronomers use megaparsecs (1 megaparsec = 1 million parsecs). Some galaxies are 3,000 to 5,000 megaparsecs from Earth—9 to 14 billion light-years away!

Brightness of Stars

Stars also differ in brightness, the amount of light they give off. The brightness of a star depends upon its size and temperature. Recall from Chapter 2 that the photosphere is the layer of a star that gives off light. Betelgeuse is fairly cool, so each square meter of its photosphere doesn't give off much light. But Betelgeuse is very large, so it shines brightly. Rigel, on the other hand, is very hot, so each square meter of Rigel's photosphere gives off a lot of light. Even though it is much smaller than Betelgeuse, Rigel also shines brightly.

How bright a star looks from Earth depends on both how far the star is from Earth and how bright the star actually is. Because of these two factors, the brightness of a star can be described in two different ways: apparent magnitude and absolute magnitude.

Apparent Magnitude

A star's **apparent magnitude** is its brightness as seen from Earth. Astronomers can measure apparent magnitude fairly easily using electronic devices.

Astronomers cannot tell how much light a star gives off just from the star's apparent magnitude. Just as a flashlight looks brighter the closer it is to you, a star looks brighter the closer it is to Earth. For example, the sun looks very bright. This does not mean that the sun gives off more light than all other stars. The sun looks so bright simply because it is so close to Earth.

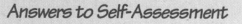

Figure 8 The constellation Orion includes the red supergiant star Betelgeuse and the blue supergiant star Rigel.

Social Studies CONNECTION

During the Middle Ages Arab astronomers in Southwest Asia and North Africa named many stars. For example, the star name Algol comes from the Arabic words *Ras al Ghul,* which mean "the demon's head." Other Arabic star names include Aldebaran ("the follower of the Pleiades"), Vega ("swooping eagle"), and Rigel ("the left leg of the giant").

In Your Journal

Many other words used in astronomy and mathematics come from Arabic. Find *zenith, nadir, algorithm,* and *algebra* in a dictionary. Write their definitions in your own words.

Brightness of Stars

Including All Students

Write the word *photosphere* on the board. Explain that this word can be broken up into two parts: *photo,* meaning "light," and *sphere,* meaning a round body like a ball. Ask students whose native language is not English for examples of similar compound words from their native languages. Challenge all students to think of other words containing *photo.* (*Samples: photography, photosensitive, photogenic*) **limited English proficiency**

Social Studies CONNECTION

Inform students that the Middle Ages coincided with a very active time in Arabic sciences. For example, the works of one Arab scholar, astronomer and mathematician Muhammad ibn Musa al-Khwarizmi, are credited with introducing Arabic numerals and algebra to European mathematics.

In Your Journal
The *zenith* is the point on the celestial sphere that appears to be directly above the observer. A *nadir* is a point on the celestial sphere directly opposite the zenith. *Algebra* is a generalized arithmetic in which letters are substituted for numbers. An *algorithm* is a step-by-step procedure for solving a mathematical problem. Challenge students to find the original Arabic meanings of *nadir* and *algebra.* (*From* Webster's Third New International Dictionary: *Nadir comes from* nazir, *which means "opposite"; algebra comes from* al-jabr, *which means "to reunite."*) **learning modality: verbal**

Answers to Self-Assessment

☑ Checkpoint
Supergiant star, giant star, medium-sized star, white dwarf star, neutron star

Caption Question
Figure 7 The sun is a medium-sized star.

Ongoing Assessment

Oral Presentation Call on students at random to name and describe the characteristics astronomers use to classify stars.

Brightness of Stars, continued

Skills Focus making models

Materials *3 flashlights, two with equal brightness, one brighter than the others*

Time 20 minutes

Tips Make sure students do not look directly into the lights.

Expected Outcome In Steps 2–3, the absolute magnitudes are the same for both flashlights. In Step 2, the apparent magnitudes are the same. The closer flashlight in Step 3 has a greater apparent magnitude. In Step 4, both absolute and apparent magnitudes are greater for the brighter flashlight.

Making Models Students could place the brighter flashlight farther away so that the two have the same apparent magnitude.

Extend Challenge students to write a paragraph speculating how astronomers determine the absolute magnitude of stars when they can only observe the apparent magnitude. **learning modality: kinesthetic**

The Hertzsprung-Russell Diagram

Including All Students

Students may need extra help using the Hertzsprung-Russell diagram. Pair students. Have partners take turns. One looks at the diagram while the other reads the text and asks questions. *(Sample: What is the relationship between surface temperature and brightness for main sequence stars? In which direction does the brightness increase? Are the brightest stars always the hottest stars?)* Emphasize that the H-R diagram is a graph—not a star chart. It does not show positions in the sky. **learning modality: visual**

Figure 9 The stars in a globular cluster are all about the same distance from Earth.

Star Bright ACTIVITY

Here's how you can compare absolute and apparent magnitudes.

1. Dim the lights. Put two equally bright flashlights next to each other on a table. Turn them on.

2. Look at the flashlights from the other side of the room. Think of the flashlights as two stars. Then compare them in terms of absolute and apparent magnitudes.

3. Move one of the flashlights closer to you and repeat Step 2.

4. Replace one of the flashlights with a brighter one. Repeat Step 1 with the unequally bright flashlights. Then repeat Step 2.

Making Models How could you place the flashlights in Step 4 so that they have the same apparent magnitude? Try it.

Absolute Magnitude A star's **absolute magnitude** is the brightness the star would have if it were at a standard distance from Earth. Finding a star's absolute magnitude is more complicated than finding its apparent magnitude. An astronomer must first find out the star's apparent magnitude and its distance from Earth. The astronomer can then calculate the star's brightness if it were at a standard distance from Earth.

Figure 9 shows a globular cluster, a group of 10,000 to 1,000,000 stars that are close together. The stars in a globular cluster are all at about the same distance from Earth. So astronomers study globular clusters to compare the brightnesses of stars. If one star in a globular cluster appears brighter than another star, it really is brighter than that other star.

The Hertzsprung-Russell Diagram

Two of the most important characteristics of stars are temperature and absolute magnitude. About 100 years ago, Ejnar Hertzsprung (EYE nahr HURT sprung) in Denmark and Henry Norris Russell in the United States each made graphs to find out if temperature and brightness are related. They plotted the temperatures of stars on the *x*-axis and their brightness on the *y*-axis. The points formed a pattern.

The graph they made is still used by astronomers. It is called the **Hertzsprung-Russell diagram,** or H-R diagram. As you can see in Figure 10, most of the stars in the H-R diagram form a diagonal line called the **main sequence.** In the main sequence, surface temperature increases as brightness increases. More than 90% of all stars are main-sequence stars. The sun is among the stars on the main sequence. Giant and supergiant stars are higher and farther to the right on the H-R diagram. White dwarfs are hot, but not very bright, so they appear at the bottom center of the diagram.

Background

History of Science The realization that the color of stars could be related to their brightness came independently to two astronomers at the same time. The result, the Hertzsprung-Russell diagram, was published in 1914 by an American, Henry Norris Russell (1877–1957), and a Dane, Ejnar Hertzsprung (1873–1967). Russell went to Princeton Preparatory School and Princeton University where he received a Ph.D. Russell returned to Princeton as a professor, then as the director of the university observatory.

Hertzsprung had no formal training in astronomy, and studied chemical engineering in technical colleges. His interest in the chemistry of photography led to work in small observatories, where he applied photography to the measurement of starlight. Like Russell, Hertzsprung later became the director of a university observatory.

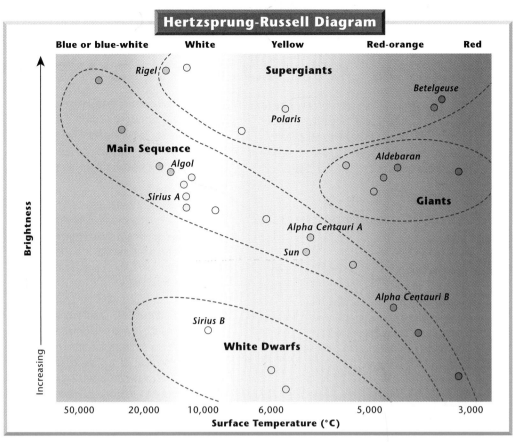

Hertzsprung-Russell Diagram

Blue or blue-white   White   Yellow   Red-orange   Red

Brightness

Increasing

Rigel
Supergiants
Betelgeuse
Polaris
Main Sequence
Algol
Aldebaran
Sirius A
Giants
Alpha Centauri A
Sun
Alpha Centauri B
Sirius B
White Dwarfs

50,000   20,000   10,000   6,000   5,000   3,000

Surface Temperature (°C)

Figure 10 The Hertzsprung-Russell diagram shows the relationship between surface temperature and brightness.
Interpreting Diagrams Which star is hotter: Rigel or Aldebaran?

Section 2 Review

1. What is parallax? How is it useful in astronomy?
2. List three characteristics used to classify stars.
3. Which is hotter—a red star or a blue star? Why?
4. **Thinking Critically Applying Concepts** Stars A and B have about the same apparent magnitude, but Star A is about twice as far from Earth as Star B. Which star has the greater absolute magnitude? Explain your answer.

Science at Home

With adult family members, go outside on a clear, dark night. Determine which way is north, south, east, and west. Using the star chart for the correct season in Appendix B, look for the constellation Orion. Find the stars Betelgeuse and Rigel in Orion and explain to your family why they are different colors.

3 Assess

Section 2 Review Answers

1. Parallax is the apparent change in an object's position when it is viewed from two different places. Astronomers can use parallax to calculate distances to nearby stars.
2. Size, temperature (or color), brightness
3. Blue stars are hotter than red stars because gas glows red at lower temperatures and blue at higher temperatures.
4. Star A has the greater absolute magnitude. Because it is farther away than Star B, but has the same apparent magnitude, it must be brighter.

Science at Home

Ask students to make sketches and take notes of their observations. Allow class time for students to share their observations. Encourage students to name and describe any other constellations they have seen. Make sure students can explain that reddish stars like Betelgeuse are cooler than bluish stars like Rigel.

Program Resources

◆ **Teaching Resources** 3-2 Review and Reinforce, p. 83; 3-2 Enrich, p. 84

Media and Technology

Transparencies "Hertzsprung-Russell Diagram," Transparency 13

Answers to Self-Assessment

Caption Question
Figure 10 Rigel is the hotter star.

Performance Assessment

Oral Presentation Challenge students to pretend they are astronomers studying a recently discovered star. Have them prepare a presentation in which they define the characteristics of the star, compare the star to our sun, and show the placement of their star on the Hertzsprung-Russell diagram.

How Far Is That Star?

Preparing for Inquiry

Key Concept Parallax is used to determine the distance to nearby stars. Parallax is an apparent motion resulting from a change in viewing position. The accuracy of the parallax method of measuring star distances decreases as the distance to the star increases.

Skills Objective Students will be able to
◆ measure distances between points;
◆ calculate the distance to an object using ratios of measured values;
◆ compare the calculated value to the measured value;
◆ predict the parallax of an object at different distances.

Time 50 minutes

Advance Planning Review ratio calculation before performing the lab. Set up two or three stations.

Guiding Inquiry

Invitation Ask students to compare how fast close and distant objects seem to move when they are viewed from the window of a moving car. *(Objects close to the car appear to move by very fast whereas objects further away do not seem to move much at all.)*

Introducing the Procedure

◆ Demonstrate the measurements students will make and show them how to mark the star on their "film."
◆ Set up several stations around the sides of the rooms. Turn the tables so that the positions of the box can be as far apart as possible.

Skills Lab

Measuring

HOW FAR IS THAT STAR?

When astronomers measure parallax, they record the positions of stars on film in cameras attached to telescopes. In this lab, you will set up a model of a telescope and use it to estimate distances.

Problem

How can parallax be used to determine distances?

Materials

masking tape   paper clips   pen
black and red pencils metric ruler   paper
meter stick   calculator
lamp without a shade, with 100-watt light bulb
copier paper box (without the lid)
flat rectangular table, about 1 m wide

Procedure

Part 1 Telescope Model

1. Place the lamp on a table in the middle of the classroom.
2. Carefully use the tip of the pen to make a small hole in the middle of one end of the box. The box represents a telescope.
3. At the front of the classroom, place the box on a flat table so the hole points toward the lamp. Line the left side of the box up with the left edge of the table.

4. Put a small piece of tape on the table below the hole. Use the pen to make a mark on the tape directly below the hole. The mark represents the position of the telescope when Earth is on one side of its orbit.

Part 2 Star 1

5. Label a sheet of paper Star 1 and place it inside the box as shown in the drawing. Hold the paper in place with two paper clips. The paper represents the film in a telescope.
6. Darken the room. Turn on the light to represent the star.
7. With the red pencil, mark the paper where you see a dot of light. Label this dot A. Dot A represents the image of the star on the film.
8. Move the box so the right edge of the box lines up with the right edge of the table. Repeat Step 4. The mark on the tape represents the position of the telescope six months later, when Earth is on the other side of its orbit.
9. Repeat Step 7, and use a black pencil to mark the second dot B. Dot B represents the image of the star as seen 6 months later from the other side of Earth's orbit.
10. Remove the paper. Before you continue, copy the data table into your notebook.
11. Measure and record the distance in millimeters between dots A and B. This distance represents the parallax shift for Star 1.

DATA TABLE

Star	Parallax Shift (mm)	Focal Length (mm)	Diameter of Orbit (mm)	Calculated Distance to Star (mm)	Calculated Distance to Star (m)	Actual Distance to Star (m)

Safety

Caution students to be careful when walking around the room so that they do not knock over the lamp or trip on a power cord. Caution them not to look directly into the lamp.

Program Resources

◆ **Teaching Resources** Skills Lab blackline masters, pp. 99–101

Media and Technology

Lab Activity Videotape
Astronomy, 6

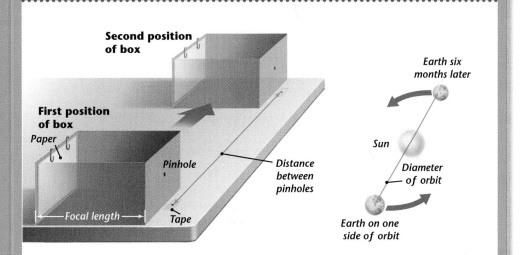

Second position of box

First position of box

Paper

Pinhole

Focal length

Tape

Distance between pinholes

Earth six months later

Sun

Diameter of orbit

Earth on one side of orbit

12. Measure and record the distance from the hole in the box to the lamp. This distance represents the actual distance to the star.

13. Measure and record the distance from the hole (lens) to the back of the box in millimeters. This distance represents the focal length of your telescope.

14. Measure and record the distance in millimeters between the marks on the two pieces of masking tape. This distance represents the diameter of Earth's orbit.

Part 3 Stars 2 and 3

15. Move the lamp away from the table—about half the distance to the back of the room. The bulb now represents Star 2. Predict what you think will happen to the light images on your paper.

16. Repeat Steps 6–12 with a new sheet of paper to find the parallax shift for Star 2.

17. Move the lamp to the back of the classroom. The bulb now represents Star 3. Repeat Steps 6–12 with a new sheet of paper to find the parallax shift for Star 3.

Analyze and Conclude

1. What caused the apparent change in position of the dots of light for each star? Explain.

2. Use the following formula to calculate the distance from the telescope to Star 1.

$$\text{Distance} = \frac{\text{Diameter} \times \text{Focal length}}{\text{Parallax shift}}$$

3. Divide your result from Question 3 by 1,000 to get the distance to the light bulb in meters.

4. Repeat Questions 3 and 4 for Stars 2 and 3.

5. Was your prediction in Step 15 correct? Why or why not?

6. Is the parallax shift greater or smaller the farther away the star is? Relate each star's parallax shift to its distance from Earth.

7. **Think About It** How did your calculation for Star 3 compare with the actual distance? What could you do to improve your results?

Design an Experiment

What would happen if you kept moving the lamp away from the box? Is there a distance at which you can no longer find the distance to the star? Design an experiment to find out.

Sample Data Table

Star	Parallax Shift (mm)	Focal Length (mm)	Diam. Orbit (mm)	Calc. Dist. Star (mm)	Calc. Dist. Star (m)	Actual Dist. Star (m)
1	80	440	460	2,530	2.53	2.52
2	40	440	460	5,060	5.06	5.09
3	20	440	460	10,120	10.12	10.22

Troubleshooting the Experiment

◆ Make sure students understand that the length of the box represents the telescope's focal length, the paper represents photographic film, and the marks on the table represent different positions of Earth in its orbit. The light bulb represents the distant star. The distances from the box to the lamp represent the distances to the stars. The change in position of the dot images represents the parallax shift.

Expected Outcome

Students will see the dot of light move from one side of the film to the other when they move the box. The dot of light will move a shorter distance when the lamp is further from the box.

Analyze and Conclude

1. The dot of light moved.
2. The light bulb (star) did not move but the image shifted because of parallax. (The viewing position changed.)
3. Distance to Star 1 is 2,530 mm using sample data.
4. Sample data: 2.53 m
5. Answers will vary. See Sample Data Table.
6. Students who predicted that the dot would move less are correct.
7. The parallax shift is smaller for stars that are farther away. The closest star, Star 1, had the greatest shift and the farthest star, Star 3, had the smallest shift.
8. See Sample Data Table. The difference was small for Star 1 (20 cm) and Star 2 (30 cm) and large for Star 3 (100 cm). Possible errors include poor measurement techniques, slight shifts in position of the box when it is moved, poor marking of exact images on paper, and possibly mathematical errors.

Extending the Inquiry

Design an Experiment The greater the distance, the smaller the parallax shift. A typical plan will duplicate this experiment in a gym or hallway, taking measurements at increasing distances until parallax is no longer observable.

Objectives

After completing the lesson, students will be able to
- describe how a star is formed;
- identify what determines how long a star will last;
- explain what happens to a star when it runs out of fuel.

Key Terms pulsar, nebula, protostar, white dwarf, supernova, neutron star, black hole, quasar

1 Engage/Explore

Activating Prior Knowledge

Ask students if they have ever watched a campfire. Have volunteers describe the stages of the burning fire. (*Most students will say that the fire started with a blaze, then the flames became smaller, gradually reduced to a glow, and eventually burned out.*) Ask students what caused the fire to go out. (*All the wood was burned.*) Point out that wood is the fuel that feeds the flame. Once the fuel is used up, the flame goes out. In the same way, stars fade away when their fuel is used up.

DISCOVER

Skills Focus inferring
Time 10 minutes
Tips Point out that a star with 0.8 times the mass of the sun has eight tenths the sun's mass, or 80% of the sun's mass.
Ask: **Does a star with 1.7 times the mass of the sun have more or less mass than the sun?** (*more*)
Answers The star with 0.8 times the sun's mass lives 14 billion years. The star with 1.7 times the sun's mass lives 2.5 billion years.
Think It Over Less massive stars live longer than more massive stars.

SECTION
3 Lives of Stars

DISCOVER ·············· ACTIVITY

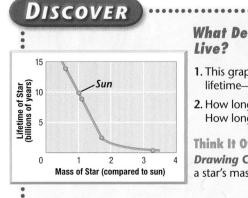

What Determines How Long Stars Live?

1. This graph shows how the mass of a star is related to its lifetime—how long the star lives before it runs out of fuel.
2. How long does a star with 0.8 times the mass of the sun live? How long does a star with 1.7 times the mass of the sun live?

Think It Over
Drawing Conclusions Describe the general relationship between a star's mass and its lifetime.

GUIDE FOR READING

- How does the life of a star begin?
- What determines how long a star will live?
- What happens to a star when it runs out of fuel?

Reading Tip As you read, make a flowchart showing the stages in the life of a medium-sized star.

Jocelyn Bell today ▼

I n 1967, Jocelyn Bell, a British astronomy student, detected an object in space that appeared to give off regular pulses of radio waves. Some astronomers hypothesized that the pulses might be a signal from an extraterrestrial civilization. At first, astronomers even named the source LGM, for the "Little Green Men" in early science-fiction stories. Eventually, astronomers concluded that the source of the radio waves was a neutron star. A neutron star is a tiny star left over when a giant star explodes. Neutron stars like the one Bell discovered are called **pulsars**, short for pulsating radio sources.

Studying the Lives of Stars

Stars do not last forever. Each star is born, goes through its life cycle, and eventually dies. (Of course, stars are not really alive. The words *born*, *live*, and *die* are just helpful comparisons.) How did astronomers figure out that the neutron star Bell discovered had been a larger star earlier in its life?

Imagine that you want to study how people age. You wish you could watch a few people for 50 years, but your assignment is due next week! You have to study a lot of people for a short time, and classify the people into different age groups. You may come up with groups like *babies, children, teenagers, young adults, middle-aged people,* and *elderly people.* You don't have time to see a single person go through all these stages, but you know the stages exist.

Astronomers have a similar problem with stars. They can't watch a single star for billions of years, so they study many stars and see how they differ from one another.

112 ◆ J

READING STRATEGIES

Reading Tip Remind students to use their own words when they make their flowcharts, as shown to the right.

Study and Comprehension Have students preview the section by reading the headings, looking at the photographs and pictures, reading the captions, and reading through "Exploring the Lives of Stars."

Gravity pulls together gas and dust in a nebula to form a protostar
↓
Nuclear fusion begins to form a star
↓
The star begins to run out of fuel
↓
Star forms a red giant
↓
Star becomes a white dwarf
↓
Star becomes a black dwarf

A Star Is Born

A star is made up of a large amount of gas in a relatively small volume. A **nebula**, on the other hand, is a large amount of gas and dust spread out in an immense volume. All stars begin their lives as parts of nebulas.

Gravity can pull some of the gas and dust in a nebula together. The contracting cloud is then called a protostar. *Proto* means "earliest" in Greek, so a **protostar** is the earliest stage of a star's life. **A star is born when the contracting gas and dust become so hot that nuclear fusion starts.** Recall from Chapter 2 that nuclear fusion is the process by which atoms of hydrogen are combined to form helium. During fusion, enormous amounts of energy are released.

Lifetimes of Stars

Before they can tell how old a star is, astronomers must determine its mass. **How long a star lives depends on how much mass it has.**

You might think that stars with more mass would last longer than stars with less mass. However, the reverse is true. You can think of stars as being like cars. A small car has a small gas tank, but it also has a small engine that burns gas slowly. A large car, on the other hand, has a larger gas tank, but it also has a larger engine that burns gas rapidly. So the small car might be able to travel farther on one small tank of gas than the larger car can on one large tank of gas. Small-mass stars use up their fuel more slowly than large-mass stars, so they have much longer lives.

Generally, stars that have less mass than the sun use their fuel slowly, and can live for up to 200 billion years. Medium-mass stars like the sun live for about 10 billion years. Astronomers think the sun is about 4.6 billion years old, so it is almost halfway through its lifetime.

Stars that have more mass than the sun have shorter lifetimes. A star that is 15 times as massive as the sun may live only about ten million years. That may seem like a long time, but it is only one tenth of one percent of the lifetime of the sun.

☑ *Checkpoint* If a star is twice as massive as the sun, will it have a longer or shorter life than the sun?

Figure 11 The Orion Nebula, top, is a giant cloud of gas and dust. The Hubble Space Telescope took this photo of a protostar, bottom, in the Orion Nebula. A protostar is a star in the earliest stage of its life. *Applying Concepts How do some of the gas and dust in a nebula become a protostar?*

Program Resources

◆ **Teaching Resources** 3-3 Lesson Plan, p. 85; 3-3 Section Summary, p. 86
◆ **Guided Study Workbook** Section 3-3

Answers to Self-Assessment

Caption Question

Figure 11 Gravity causes the gas and clouds to contract into a protostar.

☑ *Checkpoint*

A star that has twice as much mass as the sun will have a shorter life.

2 Facilitate

Studying the Lives of Stars

Building Inquiry Skills: Problem Solving

Materials *magazines, scissors, tape, posterboard*
Time: 20 minutes
Tips Have students cut out 24 pictures of people of all ages and guess their ages. Have students arrange their pictures in groups and tape them on a large piece of posterboard to make a time line. Ask students to explain how they determined the people's ages. Ask: **How do you think astronomers can determine a star's age?** *(By studying its physical features)*
learning modality: logical/ mathematical

A Star is Born

Using the Visuals: Figure 11

Ask students to explain the relationship between the object in the large image and the object in the small image. *(Some of the gas and dust in the nebula contracted to form the protostar.)* Make sure students realize that the Orion Nebula may contain hundreds of young stars. **learning modality: visual**

Ongoing Assessment

Writing Have students write paragraphs describing how a star is born and explaining what factors influence how long it will live.

Deaths of Stars

Demonstration

Materials *plastic cup, marbles, sand*
Time 20 minutes

Fill a plastic cup with marbles, then determine its mass. Empty the cup and refill with sand. Determine its mass again. Point out that glass and sand have about the same density, so why did the cup weigh more with sand than with marbles? *(Less empty space)* Explain to students that all matter is mostly empty space. When the empty space is squeezed out, as in a white dwarf or neutron star, the matter occupies a much smaller space. **learning modality: logical/ mathematical**

Predicting

Time 10 minutes
Tips Have students use the diagram on page 109 to identify the type of star and Exploring the Lives of Stars on page 115 to find the next stage. Tell students a main sequence star may become a red giant or a supergiant.
Expected Outcome Sirius B: black dwarf; Algol: red giant or supergiant; Polaris: supernova
Extend Have students identify the next stage for the other stars labeled in the H-R diagram.

Figure 12 Supernova 1987A was the brightest supernova seen in hundreds of years. The arrow in the photo at the left points to the original star, before it exploded. *Making Generalizations Why were ancient astronomers able to see supernovas?*

Predicting

Find Algol, Polaris, and Sirius B in the H-R diagram on page 109. For each star, write a sentence predicting what the next stages in its life will be.

Deaths of Stars

When a star begins to run out of fuel, the center of the star shrinks and the outer part of the star expands. The star becomes a red giant or supergiant.

All main sequence stars eventually become red giants or supergiants. However, what happens next depends on the mass of the star, as *Exploring the Lives of Stars* shows. **When a star runs out of fuel, it becomes a white dwarf, a neutron star, or a black hole.**

White Dwarfs

Small- and medium-mass stars take 10 billion or more years to use up their nuclear fuel. Then their outer layers expand, and they become red giants. Eventually, the outer parts grow bigger still and drift out into space. The blue-white hot core of the star that is left behind is a **white dwarf.**

White dwarfs are only about the size of Earth, but they have about as much mass as the sun. Since a white dwarf has the same mass as the sun but only one millionth the volume, it is one million times as dense as the sun. A spoonful of material from a white dwarf has as much mass as a large truck. White dwarfs have no fuel, but they glow faintly from leftover energy. When a white dwarf stops glowing, it is dead. Then it is called a black dwarf.

Neutron Stars

A dying giant or supergiant star can suddenly explode. Within hours, the star blazes millions of times brighter. The explosion is called a **supernova.** You can see a supernova in Figure 12. After a supernova, some of the material from the star expands into space. This material may become part of a nebula. The nebula can then contract to form a new, "recycled" star. Astronomers think the sun began as a nebula that contained material from a supernova explosion.

After the star explodes, some of the material from the star is left behind. This material forms a neutron star. **Neutron stars** are even smaller and denser than white dwarfs. A neutron star may contain as much as three times the mass of the sun but be only about 20 kilometers in diameter, the size of a large asteroid or a town on Earth.

Background

History of Science Supernovas that are visible from Earth without a telescope are very rare. Only seven supernovas were recorded before the 17th century. They occurred in 185, 393, 1006, 1054, 1181, 1572, and 1604. The 1054 supernova was so bright that it was visible even in the daytime, and it remained bright for several weeks. Rock paintings discovered in Arizona and New Mexico suggest that this supernova may have been seen by Native Americans. The supernova in 1572 was observed by Tycho Brahe and is now called Tycho's Supernova. It became as bright as Venus, and could also be seen during the day. The supernova in 1604, now called Kepler's Supernova, was first observed by Kepler's assistant. Kepler watched it until 1606 when it could no longer be seen with the unaided eye. At its brightest, Kepler's Supernova was brighter than Jupiter.

Black Holes The most massive stars—those having more than 40 times the mass of the sun—become **black holes** when they die. After this kind of star becomes a supernova, more than five times the mass of the sun may be left. The gravity of this mass is so strong that the gas is pulled inward, packing the gas into a smaller and smaller space. Eventually five times as much mass as the sun becomes packed within a sphere 30 kilometers in diameter. At that point, the gravity is so strong that nothing can escape, not even light. The remains of the star become a black hole.

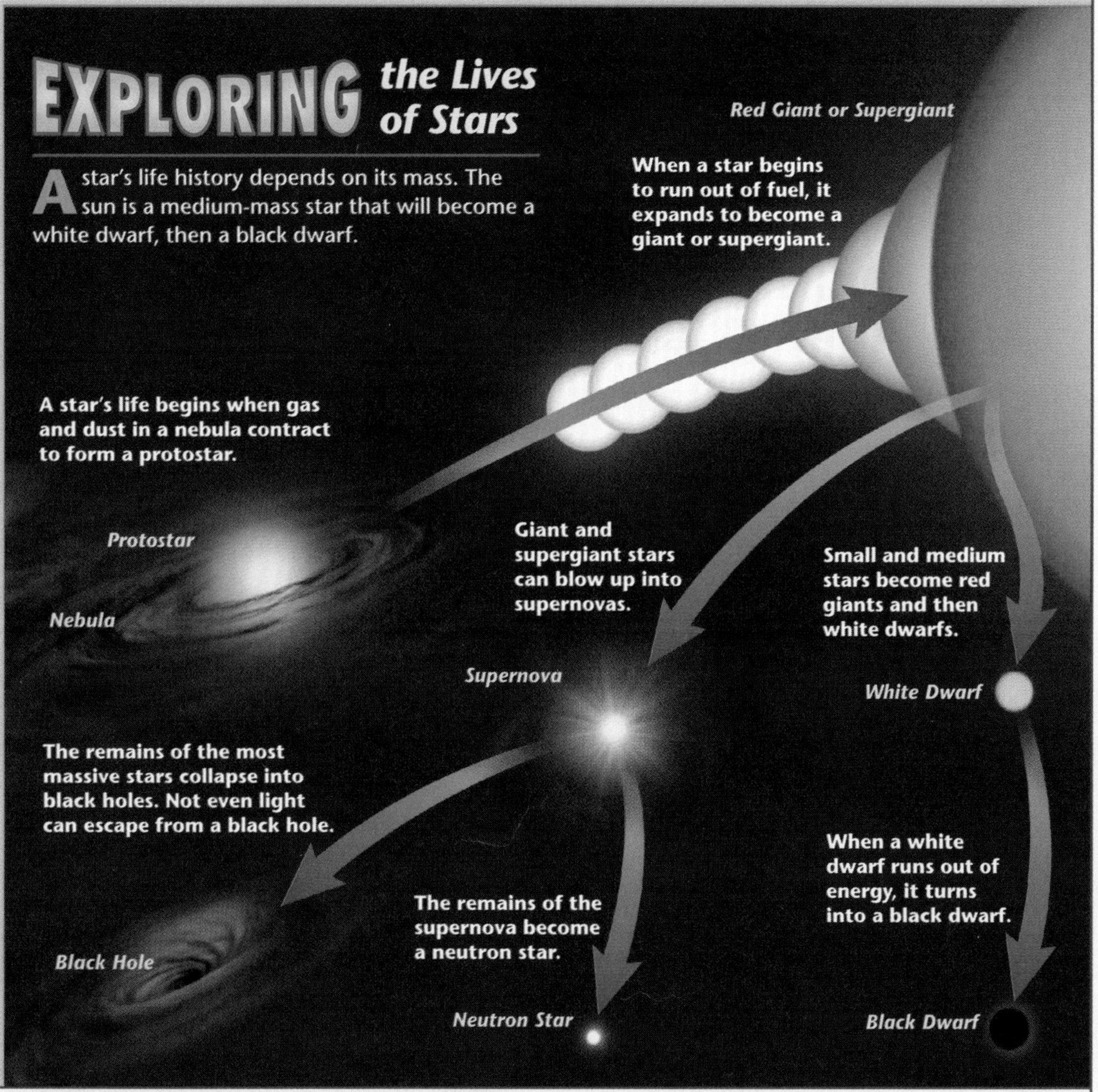

EXPLORING the Lives of Stars

A star's life history depends on its mass. The sun is a medium-mass star that will become a white dwarf, then a black dwarf.

Red Giant or Supergiant

When a star begins to run out of fuel, it expands to become a giant or supergiant.

A star's life begins when gas and dust in a nebula contract to form a protostar.

Protostar

Nebula

Giant and supergiant stars can blow up into supernovas.

Small and medium stars become red giants and then white dwarfs.

Supernova

White Dwarf

The remains of the most massive stars collapse into black holes. Not even light can escape from a black hole.

When a white dwarf runs out of energy, it turns into a black dwarf.

Black Hole

The remains of the supernova become a neutron star.

Neutron Star

Black Dwarf

EXPLORING
the Lives of Stars

As students read aloud the descriptions of the stages of the life cycle of stars, have volunteers represent the stages in sequence. Students can hold their hands overhead to represent an explosion, extend their arms horizontally to show expansion, wrap their arms around themselves to indicate condensing or shrinking, or kneel close to the ground to signify a star that has run out of fuel. Have students use this method to compare and contrast the different stages of giant stars and medium-sized stars.
learning modality: kinesthetic

Addressing Naive Conceptions

Some students may think that black holes are actually black in color. Inform students that the term *black hole* refers to the fact that the gravity of black holes is so intense that not even light can escape from them. In fact, material being pulled into a black hole can glow brightly.
learning modality: verbal

Media and Technology

Transparencies "Exploring the Lives of Stars," Transparency 14

Exploring Earth Science Videodisc Unit 1, Side 1, "Stories From the Stars"

Chapter 2

Answers to Self-Assessment

Caption Question

Figure 12 Some supernovas were bright enough to see without telescopes.

Ongoing Assessment

Drawing Have students compare and contrast white dwarfs, neutron stars, and black holes by drawing sketches with labels that indicate size and other characteristics.

Portfolio Students can save their sketches in their portfolios.

3 Assess

Section 3 Review Answers

1. The star begins as part of a nebula, a cloud of dust and gas. Some of the dust and gas condenses to form a protostar. Nuclear fusion begins, and the protostar becomes a star.

2. Small-mass stars burn their fuel more slowly than large-mass stars.

3. Giant stars collapse into neutron stars. Smaller stars form white dwarfs.

4. Scientists detect black holes by observing radiation from hot gas near the black hole, and by studying the effect of the black hole's gravity on a nearby star.

5. The sun is a medium-mass star, so it will become a red giant, then a white dwarf. When it runs out of energy, it will become a black dwarf.

Check Your Progress

CHAPTER PROJECT 3

Encourage students to allow themselves to be creative and come up with a list of several ideas before they narrow their focus to one pattern and name. If students have trouble seeing new patterns or coming up with a new name for their constellations, have them brainstorm with several classmates. As you look over students' outlines and sketches, have students explain how they chose the names for their constellations.

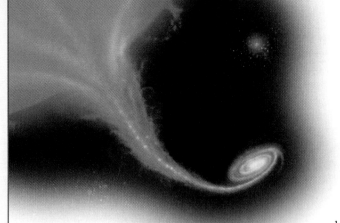

Figure 13 This artist's impression shows a black hole pulling matter from a companion star. The material glows as it is pulled into the black hole. *Applying Concepts If it is impossible to detect a black hole directly, how do astronomers find them?*

No light, radio waves, or any other form of radiation can ever get out of a black hole, so it is not possible to detect a black hole directly. But astronomers can detect black holes indirectly.

For example, gas near a black hole is pulled so strongly that it rotates faster and faster around the black hole. Friction heats the gas up. Astronomers can detect X-rays coming from the hot gas and infer that a black hole is present. Similarly, if another star is near a black hole, astronomers can calculate the mass of the black hole from the effect of its gravity on the star. Scientists are using the Chandra X-ray Observatory to look for black holes by studying sources of X-rays.

Quasars In the 1960s, astronomers discovered objects that are unusual because they are very bright, but also very far away. Many of these objects are about 12 billion light-years away, making them among the most distant objects in the universe. These distant bright objects looked almost like stars. Since *quasi* means "something like" in Latin, these objects were given the name quasi-stellar objects, or **quasars.**

What could be so bright even though it is so far away? Astronomers have concluded that quasars are actually distant galaxies with giant black holes at their centers. Each black hole has a mass a billion times or more as great as that of the sun. As enormous amounts of gas revolve around such a black hole, the gas heats up and shines brightly.

Section 3 Review

1. What is the earliest stage in the life of a star? p113

2. Why do small-mass stars have longer lifetimes than large-mass stars? p113

3. What is the difference between stars that become white dwarfs and stars that become neutron stars? p114

4. What evidence do astronomers use to detect black holes? p115

5. **Thinking Critically Inferring** What will happen to the sun when it dies? Explain your answer. p114

Check Your Progress

CHAPTER PROJECT 3

Draw and label the stars in your constellation *without* the connecting lines that form the usual image. What different patterns can you see? (*Hint:* Use a pencil to "doodle" different connections among the stars.) What does each pattern look like? Choose one pattern, and use it to name your constellation. Then write an outline of a brief story that explains why this constellation is in the sky.

Performance Assessment

Writing Have students write short biographies detailing the life cycle of a medium-sized star. Encourage students to focus on details to make the story interesting.

Portfolio Students can save their stories in their portfolios.

Answers to Self-Assessment

Caption Question

Figure 13 Astronomers can detect X-rays coming from hot gas near the black hole and infer the presence of a black hole.

Program Resources

◆ **Teaching Resources** 3-3 Review and Reinforce, p. 87; 3-3 Enrich, p. 88

SECTION
4 Star Systems and Galaxies

DISCOVER

Why Does the Milky Way Look Hazy?

1. Using a pencil, carefully poke at least 20 holes close together in a sheet of white paper.

2. Tape the paper to a chalkboard or dark-colored wall.

3. Go to the other side of the room and look at the paper. From the far side of the room, what do the dots look like? Can you see individual dots?

Think It Over

Making Models How is looking at the paper from the far side of the room like trying to see many very distant stars that are close together? How does your model compare to the photograph of the Milky Way below?

O n a clear, dark summer night in the country, you can see a hazy band of light stretched across the sky. This band of stars is called the Milky Way. It looks as if the Milky Way is very far away from Earth. Actually, though, Earth is inside the Milky Way! How is this possible? Before you can understand the answer to this question, you need to know more about how stars are grouped together.

GUIDE FOR READING

◆ What is a star system?

◆ What are the three types of galaxies?

Reading Tip Before you read, preview the boldfaced terms. As you read, look for a photograph or diagram that illustrates each term.

Star Systems and Planets

Our solar system has only one star, the sun. **But more than half of all stars are members of groups of two or more stars, called star systems.** If you were on a planet in one of these star systems, you would probably see two or more suns in the sky.

Double and Triple Stars

Star systems with two stars are called double stars or **binary stars.** (The prefix *bi* means "two.") Those with three stars are called triple stars. Proxima Centauri is probably part of a triple star system close to our sun. The other two stars in the system, Alpha Centauri A and Alpha Centauri B, form a double star. Scientists are not sure whether Proxima Centauri is really part of the system or is just passing close to the other two stars temporarily.

Astronomers can sometimes detect a binary star even if only one of the stars in the pair can be seen from Earth. For example, the darker star in the pair may pass in front of the other star and eclipse the other star. A system in which one star blocks the light from another is

The Milky Way ▶

J ◆ 117

Objectives

After completing the lesson, students will be able to

◆ describe a star system;

◆ identify and describe three types of galaxies.

Key Terms binary star, eclipsing binary, spiral galaxy, elliptical galaxy, irregular galaxy

1 Engage/Explore

Activating Prior Knowledge

Invite students to share any experiences with optical illusions. Point out that an optical illusion tricks the eye; the object appears to be different than it actually is. Ask students to recall from Section 1 that stars in constellations are optical illusions because they appear to be next to each other, but are actually at very different distances from Earth.

DISCOVER

Skills Focus making models

Materials *pencil, paper, tape*
Time 15 minutes
Tips Have students predict what the holes will look like when they observe them from the other side of the room.
Expected Outcome Students will not be able to see the individual dots from the far side of the room.
Think It Over Looking at the dots on the paper from a distance is like looking at stars because they all blur together. It is also hard to distinguish stars that are close together in the photograph of the Milky Way.

READING STRATEGIES

Reading Tip Have partners first identify and discuss each boldfaced term before finding illustrations. Encourage partners to share what they already know about the term or to predict its meaning. Partners can use information from their discussions and from the photographs to write definitions or descriptions of each term.

Program Resources

◆ **Teaching Resources** 3-4 Lesson Plan, p. 89; 3-4 Section Summary, p. 90
◆ **Guided Study Workbook** Section 3-4
   Science Explorer Series Book A, *From Bacteria to Plants,* Chapter 1

Star Systems and Planets

Using the Visuals: Figure 14

Remind students that an eclipse occurs when one body in space blocks light from another. Have students describe how eclipsing binaries appear from Earth. Encourage students to draw diagrams showing the positions of the bright star in Algol, its dim companion star, and Earth when Algol appears less bright. (*The companion star passes between the bright star and Earth.*) **learning modality: logical/ mathematical**

Inquiry Challenge

Materials *lamp with incandescent bulb, light bulbs of various wattages, plastic foam balls of three sizes, wire coat hangers, metal snips, rulers, textbooks*

Time 20 minutes

Remove the lampshade from a table or floor lamp. Place the lamp in front of the classroom so all students can see it. Have students consider this statement: *Seeing a planet around another star is like trying to see a firefly near a street light.* Pair students and assign a hanger length (6, 12, 18, 24 inches) and foam ball size (small, medium, large) to each pair. Show students how to untwist a wire hanger and straighten it, leaving the crook at one end. Snip to assigned lengths from the crook, discarding the straight section. Poke the unbent end of the hanger into a foam ball. Twist all the hangers with small balls around the neck of the lamp and observe. Ask: **Which "planet" is the easiest to see? the hardest?** (*the one farthest from the light, the one closest to the light*) Have students hold up a book or object to block the light. Discuss how this affects what they can see. Repeat with other ball sizes and compare results.

Extend Try this with different bulb wattages. Relate this to the brightness of stars. **cooperative learning**

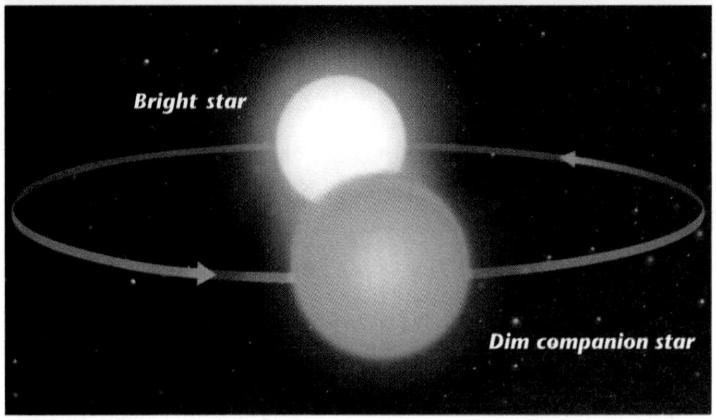

Figure 14 Algol is an eclipsing binary star system consisting of a bright star and a dim companion. Each time the dimmer star passes in front of the brighter one, Algol appears less bright. *Interpreting Diagrams When does Algol appear brighter?*

Figure 15 If you saw someone dancing but couldn't see a partner, you could infer that the partner was there by watching the dancer you could see. Astronomers use a similar method to detect faint stars in star systems.

118 ◆ J

called an **eclipsing binary.** As Figure 14 shows, the star Algol is actually an eclipsing binary.

Often astronomers can tell that there is a second star in a system only by observing the effects of its gravity. As the second star revolves around the first star, the second star's gravity makes the first star move back and forth. Imagine you are watching a pair of dancers twirling each other around. Even if one dancer were invisible, you could tell that the invisible dancer was there from watching the motion of the visible dancer.

Planets Around Other Stars In 1995, astronomers discovered a planet revolving around a star using a method similar to the one they use to detect binary stars. The star the astronomers were observing, 51 Pegasi, moved back and forth only very slightly. Therefore, they knew the invisible object could not have enough mass to be a star. They deduced that it must be a planet.

Before this discovery, there was no way to know whether stars other than the sun had planets revolving around them. Now astronomers know that our solar system is not the only one. Most of the planets found beyond our solar system so far are very large, at least half Jupiter's mass. A small planet would be difficult to detect because it would have little gravitational effect on the star it revolved around.

Astronomers are trying to find new ways to use telescopes to see planets directly. Seeing a planet around another star is like trying to see a firefly near a street light. The glare of the light makes it hard to see anything near the light. To see a planet directly, astronomers will have to shield their view from the glare of the star that the planet revolves around. In 2000, astronomers

---

Background

Facts and Figures Astronomers first started monitoring radio waves for signs of extraterrestrial life in 1960. In 1977, researchers at the Ohio State Radio Observatory picked up an unusual signal, known as the "Wow" signal for a researcher's comment on the computer printout. This signal was never detected again.

Scientists at the SETI (Search for Extraterrestrial Intelligence) Institute are using radio telescopes all over the world to search the areas near sunlike stars for artificially produced signals. Because of interference from radio sources on Earth, SETI scientists test all signals that they think might come from extraterrestrial life with a second telescope located hundreds of miles away. So far, no artificial extraterrestrial signals have been detected.

were excited by the discovery of a planet orbiting a star similar to our sun and only 10.5 light-years away.

 **INTEGRATING LIFE SCIENCE** Some scientists hypothesize that life may exist on planets revolving around other stars. A few astronomers are using radio telescopes to search for signals that could not have come from natural sources. Such a signal might be evidence that an extraterrestrial civilization existed and was sending out radio waves.

☑ *Checkpoint* *What evidence have astronomers used to conclude that there are planets around other stars?*

Galaxies

Now you are ready to learn about the Milky Way. The Milky Way is the galaxy in which our solar system is located. Like other galaxies, it contains single stars, double stars, star systems, and lots of gas and dust between the stars. The Milky Way Galaxy, often just called "our galaxy," looks milky or hazy because the stars are too close together for your eyes to see them individually. The dark blotches in the Milky Way are clouds of dust that block light coming from stars behind them.

There are billions of galaxies in the universe. **Astronomers have classified most galaxies into three main categories: spiral galaxies, elliptical galaxies, and irregular galaxies.**

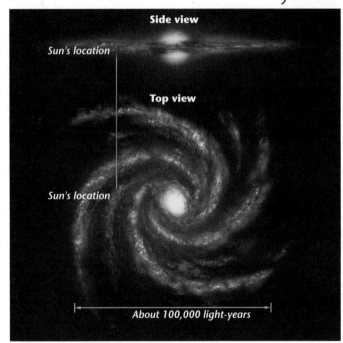

Side view

Sun's location

Top view

Sun's location

About 100,000 light-years

Figure 16 From the side, the Milky Way Galaxy appears to be a narrow disk. The spiral structure would be visible only from above the galaxy.

A Spiral Galaxy

You can make a model of our galaxy. **ACTIVITY**

1. Using pipe cleaners, make a pinwheel with two spirals.

2. View the spirals along the surface of the table. Sketch what you see. Can you see the spiral shape?

3. Next, view the spirals from above the table and sketch them.

Observing The sun is inside a flat spiral galaxy. From Earth's position on the flat surface, is it possible to get a good view of stars in the spiral arms? Why or why not?

Answers to Self-Assessment

Caption Question

Figure 14 Algol becomes brighter when the dim companion star no longer blocks light from the bright star from reaching Earth.

☑ *Checkpoint*

Astronomers can detect a planet from the effect of the planet's gravity on the motion of the star it revolves around.

Integrating Life Science

To help students understand why scientists are looking for radio signals from space, ask: **Why would scientists be unable to detect simple life forms on another planet revolving around a distant star?** (*They cannot see these planets.*) Explain that scientists hope that intelligent life forms have developed radio technology.

Cultural Diversity

Ask students to imagine that astronomers have contacted an extraterrestrial civilization and they have been chosen to meet delegates from this civilization. Have them list ten items representative of their own culture that they would like to bring with them to give the extraterrestrials a glimpse of life on Earth. **learning modality: verbal**

Galaxies

Building Inquiry Skills: Calculating

The Milky Way Galaxy may contain up to one trillion stars. Ask students how many zeros are in one trillion. (*twelve*) Have students predict how long it would take for a trillion seconds to pass. They can use calculators to test their predictions. (*About 32,000 years*) **learning modality: logical/mathematical**

TRY THIS

Skills Focus observing **ACTIVITY**
Materials *pipe cleaners*
Time 20 minutes
Tips Suggest students make their pinwheels as flat as possible.
Observing You cannot get a good view of stars in the spiral arms of Earth's galaxy, because you are inside the galaxy, looking at it edge-on.
Extend Invite students to use Figure 17 to make models of elliptical and irregular galaxies. Ask students to speculate what observers on planets within these galaxies would see. **learning modality: visual**

3 Assess

Section 4 Review Answers

1. A star system is a group of two or more stars.

2. Spiral galaxies are shaped like twin spirals, with arms that spiral out like pinwheels. Elliptical galaxies look like flattened balls; irregular galaxies do not have regular shapes.

3. The sun is about 25,000 light-years away from the center of the galaxy, about two thirds of the way out in one of the spiral arms.

4. Many binary stars consist of one brighter star and one dimmer star. When the dim star passes in front of the bright star, temporarily reducing its light as seen from Earth, it produces an effect similar to that of a partial solar eclipse.

Science at Home

Materials *binoculars, star charts from Appendix B*

Tips Students may want to make a game of looking for a particular star. Encourage students to identify a star on the chart and then try to find it in the sky. Then they can try the reverse, finding an interesting star in the sky and trying to locate it on the charts. Allow class time for volunteers to describe their experiences with their families.

Figure 17 **A.** This spiral galaxy is similar to our galaxy. **B.** An elliptical galaxy looks like a flattened ball. **C.** The Large Magellanic Cloud is an irregular galaxy.

Spiral Galaxies Figure 17A shows a galaxy that has the shape of twin spirals, called a **spiral galaxy.** Astronomers can see other spiral galaxies from different angles. These views show that spiral galaxies have arms that spiral outward, like pinwheels.

Our galaxy has the same spiral, pinwheel shape. It is hard for us to see the spiral shape of our galaxy because our solar system is inside the galaxy, about two thirds of the way out in one of the spiral arms. The Milky Way you see in the sky is the view people on Earth get when they look toward the main part of the rest of our galaxy. The center of our galaxy is about 25,000 light-years from the sun. However, we cannot see the center of our galaxy. The center is hidden from our view by the dust associated with the massive clouds of gas between the sun and the center.

Elliptical Galaxies Not all galaxies have spiral arms. **Elliptical galaxies** look like flattened balls. These galaxies contain billions of stars but have little gas and dust between the stars. Because of the lack of gas and dust, new stars cannot form in elliptical galaxies. So elliptical galaxies contain only old stars.

Irregular Galaxies Some galaxies do not have regular shapes. Because of this, they are known as **irregular galaxies.** The Large Magellanic Cloud is an irregular galaxy about 160,000 light-years away from our galaxy. At this distance it is one of the closest neighboring galaxies in the universe.

Section 4 Review

1. What is a star system?
2. Describe the three main types of galaxies.
3. Where is the sun in our galaxy?
4. **Thinking Critically Applying Concepts** Some binary stars are called eclipsing binaries. Explain why this term is appropriate. (*Hint:* Think about Algol as you come up with an answer.)

Science at Home

Plan an evening of stargazing with adult family members. Choose a dark, clear night. Use binoculars if available and the star charts in Appendix B to locate the Milky Way and some interesting stars you have learned about. Explain to your family what you know about the Milky Way and each star you observe.

Performance Assessment

Drawing Tell students to imagine they are going to teach a lesson on galaxies to some younger children. To illustrate their lessons, have students draw the three types of galaxies, then write captions describing the features of each.

Portfolio Students can save their drawings in their portfolios.

Program Resources

◆ **Teaching Resources** 3-4 Review and Reinforce, p. 91; 3-4 Enrich, p. 92

Media and Technology

Exploring Earth Science Videodisc Unit 1, Side 1, "For the Love of Astronomy"

Chapter 1

History of the Universe

DISCOVER ••••••••••••••••••••••••••••  ACTIVITY

How Does the Universe Expand?

1. Use a marker to put 10 dots on an empty balloon. The dots represent galaxies.

2. Blow up the balloon. What happens to the distances between galaxies that are close together? Galaxies that are far apart?

Think It Over

Inferring If the universe is expanding, do galaxies that are close together move apart faster or slower than galaxies that are far apart?

T he Andromeda Galaxy is the most distant object you can see with your unaided eyes. Light from this galaxy has traveled for 2 million years before reaching your eyes. When that light finally reaches your eye, you are seeing what the galaxy looked like 2 million years ago. It is as though you are looking back in time.

Astronomers have photographed galaxies that are billions of light-years away. Light from these galaxies traveled for billions of years before it reached telescopes on Earth. From these observations, astronomers have inferred that the universe is incredibly old—billions of years old.

Moving Galaxies

To study how and when the universe formed, astronomers use information about how galaxies are moving. Astronomers can measure how far away different galaxies are. By examining the spectrum of a galaxy, astronomers can tell how fast the galaxy is moving and whether it is moving toward our galaxy or away from it. Only a few nearby galaxies are moving toward our galaxy. All of the other galaxies are moving away from our galaxy.

In the 1920s, Edwin Hubble, an American astronomer, discovered that the farther away a galaxy is from us, the faster it is moving away from us. The Hubble Space Telescope was named after Hubble in honor of this and other important discoveries.

GUIDE FOR READING

◆ How did the universe form?

◆ How did the solar system form?

Reading Tip Before you read, write down what you have already heard about the big bang theory. Then read how the theory explains the history of the universe.

▼Galaxies photographed by the Hubble Space Telescope

Chapter 3 **J ◆ 121**

Objectives

After completing the lesson, students will be able to
◆ explain the big bang theory of how the universe was formed;
◆ describe how the solar system was formed.

Key Term big bang

1 Engage/Explore

Activating Prior Knowledge

Invite students who have seen a fireworks display to describe a single rocket exploding in the sky. In discussion, guide students to see that after the rocket explodes, the particles that shoot out move away from one another. Ask: **What do you think would happen if the particles from the explosion did not burn out and fade?** *(They would probably keep moving away from one another.)*

•••••••• **DISCOVER** ••••••••

Skills Focus inferring
Materials *balloon, felt-tip marker*
Time 10 minutes
Tips Make sure students mark the balloon before inflating it. Students should try to mark some dots close together and some farther apart.
Expected Outcome The dots on the balloon spread apart as the balloon expands.
Think It Over As the universe expands, galaxies that are closer together move apart more slowly than galaxies that are farther apart.

J ◆ 121

2 Facilitate

Addressing Naive Conceptions

Many students will have difficulty remembering that we see distant stars as they were in the past, not as they are in the present. Remind students that if a star is five light-years away, its light would travel five years to reach Earth. Ask: **How long would it take light from a star that is 100 light-years from Earth to reach Earth?** *(100 years)* **When we look at this star, do we see how it is now?** *(No, we see how it was 100 years ago.)* Students may think that there is a center to the universe's expansion. Explain to them that there is no such center. All distant galaxies are moving away from our galaxy and from one another. **learning modality: logical/mathematical**

Moving Galaxies

Including All Students

Students who are still mastering English may need extra help to understand analogies such as the raisin-bread dough analogy in the text. Ask students to complete the following analogies and describe the relationships. **Hat is to head as glove is to _____.** *(hand; something worn on a part of your body)* **Moon is to Earth as Earth is to _____.** *(sun; in orbit around another body)* **Planets are to solar systems as stars are to _____.** *(galaxies; part of the whole)* Then have students work in small groups to create an analogy that describes the expanding nature of the universe. *(Sample: Raisins are to bread dough as galaxies are to the universe.)* **limited English proficiency**

Figure 18 The galaxies in the expanding universe are like the raisins in rising bread dough. *Making Models How does rising raisin bread dough model the expanding universe?*

Figure 19 All of the distant galaxies astronomers have observed are moving away from our galaxy.

To understand how the galaxies are moving, think of raisin bread dough that is rising. If you could shrink yourself to sit on a raisin, you would see all the other raisins moving away from you as the bread dough rose. The farther away a raisin was from you, the faster it would move away, because there would be more bread dough to expand between you and the raisin. No matter which raisin you sat on, all the other raisins would seem to be moving away from you. You could tell that the bread dough was expanding by watching the other raisins.

The universe is like the raisin bread dough. The galaxies in the universe, like the raisins in the dough, are moving away from each other. In the universe it is space that is expanding, like the dough between the raisins.

The Big Bang Theory

To understand how the galaxies moved in the past, imagine you could run time backward. All of the galaxies would then be moving together instead of apart. All of the matter in the universe would eventually come together at a single point. At that time, billions of years ago, the universe was small, hot, and dense. The universe then exploded in what astronomers call the **big bang.** **According to the big bang theory, the universe formed in an enormous explosion about 10 to 15 billion years ago.** Since the big bang, the universe has been expanding rapidly. Because of the big bang, the universe is billions of times larger than it was billions of years ago. To understand this change in size, picture a

---

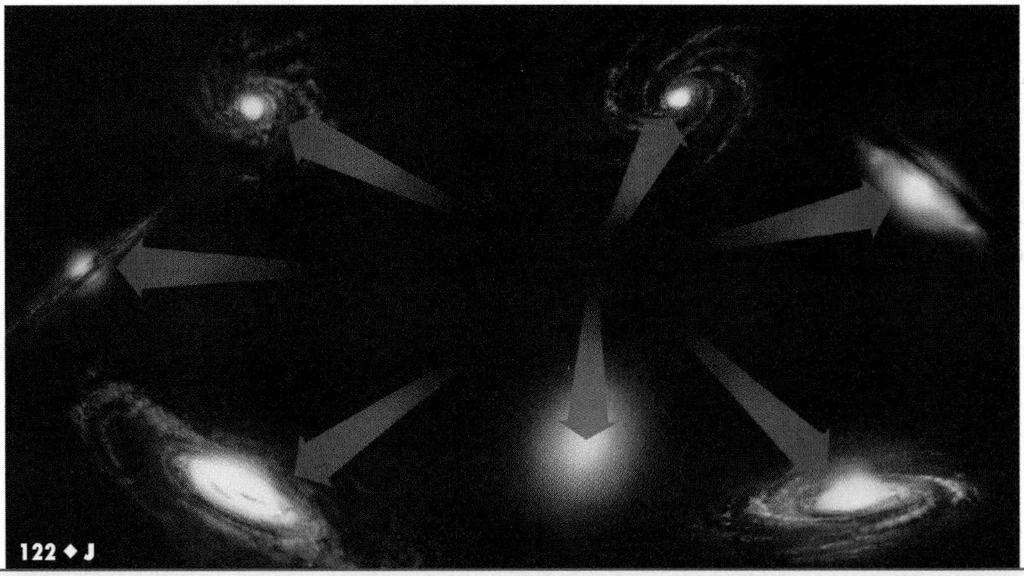

Background

History of Science Without the work of Henrietta Swan Leavitt (1868–1921), another American astronomer, Edwin Hubble could not have discovered that the farther a galaxy is from Earth, the faster it is moving away. Leavitt was born in Massachusetts and attended what is now Radcliffe College, graduating in 1892. While working at Harvard College Observatory, Leavitt found a new method of measuring distances to galaxies by studying a certain type of variable star in them.

Hubble combined his own measurements of the distances of galaxies with another astronomer's measurments of the speeds at which they are moving away and realized that the two are related.

A cloud of gas and dust formed a spinning disk.

Gas in the center of the disk collapsed to form the sun.

The remaining gas and dust formed the planets.

The solar system includes the sun, planets, and belts of rock, ice, and dust.

Figure 20 The solar system formed from a collapsing cloud of gas and dust.

tiny pea. Pretend you can blow it up to be as big as Earth. You would be inflating the pea by about a billion times. Like the pea, the universe in which you live was once very small. The universe has been growing rapidly ever since the big bang. Astronomers have concluded that the galaxies are moving away from each other as a result of the big bang.

Since astronomers know approximately how fast the universe is expanding now, they can infer how long it has been expanding. Astronomers estimate that the universe has been expanding for 10 billion to 15 billion years.

☑ *Checkpoint* *Which way are most galaxies moving relative to each other?*

Formation of the Solar System

After the big bang, matter in the universe separated into galaxies. Gas and dust spread throughout space in our galaxy. Where the solar system is now, there was only cold, dark gas and dust.

About five billion years ago, a giant cloud of gas and dust, or nebula, collapsed to form the solar system. Slowly the nebula shrank to form a spinning disk. As gravity pulled some of the gas into the center of the disk, the gas became hot and dense enough for nuclear fusion to begin. The sun was born.

Answers to Self-Assessment

Caption Question

Figure 18 As the dough expands, the raisins move farther apart. As the universe expands, its galaxies move farther apart.

☑ *Checkpoint*

The galaxies are moving away from each other.

Media and Technology

🖳 **Transparencies** "Formation of the Solar System," Transparency 16

The Big Bang Theory

Building Inquiry Skills: Predicting

Ask students to think about what might happen if they reversed the process from the Discover and slowly let the air out of the balloon. *(The balloon will shrink; the dots will move together.)* Explain that some astronomers believe that the universe will eventually begin to contract. Ask students to infer why this might happen. *(The gravitational attraction between galaxies may pull them closer together.)* Tell students to read on to find out if astronomers agree with their hypothesis. **learning modality: logical/mathematical**

Formation of the Solar System

Using the Visuals: Figure 20

Point out the spinning disk in the first image. Inform students that nonrigid round masses flatten into disks when they spin, which explains why the solar system has a flat shape. Challenge students to list other examples of round objects flattening into disks when they spin. *(One possible answer includes pizza dough being spun.)* **learning modality: visual**

Ongoing Assessment

Skills Check Have each student make a time line showing the events from the moment of the big bang to the present, including formation of the solar system. Encourage students to choose one of the theories for the future of the universe and include this on the time line.

The Future of the Universe

Building Inquiry Skills: Communicating

Challenge small groups of  students to choose one of the possible futures of the universe. Have each group prepare a presentation that describes the events predicted by this theory. Encourage groups to give an informative presentation to the class.
cooperative learning

3 Assess

Section 5 Review Answers

1. The big bang was a giant explosion in which all the matter in the universe began moving apart.
2. The solar system formed out of a collapsing, spinning disk of gas and dust. The center of the disk formed the sun. Matter toward the edge formed the planets, asteroids, and a cloud of ice and other substances.
3. The galaxies are all moving away from each other. The farther away a galaxy is from the Milky Way, the faster it moves away, because there is more space expanding between them.
4. Astronomers can infer that the universe is expanding.

> **Check Your Progress**　**CHAPTER PROJECT 3**
> Encourage students to complete their rough draft and then exchange stories for peer review before they start editing.

Elsewhere in the disk, gas and dust formed solid spheres smaller than the sun. The spheres closest to the sun lost most of their gases and became the inner planets Mercury, Venus, Earth, and Mars. The spheres farthest from the sun became the gas giants Jupiter, Saturn, Uranus, and Neptune. Between the inner planets and the gas giants, the asteroids formed. Beyond the gas giants, a huge cloud of ice and other substances formed. This cloud is probably the main source of comets. Pluto also formed in this region.

Figure 21 This engineer is checking data from the Hubble Space Telescope. The telescope can be controlled from this room.

The Future of the Universe

What will happen to the universe in the future? One possibility is that the universe will continue to expand, as it is doing now. All of the stars will eventually run out of fuel and burn out, and the universe will be cold and dark. Another possibility is that the force of gravity will begin to pull the galaxies back together. The result will be a reverse big bang, or "big crunch." All of the matter in the universe will be crushed into an enormous black hole.

Which of these possibilities is more likely? The answer depends on how strong the total force of gravity pulling the galaxies together is. This force depends on the total mass of the universe. It is very difficult for astronomers to estimate this mass because much of it is in the form of particles that do not give off electromagnetic radiation. The evidence so far suggests that the total mass of the universe is not great enough to pull the galaxies back together again. However, more research needs to be done to solve this problem.

Astronomy is one of the oldest sciences, but there are still many discoveries to be made and puzzles to be solved about this universe of ours!

Section 5 Review

1. What was the big bang?
2. Describe how the solar system formed.
3. What observations show that the universe is expanding?
4. **Thinking Critically Inferring** What can astronomers infer from the fact that other galaxies are moving away from ours?

> **Check Your Progress**　**CHAPTER PROJECT 3**
> Now you are ready to write the first draft of a story that explains your constellation's name. After you have written a first draft, read it over carefully and look for ways to improve it. Here are things to look for as you edit your first draft. Does the beginning grab the reader's interest? Does your story make sense? Should you add more details? Should you rethink your choice of words? Rewrite and revise as much as necessary.

Performance Assessment

Writing Invite students to assume the identity of a planet in our solar system. Then have them write a narrative that describes the planet as if they were a collection of gas and dust that eventually collapsed into their present state. Remind students to be scientific in their explanations.

Program Resources

◆ **Teaching Resources** 3-5 Review and Reinforce, p. 95; 3-5 Enrich, p. 96

SECTION 1 — Tools of Modern Astronomy
INTEGRATING PHYSICS

Key Ideas
- The electromagnetic spectrum includes radio waves, infrared radiation, visible light, ultraviolet radiation, X-rays, and gamma rays.
- Telescopes collect and focus different types of electromagnetic radiation.
- Astronomers use spectrographs to get information about stars.

Key Terms

constellation	refracting telescope
visible light	convex lens
electromagnetic radiation	reflecting telescope
	radio telescope
wavelength	observatory
spectrum	spectrograph

SECTION 2 — Characteristics of Stars

Key Ideas
- Astronomers use parallax to measure distances to nearby stars.
- The main characteristics used to classify stars are size, temperature, and brightness.

Key Terms

galaxy	apparent magnitude
universe	absolute magnitude
light-year	Hertzsprung-Russell diagram
parallax	main sequence
giant star	

SECTION 3 — Lives of Stars

Key Ideas
- A star is born when nuclear fusion starts.
- The length of a star's life depends on its mass.
- When a star runs out of fuel, it becomes a white dwarf, a neutron star, or a black hole.

Key Terms

pulsar	white dwarf	black hole
nebula	supernova	quasar
protostar	neutron star	

SECTION 4 — Star Systems and Galaxies

Key Ideas
- More than half of all stars are members of groups of two or more stars, called star systems.
- There are three types of galaxies: spiral galaxies, elliptical galaxies, and irregular galaxies.

Key Terms

binary star	elliptical galaxy
eclipsing binary	irregular galaxy
spiral galaxy	

SECTION 5 — History of the Universe

Key Ideas
- According to the big bang theory, the universe formed in an enormous explosion about 10 to 15 billion years ago.
- About five billion years ago, a cloud of gas and dust collapsed to form the solar system.

Key Term
big bang

Organizing Information

Concept Map Copy the concept map about telescopes onto a separate sheet of paper. Then complete it and add a title. (For more on concept maps, see the Skills Handbook.)

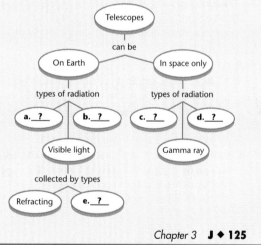

Organizing Information

Concept Map Sample Title: *Types of Telescopes;* **a.** radio waves **b.** infrared **c.** ultraviolet **d.** X-rays **e.** reflecting

Media and Technology

Interactive Student Tutorial CD-ROM J-3

Computer Test Bank *Astronomy,* Chapter 3 Test

Program Resources

- **Teaching Resources** Chapter 3 Project Scoring Rubric, p. 76; Chapter 3 Performance Assessment, pp. 128-130; Chapter 3 Test, pp. 131-134; Astronomy Book Test, pp. 135-138

Reviewing Content
Multiple Choice
1. b 2. a 3. c 4. c 5. d

True or False
6. electromagnetic spectrum 7. true
8. true 9. double or triple 10. true

Checking Concepts
11. Radio, infrared, visible light, ultraviolet, X-rays, gamma rays
12. The spectrum of a star can show chemical composition and temperature.
13. The sun will become a white dwarf and then a black dwarf.
14. We are outside the Andromeda Galaxy, so we can see it more clearly than the Milky Way.
15. The sun was formed when contracting gas and dust became so hot that nuclear fusion started.
16. Students' letters would describe a relatively short trip to Proxima Centauri, a much longer trip (6,000 times longer) to the center of our galaxy, and then a very long trip (almost a million times longer than to Proxima Centauri) to the nearest galaxy, Andromeda.

Thinking Critically
17. The star is part of an eclipsing binary system. An unseen companion star is moving in front of the bright star, preventing much of its light from reaching Earth.
18. One real-world example is car headlights. High beams have a greater absolute magnitude than low beams. The closer the car is to you, the greater the apparent magnitude of its headlights (on low or high).
19. Both stars begin as nebulas, become protostars, and eventually run out of fuel and die. The difference is in what happens when each star runs out of fuel. A medium-mass star becomes a white dwarf, then a black dwarf; a large-mass star becomes a supernova, then a neutron star.
20. Knowing how fast the universe is expanding and knowing the size of the universe allows astronomers to calculate when the big bang occurred.
21. A light-year is a unit of distance: it is the distance that light travels in one year, or 9,460,000 million kilometers.

Reviewing Content

For more review of key concepts, see the Interactive Student Tutorial CD-ROM.

Multiple Choice
Choose the letter of the answer that best completes each statement.

1. The Hubble Space Telescope is a
   a. gamma ray telescope.
   b. reflecting telescope.
   c. refracting telescope.
   d. radio telescope.
2. The most common chemical element in a star is
   a. hydrogen.
   b. helium.
   c. carbon.
   d. sodium.
3. To measure the distance to a nearby star, an astronomer would use
   a. visible light.
   b. quasars.
   c. parallax.
   d. a spectrograph.
4. Stars more massive than the sun
   a. live longer than the sun.
   b. are redder than the sun.
   c. have shorter lives than the sun.
   d. live as long as the sun.
5. The sun formed out of a
   a. pulsar.   b. supergiant star.
   c. black hole.   d. nebula.

True or False
If the statement is true, write true. If it is false, change the underlined word or words to make the statement true.

6. Gamma rays, X-rays, ultraviolet radiation, visible light, infrared radiation, and radio waves make up the Hertzsprung-Russell diagram. *electromagnetic spectrum*
7. The sun is a main-sequence star. T
8. Pulsars are a kind of neutron star. T
9. More than half of all stars are single stars. *double or triple*
10. Acccording to the big bang theory, T the universe has been growing for 10–15 billion years.

3T 2F

Checking Concepts
11. What types of radiation are included in the electromagnetic spectrum?
12. What kinds of information can astronomers obtain by studying the spectrum of a star?
13. Describe what will happen to the sun when it runs out of fuel.
14. Why can astronomers see the spiral arms of the Andromeda Galaxy more clearly than the spiral arms of the Milky Way Galaxy?
15. Describe the process by which the sun was formed.
16. **Writing to Learn** Imagine you have a spaceship that can travel much faster than the speed of light. Write a letter describing your three-part trip from Earth: to the nearest star other than the sun, to the center of our galaxy, and to the next nearest spiral galaxy.

Thinking Critically
17. **Relating Cause and Effect** Once every three days a small, bright star becomes much dimmer, only to return to its original brightness within six hours. Based on this information, what is causing the small star to become dimmer?
18. **Applying Concepts** Describe a real-world situation involving absolute and apparent magnitudes. (*Hint:* Think about riding in a car at night.)
19. **Comparing and Contrasting** Compare the life histories of a medium-mass star and a high-mass star. How are they similar? How are they different?
20. **Making Generalizations** What does knowing the rate at which the universe is expanding tell astronomers about the big bang?
21. **Applying Concepts** Is a light-year a unit of distance or a unit of time? Explain.

Applying Skills
22. Student graphs should show a straight diagonal line pointing up and to the right.
23. The graph is a straight line, so the two variables, speed and distance, are directly related.
24. The graph shows that the galaxies are moving apart, that is, it shows the expansion of the universe.

Applying Skills

Use the data about moving galaxies in the table below to answer Questions 22–24.

Cluster of Galaxies	Distance (millions of light-years)	Speed (kilometers per second)
Virgo	80	1,200
Ursa Major	980	15,000
Bootes	2,540	39,000
Hydra	3,980	61,000

22. **Graphing** Make a line graph showing how each cluster's distance from our galaxy is related to its speed. Put distance on the *x*-axis and speed on the *y*-axis.

23. **Interpreting Data** How are the distance and speed of a galaxy related?

24. **Drawing Conclusions** Does your graph indicate that the universe is expanding, contracting, or staying the same size? Explain.

Performance CHAPTER PROJECT 3 **Assessment**

Project Wrap Up Check the final draft of your story for correct spelling, grammar, punctuation, and usage. Make any necessary changes. Then decide how you will present your new constellation story. For example, you can make a poster showing the constellation, its star pattern, and your story. You can read your story aloud or perform it as a skit or play.

Reflect and Record This project has given you a chance to research information and then present it in writing. In your journal, write what you found easiest and hardest about researching and writing.

Test Preparation

Use these questions to prepare for standardized tests.

Study the diagram. Then answer Questions 25–29.

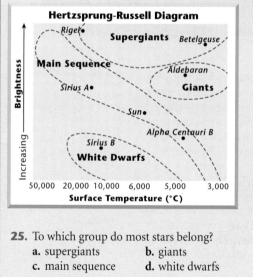

Hertzsprung-Russell Diagram

25. To which group do most stars belong?
    a. supergiants   b. giants
    c. main sequence   d. white dwarfs

26. Which star is hotter than the sun?
    a. Betelgeuse
    b. Aldebaran
    c. Alpha Centauri B
    d. Sirius B

27. Which star is most likely to be red?
    a. Rigel
    b. Sirius A
    c. Sirius B
    d. Betelgeuse

28. Compared to Rigel, Alpha Centauri B is
    a. cooler and brighter.
    b. cooler and dimmer.
    c. hotter and brighter.
    d. hotter and dimmer.

29. Which star has a greater absolute magnitude?
    a. Rigel
    b. Betelgeuse
    c. Sirius B
    d. Aldebaran

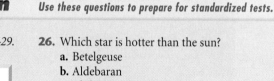
Performance CHAPTER PROJECT 3 **Assessment**

Project Wrap Up Students should be able to answer questions about the classical myth associated with their constellation. Encourage students who have studied the same constellation to compare their different approaches to writing a new story for it.

Reflect and Record Encourage students to reflect on the research and writing process. Ask students to identify places where they got stuck or spent too much time and places where they should have concentrated more of their efforts. Have students make suggestions on how they would improve their projects.

Test Preparation

25. c 26. d 27. d 28. b 29. a

Program Resources

♦ **Inquiry Skills Activity Book** Provides teaching and review of all inquiry skills
♦ **Standardized Test Preparation Book** Provides standardized test practice
♦ **Reading in the Content Area** Provides strategies to improve science reading skills
♦ **Teacher's ELL Handbook** Provides multiple strategies for English language learners

Journey to Mars

This interdisciplinary feature presents the central theme of exploring Mars by connecting four different disciplines: science, social studies, mathematics, and language arts. The four explorations are designed to capture students' interest and help them see how the content they are studying in science relates to other school subjects and to real-world events. The unit is particularly suitable for team teaching.

1 Engage/Explore

Activating Prior Knowledge

Help students recall what they learned in Chapter 2, Section 3, The Inner Planets, by asking questions such as: **How many moons does Mars have?** *(two)* and **How does Mars compare in size to Earth?** *(Mars has a diameter a little more than half that of Earth.)* Ask students if they remember when the Pathfinder landed and explored Mars in 1997. Ask: **What did you learn about Mars?** *(Accept all responses without comment at this time.)*

Introducing the Unit

Discuss the fact that space exploration is a popular theme in entertainment. However, humans have explored very little of space so far. Ask: **Why is it so difficult for humans to explore space?** *(Accept all reasonable responses.)* Ask: **Where have humans been in the solar system outside of Earth?** *(In space stations orbiting around Earth and on the moon)*

JOURNEY TO MARS

The little six-wheeled rover inched down the steep ramp of the lander and onto the surface of Mars. Scientists on Earth held their breaths. Then, Sojourner hummed into action.

Sojourner became the star of the 1997 *Pathfinder* mission. Engineers at the Jet Propulsion Laboratory in Pasadena, California, guided the rover from remote controls on Earth. It rolled from rock to rock, collecting scientific data and checking the mineral content of each rock. Back on Earth, the *Pathfinder* team named the rocks after cartoon characters—Barnacle Bill, Scooby Doo, and Casper. They named a bear-shaped rock Yogi.

Pathfinder had landed in a region of Mars that no one had seen closely before. The lander took photographs of Martian landscapes, sunrises, and sunsets. Running on energy from solar panels, *Pathfinder's* instruments sent back huge amounts of information for scientists on Earth to analyze. This mission was just one of many that would study the Martian landscape.

Sojourner—about the size of a microwave oven—explores the rocky surface of Mars. Here it bumps into a rock that scientists called Yogi. The electronic image was transmitted by Pathfinder from Mars to Earth.

Program Resources

◆ **Teaching Resources** Interdisciplinary Explorations, Science, pp. 105–107; Mathematics, pp. 111-113; Social Studies, pp. 108–110; Language Arts, pp. 102–104

Sojourner Truth (above), a powerful speaker against slavery, and Valerie Ambroise (right).

Honor in a Name

Would you like to name a spacecraft? A 13-year-old student from Connecticut got that chance. Valerie Ambroise chose the name *Sojourner* for the small Pathfinder rover that explored the Martian surface in 1997. In a contest sponsored by NASA and The Planetary Society, Valerie wrote the winning essay for the best name. There were 3,500 student entries.

Valerie named *Sojourner* after Sojourner Truth, an African American reformer in the 1840s and 1850s. Here is Valerie Ambroise's essay.

The name of the Pathfinder should be Sojourner Truth. I chose Sojourner because she was a heroine to Blacks, slaves, and women. She acted on her strong feelings about life and the way it should be. Her greatest companions were God and her beliefs. Her greatest achievements included the book of her life written through her by a friend, meeting President Lincoln, meeting President Grant, her speeches and tours, her work at hospitals for soldiers during the Civil War, and her intellect (considering that she was illiterate). She went on many journeys and told many truths. She spoke with such eloquence that she moved people with simple words and understandings.

It's only logical that the Pathfinder be named Sojourner Truth, because she is on a journey to find truths about Mars. The Pathfinder should be able to have strong personalities in order to go under harsh conditions like that on Mars. Truth, while on tours, went under many harsh conditions. Even before, she went under harsh conditions as a slave.

Like Sojourner, the Pathfinder should be able to survive with what she already has. She should not need any extra equipment for surviving. The Pathfinder could use its feet like wheels, for transportation. Sojourner used her feet to travel a lot.

To research Mars, first, Sojourner would find out all she could about it. She always tried to understand further about what she was fighting for. When she got her information; she would use this information in Mars to study it more and add it to hers. She would act quickly to get what she wanted or what she felt was needed. Her talents in her work would be the same on Mars. She would use her eloquent voice and powerful actions.

You must admit, Sojourner and the Pathfinder are important.

Language Arts Activity

You have the chance to name the first research station on Mars, honoring an important person in scientific exploration or discovery. Research your hero or heroine. Then write a persuasive essay explaining why the research station should be named after him or her.

2 Facilitate

◆ Have three volunteers each read one third of the essay aloud. Students may need help pronouncing "Sojourner." Have students use a dictionary to look up the meanings of words they are not familiar with, such as "reformer" or "eloquence."

◆ After students have read the essay, make two columns on the board titled "Person" and "Pathfinder." Have students review the essay and name ways in which Sojourner Truth and the *Sojourner* rover are similar.

◆ Challenge interested students to find out more about Sojourner Truth's life and make a bulletin board display for the class.

Language Arts Activity

Students can use reference books such as almanacs or the *New York Public Library Science Desk Reference* to find the names and achievements of some of the most famous scientists. Students can then research further those scientists they are most interested in. Urge students to include in their essays the ways in which the scientist is similar to the research station.

Teaching Resources The following worksheets correlate with this page: Ain't I A Woman?, page 102; Words From Mars Fiction, page 103; and Move to Mars!, page 104.

3 Assess

Activity Assessment

Make sure students choose a person from science exploration or discovery, not a sports or entertainment figure. Make sure students' essays are persuasive. Look for students who clearly explained why the research station should be named after the person they chose.

Background

Facts and Figures The "Name the Rover" competition was announced in 1994. The rules were:

◆ the writer had to be born after January 1, 1976

◆ the essay had to be 300 words;

◆ the essay had to be fully researched;

◆ the rover could be named for any heroine from mythology, fiction, or history who was not living;

◆ the essay had to explain how the person's name was appropriate for the rover.

The essay organizers received 3,800 essays, of which 1,700 followed the rules. The essays came from all over the world. The second place essay proposed that the rover be named after Marie Curie. Curie's work in radioactivity related to the Mars mission because the rover used radioactivity to analyze rocks and soil.

2 Facilitate

◆ To extend this exploration, challenge students to find out more about the surface conditions on Mars. Students who have access to the Internet can look at NASA's Web Site, **www.nasa.gov**, to find out what the rover *Sojourner* learned about conditions on Mars.

Science Activity

Divide students into groups of four. Have each group perform the activity. Urge students to use the amount of plant food marked on the container. Students who use more plant food than is recommended may damage their plants.

Assign a few minutes twice a week for the following three weeks for students to check that their plants have sufficient water and to record their progress.

Use this experiment to help students understand the scientific process. Scientists try to test every hypothesis rather than just assume it is true. Scientists can learn as much from hypotheses that are proved to be false as they can from hypotheses that are supported by scientific evidence.
Teaching Resources The following worksheets correlate with this page: Gravity on Mars, page 105; The Polar Caps of Mars, page 106; and History of Mars Exploration, page 107.

3 Assess

Activity Assessment

Schedule time for students to explain their experiments and describe what conclusions they have drawn. Look for students who have recorded their measurements in an organized table.

An artist imagines a scene in the future in which humans walk on the rocky plains of Mars.

Essentials for Survival

You step out of your spacecraft onto a dusty red landscape under a pinkish-red sky. Now you know why Mars is called the "red planet." Water vapor in the air forms thin clouds, even fog. Because the air is so thin, the sun glares down. It's windy, too. Thick clouds of reddish dust, rich in iron, blow around you.

Without a pressurized spacesuit, you would not survive in the thin Martian air. Unlike the thick layers of atmosphere around Earth, this atmosphere gives almost no protection against harmful ultraviolet radiation. You also must carry oxygen. Martian air is about 95 percent carbon dioxide, which humans can't breathe.

Your spacesuit must keep you warm. Even at the Martian equator, daytime temperatures are rarely above freezing. At night they plunge to about –100°C. Walk carefully, too, because Martian gravity is weak. You'll feel only 38 percent of your Earth weight!

This is a 360-degree image taken from *Pathfinder.* On the rugged Martian landscape, sand and dust storms have carved rocks into fantastic shapes. Deep canyons and huge volcanoes also shape the surface.

130 ◆ J

Science Activity

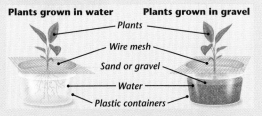

Plants grown in water   Plants grown in gravel
Plants
Wire mesh
Sand or gravel
Water
Plastic containers

Any human settlement on Mars would have to grow some of its own food. Experiment with a method called hydroponics—growing plants mainly in water, without soil. Set up two plant containers to grow tomatoes or peppers.
◆ Decide what variables to control.
◆ In one container, use just water and plant food, with a wire mesh support.
◆ In the other, add sand or gravel to root plants; add water and plant food.
◆ Record the rate of growth and strength of each plant over a two-to three-week period.

Which technique worked the best? How do you think hydroponics would work on Mars?

Background

Facts and Figures If you've ever been in the rocky western deserts of the United States, the rugged Martian landscape of reddish rocks may look familiar. Mars has a "Grand Canyon," too, a series of huge canyons called Valles Marineris (named after the U.S. *Mariner* probe). These canyons are five times as deep as the Grand Canyon and more than 4,500 kilometers long, about the width of the continental United States.

Since there are no oceans, the total land area of Mars is about equal to the continents and islands on Earth. In the south, the rugged surface is pitted with craters. The northern hemisphere is sandy dunes or rolling plains covered with thin lava. Volcanoes have been important in forming Mars's landscape. One huge volcano, Olympus Mons, towers about 24 kilometers above the surface, three times as high as Mt. Everest.

Astronaut Shannon Lucid and a Russian cosmonaut examine food bins on *Mir* (left).

A cosmonaut, floating in space, repairs equipment on *Mir* (above).

Partners in Space

Many engineers and scientists are confident that humans will travel to Mars sometime in the next 25 years. Meanwhile, people have gotten a preview of a space voyage from astronauts and cosmonauts traveling on space shuttles, on *Mir*, Russia's former space station, and on the new International Space Station.

For years, the United States and the Soviet Union competed in a race to send missions into space. Beginning in 1997, Russia and the United States cooperated on *Mir*. Americans worked with cosmonauts to solve problems, make repairs, take spacewalks, and run the ship's computers. More recently, scientists from 16 countries have cooperated to construct and operate the International Space Station, which is being built in orbit.

What's it like for crew members from different backgrounds to live and work together in a cramped spacecraft? Besides

having cultural and language differences, Russian and American crews have different training and different equipment. Even spacesuits are not the same.

Because *Mir* was an old station, space crews gained experience dealing with emergencies. On a long flight, such as one to Mars, those skills would be essential.

All this experience on *Mir* and the International Space Station should prove invaluable for a future expedition to Mars.

Social Studies Activity

The first trips to Mars will probably take at least 6 to 8 months. Think about the difficulties you would have spending 7 months in a spacecraft about the size of a school bus. Set up rules and guidelines for your voyage. Plan for five astronauts from two different countries. Consider these issues:

◆ who will make decisions and give orders
◆ how you will communicate
◆ how you'll adjust for different living habits and backgrounds
◆ how you'll avoid getting bored
◆ how you'll resolve conflicts among crew members or with mission-control scientists on Earth.

Background

Integrating Science and Technology
After Shannon Lucid returned from her 188 days in space, the longest of any United States astronaut, she wrote an account of her experiences for *Scientific American* magazine. Her account included her insights into how the crew of the International Space Station should be chosen and trained. She said foremost that the crew should enjoy working together; otherwise the long

durations in space would be miserable experiences. She proposed that the crew be given more control over their daily schedules rather than have every moment of their time assigned by NASA's ground controllers.

Rather than train crew members to practice every possible procedure, they should instead learn some key skills and then train for specific procedures at the time they would need those new skills.

---

2 Facilitate

◆ *Mir* is pronounced "mere" and means "peace."
◆ Mention that the International Space Station was begun in 1999 and that *Mir* re-entered Earth's atmosphere on a controlled trajectory and crashed into the Pacific Ocean in March 2001. Russia has more extensive experience than the United States with long stays in a space station. This experience will be useful both for the space station and for future trips to Mars.
◆ To extend this exploration, have students think about experiences they have had where people had to cooperate in cramped conditions. Ask students to brainstorm things they learned about how to get along with others under stressful conditions.

Social Studies Activity

Have students first work alone, then in groups. Have students share and discuss their ideas. As conflicts arise within student groups, use this as an opportunity to discuss ways the astronauts might have conflicts. Ask students to suggest strategies that people can use to make group decision-making easier. Ask: **What kinds of behavior help the group get along?**
Teaching Resources The following worksheets correlate with this page: Earth from Space, page 108; The Search for Life on Mars, page 109; and Map of Mars, page 110.

3 Assess

Activity Assessment
Evaluate the reasonableness of students' ideas. Watch for students who need concrete suggestions on how the astronauts can resolve conflicts. Watch for students who are unrealistic about the amount of stress that can occur when too many people are sharing too small a space.

Mathematics

2 Facilitate

♦ Review what causes days, years, and seasons. Ask: **Could a planet have a day shorter than an Earth day but have a year longer than an Earth year?** *(Yes, if the planet was spinning on its axis faster than Earth but revolving around the sun slower than Earth.)*

♦ To extend this exploration, encourage interested students to read books or magazine articles about what it is like to live in harsh climates. Eric Pinder's book, *Life at the Top*, describes living conditions at the Mount Washington weather observatory on top of Mount Washington, New Hampshire, which is known as the location of Earth's worst weather.

Math Activity

Point out that the values of the percents should correspond to the relative sizes of the segments. Remind students that the northern and southern hemispheres have seasons of different lengths, unlike on Earth.

Teaching Resources The following worksheets correlate with this page: A Year on Mars, page 111; Model the Mars Neighborhood, page 112; and Martian Seasons in Days, page 113.

3 Assess

Activity Assessment

Northern Hemisphere: Fall 21%, Spring 29%; Southern Hemisphere: Fall 29%, Spring 21%. Make sure the size of each segment is the right size for the percent.

Sols of Mars

Mars is the planet most like Earth. But its smaller size, greater distance from the sun, and different orbit cause some immense differences. A Martian day, called a sol, is only about 40 minutes longer than an Earth day. The Martian year, however, is much longer—669 sols.

Mars, like Earth, tilts on its axis, so it has seasons. Each Martian season lasts longer than an Earth season because the Martian year is longer. The shape of Mars's orbit makes the seasons unequal in length (see table below).

The climate in the southern hemisphere is more extreme than in the northern hemisphere. Winters in the south are longer and colder, while summers are shorter and warmer. Winter in the south, for instance, lasts 177 sols. In the northern hemisphere, winter lasts only 156 sols.

Seasonal changes affect Mars's north and south poles, which are covered with polar ice caps made of water and carbon dioxide. During winter in the southern hemisphere, the polar cap covers almost half the hemisphere. Here the ice cap is mainly frozen carbon dioxide—like dry ice. In spring, the ice cap partially melts, releasing carbon dioxide into the air. In a similar way, when spring comes in the northern hemisphere, the north polar cap melts. But in the north, the frozen core is made mainly of water ice.

An ice cap covers the northern polar region of Mars.

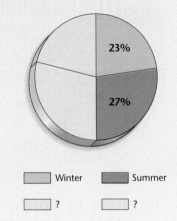

Northern Hemisphere of Mars

23%

27%

Winter   Summer

?   ?

Martian Seasons in Sols (Martian Days)		
	Northern Hemisphere	Southern Hemisphere
Winter	156	177
Spring	194	142
Summer	177	156
Fall	142	194

The sun rises on Mars.

Background

Integrating Science and Technology
Space scientists and engineers who have considered missions to Mars have taken two different approaches. One approach, in general, depends on transporting buildings, supplies, rocket fuel, and billions of dollars worth of other equipment to the planet—in short, taking along everything necessary to get along for two or three years. By contrast, the other approach depends on the pioneer settlers quickly making use of what is available on Mars. For example, an initial uncrewed flight would take just the equipment needed to use chemicals in the Martian atmosphere to make enough rocket fuel to return home.

Southern Hemisphere of Mars

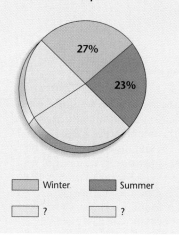

27%

23%

☐ Winter ☐ Summer

☐ ? ☐ ?

Math Activity

People working on Mars would probably go by Martian time. You know that there are 669 sols (Martian days) in a Martian year. Knowing the number of sols in a season, you can figure the percent of the year that's winter. For example, winter in the northern hemisphere is 156 sols ÷ 669 sols ≈ 0.233 ≈ 23%.

◆ Use the table on page 132 to figure out what percent of the Martian year in each hemisphere is winter, spring, summer, and fall. Round to the nearest hundredth.

◆ Make two circle graphs like those on pages 132 and 133. Label, color, and write the percent for each season in the northern and southern hemispheres.

◆ Choose a different color for each.

If you had a choice, which hemisphere would you choose to live in?

Plan a Martian Station

At last, you will be going to Mars to set up the first human research station. For an expedition this long, good planning is essential. Review the major problems that Mars presents to humans, such as thin atmosphere, no oxygen, extreme temperatures, and so on. Remember that it's too expensive to send most supplies to Mars. Work in groups to make a plan for setting up Earth's research station. Include maps and drawings. As you make your plan, consider questions such as these:

◆ How will you supply oxygen? Water? Fuel?

◆ What site will you choose for your settlement? Consider the landscape and climate on Mars.

◆ What supplies will you bring with you?

◆ What will you use for building materials?

◆ What kinds of food will you get? How will you get food?

This painting shows how one artist imagined a human home on another planet.

Time 1 week (1 day for planning, 2 days for research, 2 days for preparing maps, plans, and drawings)

Tips Have students work in groups of four or five. If possible, group students so that each group contains at least one student who knows how to research on the Internet or who can ask an adult for help.

◆ Most of the information that students' are searching for should be readily available from encyclopedias.

◆ Ask questions such as the following to prompt student thinking: **Will you construct domes like those in research stations in Antarctica? Could you make bricks out of frozen soil? How will you supply oxygen, water, food, and fuel? How can you grow food indoors in a laboratory or greenhouse? Can you use hydroponics or aquaculture? Keeping in mind what you have learned about the landscape and climate of Mars, what kind of site will you choose for a settlement? Do you want the protection of a valley or canyon? Do you want the smoother terrain and milder climate of the northern hemisphere?**

Extend Challenge students to find out what scientists have learned about building self-contained biospheres containing people.

Developing scientific thinking in students is important for a solid science education. To learn how to think scientifically, students need frequent opportunities to practice science process skills, critical thinking skills, as well as other skills that support scientific inquiry. The *Science Explorer* Skills Handbook introduces the following key science skills:

◆ Science Process Skills
◆ SI Measuring Skills
◆ Skills for Conducting a Scientific Investigation
◆ Critical Thinking Skills
◆ Information Organizing Skills
◆ Data Table and Graphing Skills

   The Skills Handbook is designed as a reference for students to use whenever they need to review a science skill. You can use the activities provided in the Skills Handbook to teach or reinforce the skills.

Think Like a Scientist

Observing

Before students look at the photograph, remind them that an observation is what they can see, hear, smell, taste, or feel. Ask: **Which senses will you use to make observations from this photograph?** (*Sight is the only sense that can be used to make observations from the photograph.*) **What are some observations you can make from the photograph?** (*Answers may vary. Sample answers: The boy is wearing sneakers, sports socks, shorts, and a T-shirt; the boy is sitting in the grass holding something blue against his knee; the boy is looking at his knee; there is a soccer ball lying beside the boy.*) List the observations on the board. If students make any inferences or predictions about the boy at this point, ask: **Can you be sure your statement is accurate from just observing the photograph?** Help students understand how observations differ from inferences and predictions.

Inferring

Review students' observations from the photograph. Then ask: **What inferences can you make from your observations?** (*Students may*

Think Like a Scientist

Although you may not know it, you think like a scientist every day. Whenever you ask a question and explore possible answers, you use many of the same skills that scientists do. Some of these skills are described on this page.

Observing

When you use one or more of your five senses to gather information about the world, you are **observing.** Hearing a dog bark, counting twelve green seeds, and smelling smoke are all observations. To increase the power of their senses, scientists sometimes use microscopes, telescopes, or other instruments that help them make more detailed observations.

   An observation must be an accurate report of what your senses detect. It is important to keep careful records of your observations in science class by writing or drawing in a notebook. The information collected through observations is called evidence, or data.

Inferring

When you interpret an observation, you are **inferring,** or making an inference. For example, if you hear your dog barking, you may infer that someone is at your front door. To make this inference, you combine the evidence—the barking dog—and your experience or knowledge—you know that your dog barks when strangers approach—to reach a logical conclusion.

   Notice that an inference is not a fact; it is only one of many possible interpretations for an observation. For example, your dog may be barking because it wants to go for a walk. An inference may turn out to be incorrect even if it is based on accurate observations and logical reasoning. The only way to find out if an inference is correct is to investigate further.

Predicting

When you listen to the weather forecast, you hear many predictions about the next day's weather—what the temperature will be, whether it will rain, and how windy it will be. Weather forecasters use observations and knowledge of weather patterns to predict the weather. The skill of **predicting** involves making an inference about a future event based on current evidence or past experience.

   Because a prediction is an inference, it may prove to be false. In science class, you can test some of your predictions by doing experiments. For example, suppose you predict that larger paper airplanes can fly farther than smaller airplanes. How could you test your prediction?

ACTIVITY Use the photograph to answer the questions below.

Observing Look closely at the photograph. List at least three observations.

Inferring Use your observations to make an inference about what has happened. What experience or knowledge did you use to make the inference?

Predicting Predict what will happen next. On what evidence or experience do you base your prediction?

---

say that the boy hurt his knee playing soccer and is holding a coldpack against his injured knee.) **What experience or knowledge helped you make this inference?** (*Students may have experienced knee injuries from playing soccer, and they may be familiar with coldpacks like the one the boy is using.*) **Can anyone suggest another possible interpretation for these observations?** (*Answers may vary. Sample answer: The boy hurt his knee jogging, and he just happened to sit beside a soccer ball his sister left in the yard.*) **How can you find out whether an inference is correct?** (*by further investigation*)

Predicting

After students come to some consensus about the inference that the boy hurt his knee, encourage them to make predictions about what will happen next. (*Students' predictions may vary. Sample answers: The boy will go to the doctor. A friend will help the boy home. The boy will get up and continue playing soccer.*)

Classifying

Could you imagine searching for a book in the library if the books were shelved in no particular order? Your trip to the library would be an all-day event! Luckily, librarians group together books on similar topics or by the same author. Grouping together items that are alike in some way is called **classifying.** You can classify items in many ways: by size, by shape, by use, and by other important characteristics.

Like librarians, scientists use the skill of classifying to organize information and objects. When things are sorted into groups, the relationships among them become easier to understand.

 Classify the objects in the photograph into two groups based on any characteristic you choose. Then use another characteristic to classify the objects into three groups.

Making Models

Have you ever drawn a picture to help someone understand what you were saying? Such a drawing is one type of model. A model is a picture, diagram, computer image, or other representation of a complex object or process. **Making models** helps people understand things that they cannot observe directly.

Scientists often use models to represent things that are either very large or very small, such as the planets in the solar system, or the parts of a cell. Such models are physical models—drawings or three-dimensional structures that look like the real thing. Other models are mental models—mathematical equations or words that describe how something works.

ACTIVITY This student is using a model to demonstrate what causes day and night on Earth. What do the flashlight and the tennis ball in the model represent?

Communicating

Whenever you talk on the phone, write a letter, or listen to your teacher at school, you are communicating. **Communicating** is the process of sharing ideas and information with other people. Communicating effectively requires many skills, including writing, reading, speaking, listening, and making models.

Scientists communicate to share results, information, and opinions. Scientists often communicate about their work in journals, over the telephone, in letters, and on the Internet. They also attend scientific meetings where they share their ideas with one another in person.

 ACTIVITY On a sheet of paper, write out clear, detailed directions for tying your shoe. Then exchange directions with a partner. Follow your partner's directions exactly. How successful were you at tying your shoe? How could your partner have communicated more clearly?

On what did you base your prediction? *(Scientific predictions are based on knowledge and experience.)* Point out that in science, predictions can often be tested with experiments.

Classifying

Encourage students to think of other common things that are classified. Then ask: **What things at home are classified?** *(Clothing might be classified in order to place it in the appropriate dresser drawer; glasses, plates, and silverware are grouped in different parts of the kitchen; screws, nuts, bolts, washers, and nails might be separated into small containers.)* **What are some things that scientists classify?** *(Scientists classify many things they study, including organisms, geological features and processes, and kinds of machines.)* After students have classified the different fruits in the photograph, have them share their criteria for classifying them. *(Some characteristics students might use include shape, color, size, and where they are grown.)*

Making Models

Ask students: **What are some models you have used to study science?** *(Students may have used human anatomical models, solar system models, maps, stream tables.)* **How did these models help you?** *(Models can help you learn about things that are difficult to study, because they are either too big, too small, or complex.)* Be sure students understand that a model does not have to be three-dimensional. For example, a map in a textbook is a model. Ask: **What do the flashlight and tennis ball represent?** *(The flashlight represents the sun, and the ball represents Earth.)* **What quality of each item makes this a good model?** *(The flashlight gives off light, and the ball is round and can be rotated by the student.)*

Communicating

Challenge students to identify the methods of communication they've used today. Then ask: **How is the way you communicate with a friend similar to and different from the way scientists communicate about their work to other scientists?** *(Both may communicate using various methods, but scientists must be very detailed and precise, whereas communication between friends may be less detailed and precise.)* Encourage students to communicate like a scientist as they carry out the activity. *(Students' directions should be detailed and precise enough for another person to successfully follow.)*

Making Measurements

Measuring in SI

Review SI units in class with students. Begin by providing metric rulers, graduated cylinders, balances, and Celsius thermometers. Use these tools to reinforce that the meter is the unit of length, the liter is the unit of volume, the gram is the unit of mass, and the degree Celsius is the unit for temperature. Ask: **If you want to measure the length and width of your classroom, which SI unit would you use?** *(meter)* **Which unit would you use to measure the amount of matter in your textbook?** *(gram)* **Which would you use to measure how much water a drinking glass holds?** *(liter)* **When would you use the Celsius scale?** *(To measure the temperature of something)* Then use the measuring equipment to review SI prefixes. For example, ask: **What are the smallest units on the metric ruler?** *(millimeters)* **How many millimeters are there in 1 cm?** *(10 mm)* **How many in 10 cm?** *(100 mm)* **How many centimeters are there in 1 m?** *(100 cm)* **What does 1,000 m equal?** *(1 km)*

Length *(Students should state that the shell is 4.6 centimeters, or 46 millimeters, long.)* If students need more practice measuring length, have them use meter sticks and metric rulers to measure various objects in the classroom.

Liquid Volume *(Students should state that the volume of water in the graduated cylinder is 62 milliliters.)* If students need more practice measuring liquid volume, have them use a graduated cylinder to measure different volumes of water.

Making Measurements

When scientists make observations, it is not sufficient to say that something is "big" or "heavy." Instead, scientists use instruments to measure just how big or heavy an object is. By measuring, scientists can express their observations more precisely and communicate more information about what they observe.

Measuring in SI

The standard system of measurement used by scientists around the world is known as the International System of Units, which is abbreviated as SI (in French, *Système International d'Unités*). SI units are easy to use because they are based on multiples of 10. Each unit is ten times larger than the next smallest unit and one tenth the size of the next largest unit. The table lists the prefixes used to name the most common SI units.

Common SI Prefixes		
Prefix	**Symbol**	**Meaning**
kilo-	k	1,000
hecto-	h	100
deka-	da	10
deci-	d	0.1 (one tenth)
centi-	c	0.01 (one hundredth)
milli-	m	0.001 (one thousandth)

Length To measure length, or the distance between two points, the unit of measure is the **meter (m).** The distance from the floor to a doorknob is approximately one meter. Long distances, such as the distance between two cities, are measured in kilometers (km). Small lengths are measured in centimeters (cm) or millimeters (mm). Scientists use metric rulers and meter sticks to measure length.

Common Conversions
1 km = 1,000 m
1 m = 100 cm
1 m = 1,000 mm
1 cm = 10 mm

The larger lines on the metric ruler in the picture show centimeter divisions, while the smaller, unnumbered lines show millimeter divisions. How many centimeters long is the shell? How many millimeters long is it?

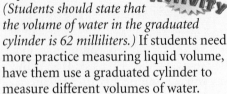

Liquid Volume To measure the volume of a liquid, or the amount of space it takes up, you will use a unit of measure known as the **liter (L).** One liter is the approximate volume of a medium-size carton of milk. Smaller volumes are measured in milliliters (mL). Scientists use graduated cylinders to measure liquid volume.

Common Conversion
1 L = 1,000 mL

The graduated cylinder in the picture is marked in milliliter divisions. Notice that the water in the cylinder has a curved surface. This curved surface is called the *meniscus*. To measure the volume, you must read the level at the lowest point of the meniscus. What is the volume of water in this graduated cylinder?

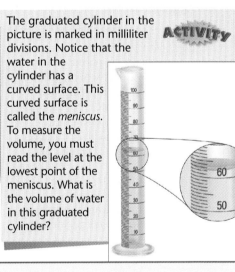

Mass To measure mass, or the amount of matter in an object, you will use a unit of measure known as the **gram** (**g**). One gram is approximately the mass of a paper clip. Larger masses are measured in kilograms (kg). Scientists use a balance to find the mass of an object.

Common Conversion

1 kg = 1,000 g

The mass of the apple in the picture is measured in kilograms. What is the mass of the apple? Suppose a recipe for applesauce called for one kilogram of apples. About how many apples would you need?

ACTIVITY

Temperature
To measure the temperature of a substance, you will use the **Celsius scale**. Temperature is measured in degrees Celsius (°C) using a Celsius thermometer. Water freezes at 0°C and boils at 100°C.

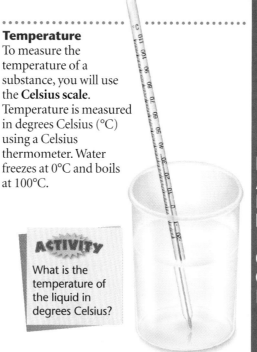

ACTIVITY

What is the temperature of the liquid in degrees Celsius?

Converting SI Units

To use the SI system, you must know how to convert between units. Converting from one unit to another involves the skill of **calculating**, or using mathematical operations. Converting between SI units is similar to converting between dollars and dimes because both systems are based on multiples of ten.

Suppose you want to convert a length of 80 centimeters to meters. Follow these steps to convert between units.

1. Begin by writing down the measurement you want to convert—in this example, 80 centimeters.
2. Write a conversion factor that represents the relationship between the two units you are converting. In this example, the relationship is *1 meter = 100 centimeters*. Write this conversion factor as a fraction, making sure to place the units you are converting from (centimeters, in this example) in the denominator.

3. Multiply the measurement you want to convert by the fraction. When you do this, the units in the first measurement will cancel out with the units in the denominator. Your answer will be in the units you are converting to (meters, in this example).

Example

80 centimeters = ___?___ meters

$$80 \text{ centimeters} \times \frac{1 \text{ meter}}{100 \text{ centimeters}} = \frac{80 \text{ meters}}{100}$$

$$= 0.8 \text{ meters}$$

ACTIVITY

Convert between the following units.
1. 600 millimeters = _?_ meters
2. 0.35 liters = _?_ milliliters
3. 1,050 grams = _?_ kilograms

Mass *(Students should state that the mass of the apple is 0.1 kilograms. They would need 10 apples to make 1 kilogram.)* If students need practice determining mass, have them use a balance to determine the mass of various common objects, such as coins, paper clips, and books.

ACTIVITY

Temperature *(Students should state that the temperature of the liquid is 35°C.)* If students need practice measuring temperature, have them use a Celsius thermometer to measure the temperature of various water samples.

ACTIVITY

Converting SI Units

ACTIVITY

Review the steps for converting SI units and work through the example with students. Then ask: **How many millimeters are in 80 centimeters?** *(Students should follow the steps to calculate that 80 centimeters is equal to 800 millimeters.)*

Have students do the conversion problems in the activity. (**1.** *600 millimeters = 0.6 meters;* **2.** *0.35 liters = 350 milliliters;* **3.** *1,050 grams = 1.05 kilograms)* If students need more practice converting SI units, have them make up conversion problems and trade with a partner.

Conducting a Scientific Investigation

Posing Questions

Before students do the activity on the next page, walk them through the steps of a typical scientific investigation. Begin by asking: **Why is a scientific question important to a scientific investigation?** (*It is the reason for conducting a scientific investigation.*) **What is the scientific question in the activity at the bottom of the next page?** (*Is a ball's bounce affected by the height from which it is dropped?*)

Developing a Hypothesis

Emphasize that a hypothesis is a possible explanation for a set of observations or answer to a scientific question, but it is *not* a guess. Ask: **On what information do scientists base their hypotheses?** (*Their observations and previous knowledge or experience*) Point out that a hypothesis does not always turn out to be correct. Ask: **In that case, do you think the scientist wasted his or her time? Explain your answer.** (*No, because the scientist probably learned from the investigation and may be able to develop another hypothesis that could be supported.*)

Designing an Experiment

Have a volunteer read the Experimental Procedure in the box. Then call on students to identify the manipulated variable (*amount of salt added to water*), the variables that are kept constant (*amount and starting temperature of water, placing containers in freezer*), the responding variable (*time it takes water to freeze*), and the control (*Container 3*).

Ask: **How might the experiment be affected if Container 1 had only 100 mL of water?** (*It wouldn't be a fair comparison with the containers that have more water.*) **What if Container 3 was not included in the experiment?** (*You wouldn't have anything to compare the other two containers with to know if their freezing times were faster or slower than normal.*) Help students understand the importance of keeping all variables constant except the manipulated variable. Also, be sure

Conducting a Scientific Investigation

In some ways, scientists are like detectives, piecing together clues to learn about a process or event. One way that scientists gather clues is by carrying out experiments. An experiment tests an idea in a careful, orderly manner. Although experiments do not all follow the same steps in the same order, many follow a pattern similar to the one described here.

Posing Questions

Experiments begin by asking a scientific question. A scientific question is one that can be answered by gathering evidence. For example, the question "Which freezes faster—fresh water or salt water?" is a scientific question because you can carry out an investigation and gather information to answer the question.

Developing a Hypothesis

The next step is to form a hypothesis. A **hypothesis** is a possible explanation for a set of observations or answer to a scientific question. In science, a hypothesis must be something that can be tested. A hypothesis can be worded as an *If…then…* statement. For example, a hypothesis might be "*If I add salt to fresh water, then the water will take longer to freeze.*" A hypothesis worded this way serves as a rough outline of the experiment you should perform.

they understand the role of the control. Then ask: **What operational definition is used in this experiment?** (*"Frozen" means the time at which a wooden stick can no longer move in a container.*)

Designing an Experiment

Next you need to plan a way to test your hypothesis. Your plan should be written out as a step-by-step procedure and should describe the observations or measurements you will make.

Two important steps involved in designing an experiment are controlling variables and forming operational definitions.

Controlling Variables In a well-designed experiment, you need to keep all variables the same except for one. A **variable** is any factor that can change in an experiment. The factor that you change is called the **manipulated variable.** In this experiment, the manipulated variable is the amount of salt added to the water. Other factors, such as the amount of water or the starting temperature, are kept constant.

The factor that changes as a result of the manipulated variable is called the responding variable. The **responding variable** is what you measure or observe to obtain your results. In this experiment, the responding variable is how long the water takes to freeze.

An experiment in which all factors except one are kept constant is a **controlled experiment.** Most controlled experiments include a test called the control. In this experiment, Container 3 is the control. Because no salt is added to Container 3, you can compare the results from the other containers to it. Any difference in results must be due to the addition of salt alone.

Forming Operational Definitions

Another important aspect of a well-designed experiment is having clear operational definitions. An **operational definition** is a statement that describes how a particular variable is to be measured or how a term is to be defined. For example, in this experiment, how will you determine if the water has frozen? You might decide to insert a stick in each container at the start of the experiment. Your operational definition of "frozen" would be the time at which the stick can no longer move.

EXPERIMENTAL PROCEDURE

1. Fill 3 containers with 300 milliliters of cold tap water.

2. Add 10 grams of salt to Container 1; stir. Add 20 grams of salt to Container 2; stir. Add no salt to Container 3.

3. Place the 3 containers in a freezer.

4. Check the containers every 15 minutes. Record your observations.

Interpreting Data

The observations and measurements you make in an experiment are called data. At the end of an experiment, you need to analyze the data to look for any patterns or trends. Patterns often become clear if you organize your data in a data table or graph. Then think through what the data reveal. Do they support your hypothesis? Do they point out a flaw in your experiment? Do you need to collect more data?

Drawing Conclusions

A conclusion is a statement that sums up what you have learned from an experiment. When you draw a conclusion, you need to decide whether the data you collected support your hypothesis or not. You may need to repeat an experiment several times before you can draw any conclusions from it. Conclusions often lead you to pose new questions and plan new experiments to answer them.

Is a ball's bounce affected by the height from which it is dropped? Using the steps just described, plan a controlled experiment to investigate this problem. **ACTIVITY**

Interpreting Data

Emphasize the importance of collecting accurate and detailed data in a scientific investigation. Ask: **What if you forgot to record some data during your investigation?** *(They wouldn't be able to completely analyze their data to draw valid conclusions.)* Then ask: **Why are data tables and graphs a good way to organize data?** *(They often make it easier to compare and analyze data.)* You may wish to have students review the Skills Handbook pages on Creating Data Tables and Graphs at this point.

Drawing Conclusions

Help students understand that a conclusion is not necessarily the end of a scientific investigation. A conclusion about one experiment may lead right into another experiment. Point out that in scientific investigations, a conclusion is a summary and explanation of the results of an experiment.

Tell students to suppose that for the Experimental Procedure described on this page, they obtained the following results: Container 1 froze in 45 minutes, Container 2 in 80 minutes, and Container 3 in 25 minutes. Ask: **What conclusions can you draw about this experiment?** *(Students might conclude that the more salt that is added to fresh water, the longer it takes the water to freeze. The hypothesis is supported, and the question of which freezes faster is answered—fresh water.)*

You might wish to have students work in pairs to plan the controlled experiment. **ACTIVITY** *(Students should develop a hypothesis, such as "If I increase the height from which a ball is dropped, then the height of its bounce will increase." They can test the hypothesis by dropping balls from varying heights (the manipulated variable). All trials should be done with the same kind of ball and on the same surface (constant variables). For each trial, they should measure the height of the bounce (responding variable).)* After students have designed the experiment, provide rubber balls and invite them to carry out the experiment so they can collect and interpret data and draw conclusions.

Thinking Critically

Comparing and Contrasting

Emphasize that the skill of comparing and contrasting often relies on good observation skills, as in this activity. *(Students' answers may vary. Sample answer: Similarities—both are dogs and have four legs, two eyes, two ears, brown and white fur, black noses, pink tongues; Differences—smooth coat vs. rough coat, more white fur vs. more brown fur, shorter vs. taller, long ears vs. short ears.)*

Applying Concepts

Point out to students that they apply concepts that they learn in school in their daily lives. For example, they learn to add, subtract, multiply, and divide in school. If they get a paper route or some other part-time job, they can apply those concepts. Challenge students to practice applying concepts by doing the activity. *(Antifreeze lowers the temperature at which the solution will freeze, and thus keeps the water in the radiator from freezing.)*

Interpreting Illustrations

Again, point out the need for good observation skills. Ask: **What is the difference between "interpreting illustrations" and "looking at the pictures"?** *("Interpreting illustrations" requires thorough examination of the illustrations, captions, and labels, while "looking at the pictures" implies less thorough examination.)* Encourage students to thoroughly examine the diagram as they do the activity. *(Students' paragraphs will vary, but should describe the internal anatomy of an earthworm, including some of the organs in the earthworm.)*

Thinking Critically

Has a friend ever asked for your advice about a problem? If so, you may have helped your friend think through the problem in a logical way. Without knowing it, you used critical-thinking skills to help your friend. Critical thinking involves the use of reasoning and logic to solve problems or make decisions. Some critical-thinking skills are described below.

Comparing and Contrasting

When you examine two objects for similarities and differences, you are using the skill of **comparing and contrasting.** Comparing involves identifying similarities, or common characteristics. Contrasting involves identifying differences. Analyzing objects in this way can help you discover details that you might otherwise overlook.

Compare and contrast the two animals in the photo. First list all the similarities that you see. Then list all the differences.

Applying Concepts

When you use your knowledge about one situation to make sense of a similar situation, you are using the skill of **applying concepts.** Being able to transfer your knowledge from one situation to another shows that you truly understand a concept. You may use this skill in answering test questions that present different problems from the ones you've reviewed in class.

You have just learned that water takes longer to freeze when other substances are mixed into it. Use this knowledge to explain why people need a substance called antifreeze in their car's radiator in the winter.

Interpreting Illustrations

Diagrams, photographs, and maps are included in textbooks to help clarify what you read. These illustrations show processes, places, and ideas in a visual manner. The skill called **interpreting illustrations** can help you learn from these visual elements. To understand an illustration, take the time to study the illustration along with all the written information that accompanies it. Captions identify the key concepts shown in the illustration. Labels point out the important parts of a diagram or map, while keys identify the symbols used in a map.

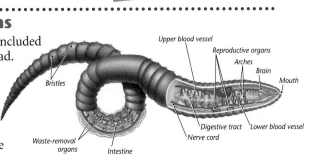

▲ Internal anatomy of an earthworm

Study the diagram above. Then write a short paragraph explaining what you have learned.

Relating Cause and Effect

If one event causes another event to occur, the two events are said to have a cause-and-effect relationship. When you determine that such a relationship exists between two events, you use a skill called **relating cause and effect.** For example, if you notice an itchy, red bump on your skin, you might infer that a mosquito bit you. The mosquito bite is the cause, and the bump is the effect.

It is important to note that two events do not necessarily have a cause-and-effect relationship just because they occur together. Scientists carry out experiments or use past experience to determine whether a cause-and-effect relationship exists.

You are on a camping **ACTIVITY** trip and your flashlight has stopped working. List some possible causes for the flashlight malfunction. How could you determine which cause-and-effect relationship has left you in the dark?

Making Generalizations

When you draw a conclusion about an entire group based on information about only some of the group's members, you are using a skill called **making generalizations.** For a generalization to be valid, the sample you choose must be large enough and representative of the entire group. You might, for example, put this skill to work at a farm stand if you see a sign that says, "Sample some grapes before you buy." If you sample a few sweet grapes, you may conclude that all the grapes are sweet—and purchase a large bunch.

A team of scientists **ACTIVITY** needs to determine whether the water in a large reservoir is safe to drink. How could they use the skill of making generalizations to help them? What should they do?

Making Judgments

When you evaluate something to decide whether it is good or bad, or right or wrong, you are using a skill called **making judgments.** For example, you make judgments when you decide to eat healthful foods or to pick up litter in a park. Before you make a judgment, you need to think through the pros and cons of a situation, and identify the values or standards that you hold.

Should children and teens be required to wear helmets when bicycling? Explain why you feel the way you do.

Problem Solving

When you use critical-thinking skills to resolve an issue or decide on a course of action, you are using a skill called **problem solving.** Some problems, such as how to convert a fraction into a decimal, are straightforward. Other problems, such as figuring out why your computer has stopped working, are complex. Some complex problems can be solved using the trial and error method—try out one solution first, and if that doesn't work, try another. Other useful problem-solving strategies include making models and brainstorming possible solutions with a partner.

J ♦ 141

Relating Cause and Effect

Emphasize that not all events that occur together have a cause-and-effect relationship. For example, tell students that you went to the grocery and your car stalled. Ask: **Is there a cause-and-effect relationship in this situation? Explain your answer.** (*No, because going to the grocery could not cause a car to stall. There must be another cause to make the car stall.*) Have students do the activity to practice relating cause and effect. (*Students should identify that the flashlight not working is the effect. Some possible causes include dead batteries, a burned-out light bulb, or a loose part.*)

Making Generalizations

Point out the importance of having a large, representative sample before making a generalization. Ask: **If you went fishing at a lake and caught three catfish, could you make the generalization that all fish in the lake are catfish? Why or why not?** (*No, because there might be other kinds of fish you didn't catch because they didn't like the bait or they may be in other parts of the lake.*) **How could you make a generalization about the kinds of fish in the lake?** (*By having a larger sample*) Have students do the activity in the Student Edition to practice making generalizations. (*The scientists should collect and test water samples from a number of different parts of the reservoir.*)

Making Judgments

Remind students that they make a judgment almost every time they make a decision. Ask: **What steps should you follow to make a judgment?** (*Gather information, list pros and cons, analyze values, make judgment*) Invite students to do the activity, and then to share and discuss the judgments they made. (*Students' judgments will vary, but should be supported by valid reasoning. Sample answer: Children and teens should be required to wear helmets when bicycling because helmets have been proven to save lives and reduce head injuries.*)

Problem Solving

Challenge student pairs to solve a problem about a soapbox derby. Explain that their younger brother is building a car to enter in the race. The brother wants to know how to make his soapbox car go faster. After student pairs have considered the problem, have them share their ideas about solutions with the class. (*Most will probably suggest using trial and error by making small changes to the car and testing the car after each change. Some students may suggest making and manipulating a model.*)

Organizing Information

Concept Maps

Challenge students to make a concept map with at least three levels of concepts to organize information about types of transportation. All students should start with the phrase *types of transportation* at the top of the concept map. After that point, their concept maps may vary. *(For example, some students might place* private transportation *and* public transportation *at the next level, while other students might have* human-powered *and* gas-powered. *Make sure students connect the concepts with linking words. Challenge students to include cross-linkages as well.)*

Compare/ Contrast Tables

Have students make their own compare/contrast tables using two or more different sports or other activities, such as playing musical instruments. Emphasize that students should select characteristics that highlight the similarities and differences between the activities. *(Students' compare/contrast tables should include several appropriate characteristics and list information about each activity for every characteristic.)*

Organizing Information

As you read this textbook, how can you make sense of all the information it contains? Some useful tools to help you organize information are shown on this page. These tools are called **graphic organizers** because they give you a visual picture of a topic, showing at a glance how key concepts are related.

Concept Maps

Concept maps are useful tools for organizing information on broad topics. A concept map begins with a general concept and shows how it can be broken down into more specific concepts. In that way, relationships between concepts become easier to understand.

A concept map is constructed by placing concept words (usually nouns) in ovals and connecting them with linking words. Often, the most general concept word is placed at the top, and the words become more specific as you move downward. Often the linking words, which are written on a line extending between two ovals, describe the relationship between the two concepts they connect. If you follow any string of concepts and linking words down the map, it should read like a sentence.

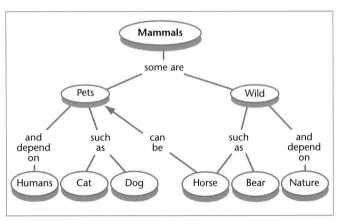

Some concept maps include linking words that connect a concept on one branch of the map to a concept on another branch. These linking words, called cross-linkages, show more complex interrelationships among concepts.

Compare/Contrast Tables

Compare/contrast tables are useful tools for sorting out the similarities and differences between two or more items. A table provides an organized framework in which to compare items based on specific characteristics that you identify.

To create a compare/contrast table, list the items to be compared across the top of a table. Then list the characteristics that will form the basis of your comparison in the left-hand

Characteristic	Baseball	Basketball
Number of Players	9	5
Playing Field	Baseball diamond	Basketball court
Equipment	Bat, baseball, mitts	Basket, basketball

column. Complete the table by filling in information about each characteristic, first for one item and then for the other.

Venn Diagrams

Another way to show similarities and differences between items is with a Venn diagram. A Venn diagram consists of two or more circles that partially overlap. Each circle represents a particular concept or idea. Common characteristics, or similarities, are written within the area of overlap between the two circles. Unique characteristics, or differences, are written in the parts of the circles outside the area of overlap.

To create a Venn diagram, draw two overlapping circles. Label the circles with the names of the items being compared. Write the

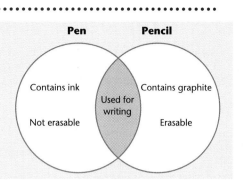

unique characteristics in each circle outside the area of overlap. Then write the shared characteristics within the area of overlap.

Flowcharts

A flowchart can help you understand the order in which certain events have occurred or should occur. Flowcharts are useful for outlining the stages in a process or the steps in a procedure.

To make a flowchart, write a brief description of each event in a box. Place the first event at the top of the page, followed by the second event, the third event, and so on. Then draw an arrow to connect each event to the one that occurs next.

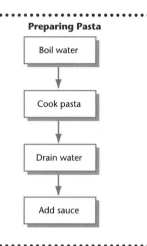

Cycle Diagrams

A cycle diagram can be used to show a sequence of events that is continuous, or cyclical. A continuous sequence does not have an end because, when the final event is over, the first event begins again. Like a flowchart, a cycle diagram can help you understand the order of events.

To create a cycle diagram, write a brief description of each event in a box. Place one event at the top of the page in the center. Then, moving in a clockwise direction around an imaginary circle, write each event in its proper sequence. Draw arrows that connect each event to the one that occurs next, forming a continuous circle.

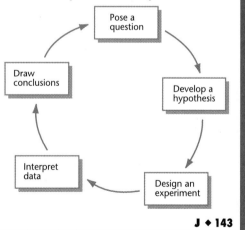

J ◆ 143

Venn Diagrams

Students can use the same information from their compare/contrast tables to create a Venn diagram. Make sure students understand that the overlapping area of the circles is used to list similarities and the parts of the circles outside the overlap area are used to show differences. If students want to list similarities and differences among three activities, show them how to add a third circle that overlaps each of the other two circles and has an area of overlap for all three circles. *(Students' Venn diagrams will vary. Make sure they have accurately listed similarities in the overlap area and differences in the parts of the circles that do not overlap.)*

Flowcharts

Encourage students to create a flowchart to show the things they did this morning as they got ready for school. Remind students that a flowchart should show the correct order in which events occurred or should occur. *(Students' flowcharts will vary somewhat. A typical flowchart might include: got up → ate breakfast → took a shower → brushed teeth → got dressed → gathered books and homework → put on jacket.)*

Cycle Diagrams

Review that a cycle diagram shows a sequence of events that is continuous. Then challenge students to create a cycle diagram that shows how the weather changes with the seasons where they live. *(Students' cycle diagrams may vary, though most will include four steps, one for each season.)*

Creating Data Tables and Graphs

Data Tables

Have students create a data table to show how much time they spend on different activities during one week. Suggest that students first list the main activities they do every week. Then they should determine the amount of time they spend on each activity each day. Remind students to give this data table a title. *(Students' data tables will vary. A sample data table is shown below.)*

Bar Graphs

Students can use the data from the data table they created to make a bar graph showing how much time they spend on different activities during a week. The vertical axis should be divided into units of time, such as hours. Remind students to label both axes and give their graph a title. *(Students' bar graphs will vary. A sample bar graph is shown below.)*

Creating Data Tables and Graphs

How can you make sense of the data in a science experiment? The first step is to organize the data to help you understand them. Data tables and graphs are helpful tools for organizing data.

Data Tables

You have gathered your materials and set up your experiment. But before you start, you need to plan a way to record what happens during the experiment. By creating a data table, you can record your observations and measurements in an orderly way.

Suppose, for example, that a scientist conducted an experiment to find out how many Calories people of different body masses burn while doing various activities. The data table shows the results.

Notice in this data table that the manipulated variable (body mass) is the heading of one column. The responding

variable (for Experiment 1, the number of Calories burned while bicycling) is the heading of the next column. Additional columns were added for related experiments.

CALORIES BURNED IN 30 MINUTES OF ACTIVITY			
Body Mass	Experiment 1 Bicycling	Experiment 2 Playing Basketball	Experiment 3 Watching Television
30 kg	60 Calories	120 Calories	21 Calories
40 kg	77 Calories	164 Calories	27 Calories
50 kg	95 Calories	206 Calories	33 Calories
60 kg	114 Calories	248 Calories	38 Calories

Bar Graphs

To compare how many Calories a person burns doing various activities, you could create a bar graph. A bar graph is used to display data in a number of separate, or distinct, categories. In this example, bicycling, playing basketball, and watching television are three separate categories.

To create a bar graph, follow these steps.
1. On graph paper, draw a horizontal, or *x*-, axis and a vertical, or *y*-, axis.
2. Write the names of the categories to be graphed along the horizontal axis. Include an overall label for the axis as well.
3. Label the vertical axis with the name of the responding variable. Include units of measurement. Then create a scale along the axis by marking off equally spaced numbers that cover the range of the data collected.
4. For each category, draw a solid bar using the scale on the vertical axis to determine the

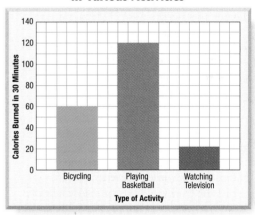

Calories Burned by a 30-kilogram Person in Various Activities

appropriate height. For example, for bicycling, draw the bar as high as the 60 mark on the vertical axis. Make all the bars the same width and leave equal spaces between them.
5. Add a title that describes the graph.

Time Spent on Different Activities in a Week (in hours)				
	Going to Classes	Eating Meals	Playing Soccer	Watching Television
Monday	6	2	2	0.5
Tuesday	6	1.5	1.5	1.5
Wednesday	6	2	1	2
Thursday	6	2	2	1.5
Friday	6	2	2	0.5
Saturday	0	2.5	2.5	1
Sunday	0	3	1	2

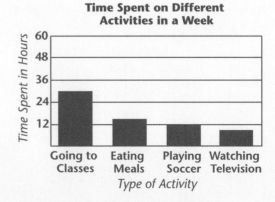

Time Spent on Different Activities in a Week

Line Graphs

To see whether a relationship exists between body mass and the number of Calories burned while bicycling, you could create a line graph. A line graph is used to display data that show how one variable (the responding variable) changes in response to another variable (the manipulated variable). You can use a line graph when your manipulated variable is *continuous*, that is, when there are other points between the ones that you tested. In this example, body mass is a continuous variable because there are other body masses between 30 and 40 kilograms (for example, 31 kilograms). Time is another example of a continuous variable.

Line graphs are powerful tools because they allow you to estimate values for conditions that you did not test in the experiment. For example, you can use the line graph to estimate that a 35-kilogram person would burn 68 Calories while bicycling.

To create a line graph, follow these steps.

1. On graph paper, draw a horizontal, or *x*-, axis and a vertical, or *y*-, axis.
2. Label the horizontal axis with the name of the manipulated variable. Label the vertical axis with the name of the responding variable. Include units of measurement.
3. Create a scale on each axis by marking off equally spaced numbers that cover the range of the data collected.
4. Plot a point on the graph for each piece of data. In the line graph above, the dotted lines show how to plot the first data point (30 kilograms and 60 Calories). Draw an imaginary vertical line extending up from the horizontal axis at the 30-kilogram mark. Then draw an imaginary horizontal line extending across from the vertical axis at the 60-Calorie mark. Plot the point where the two lines intersect.

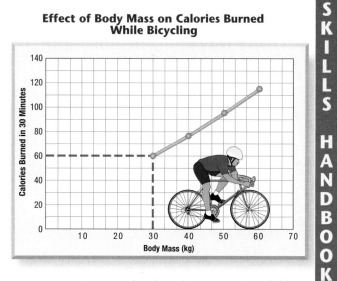

Effect of Body Mass on Calories Burned While Bicycling

5. Connect the plotted points with a solid line. (In some cases, it may be more appropriate to draw a line that shows the general trend of the plotted points. In those cases, some of the points may fall above or below the line. Also, not all graphs are linear. It may be more appropriate to draw a curve to connect the points.)
6. Add a title that identifies the variables or relationship in the graph.

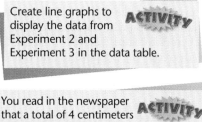

Create line graphs to display the data from Experiment 2 and Experiment 3 in the data table. **ACTIVITY**

You read in the newspaper that a total of 4 centimeters of rain fell in your area in June, 2.5 centimeters fell in July, and 1.5 centimeters fell in August. What type of graph would you use to display these data? Use graph paper to create the graph. **ACTIVITY**

Line Graphs

Walk students through the steps involved in creating a line graph using the example illustrated on the page. For example, ask: **What is the label on the horizontal axis? On the vertical axis?** *(Body Mass (kg); Calories Burned in 30 Minutes)* **What scales are used on each axis?** *(3 squares per 10 kg on the x-axis and 2 squares per 20 calories on the y-axis)* **What does the second data point represent?** *(77 Calories burned for a body mass of 40 kg)* **What trend or pattern does the graph show?** *(The number of Calories burned in 30 minutes of cycling increases with body mass.)*

Have students follow the steps to carry out the first activity. *(Students should make a different graph for each experiment with different y-axis scales to practice making scales appropriate for data. See sample graphs below.)*

Have students carry out the second activity. *(Students should conclude that a bar graph would be best for displaying the data. A sample bar graph for these data is shown below.)*

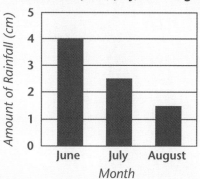

Rainfall in June, July, and August

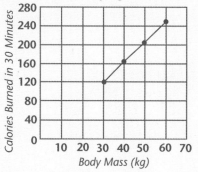

Effect of Body Mass on Calories Burned While Playing Basketball

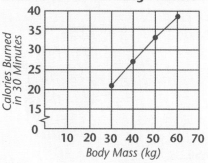

Effect of Body Mass on Calories Burned While Watching Television

Circle Graphs

Emphasize that a circle graph has to include 100 percent of the categories for the topic being graphed. For example, ask: **Could the data in the bar graph titled "Calories Burned by a 30-kilogram Person in Various Activities" (on page 144) be shown in a circle graph? Why or why not?** *(No, because it does not include all the possible ways a 30-kilogram person can burn Calories.)* Then walk students through the steps for making a circle graph. Help students to use a compass and a protractor. Use the protractor to illustrate that a circle has 360 degrees. Make sure students understand the mathematical calculations involved in making a circle graph.

You might wish to have students work in pairs to complete the activity. *(Students' circle graphs should look like the graph below.)*

Circle Graphs

Like bar graphs, circle graphs can be used to display data in a number of separate categories. Unlike bar graphs, however, circle graphs can only be used when you have data for *all* the categories that make up a given topic. A circle graph is sometimes called a pie chart because it resembles a pie cut into slices. The pie represents the entire topic, while the slices represent the individual categories. The size of a slice indicates what percentage of the whole a particular category makes up.

The data table below shows the results of a survey in which 24 teenagers were asked to identify their favorite sport. The data were then used to create the circle graph at the right.

Sports That Teens Prefer

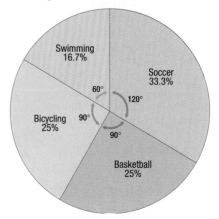

FAVORITE SPORTS

Sport	Number of Students
Soccer	8
Basketball	6
Bicycling	6
Swimming	4

To create a circle graph, follow these steps.
1. Use a compass to draw a circle. Mark the center of the circle with a point. Then draw a line from the center point to the top of the circle.
2. Determine the size of each "slice" by setting up a proportion where *x* equals the number of degrees in a slice. (NOTE: A circle contains 360 degrees.) For example, to find the number of degrees in the "soccer" slice, set up the following proportion:

$$\frac{\text{students who prefer soccer}}{\text{total number of students}} = \frac{x}{\text{total number of degrees in a circle}}$$

$$\frac{8}{24} = \frac{x}{360}$$

Cross-multiply and solve for *x*.
$$24x = 8 \times 360$$
$$x = 120$$
The "soccer" slice should contain 120 degrees.

3. Use a protractor to measure the angle of the first slice, using the line you drew to the top of the circle as the 0° line. Draw a line from the center of the circle to the edge for the angle you measured.
4. Continue around the circle by measuring the size of each slice with the protractor. Start measuring from the edge of the previous slice so the wedges do not overlap. When you are done, the entire circle should be filled in.
5. Determine the percentage of the whole circle that each slice represents. To do this, divide the number of degrees in a slice by the total number of degrees in a circle (360), and multiply by 100%. For the "soccer" slice, you can find the percentage as follows:

$$\frac{120}{360} \times 100\% = 33.3\%$$

6. Use a different color to shade in each slice. Label each slice with the name of the category and with the percentage of the whole it represents.
7. Add a title to the circle graph.

ACTIVITY In a class of 28 students, 12 students take the bus to school, 10 students walk, and 6 students ride their bicycles. Create a circle graph to display these data.

Ways Students Get to School

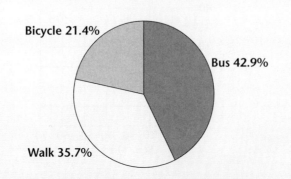

Safety Symbols

These symbols alert you to possible dangers in the laboratory and remind you to work carefully.

Safety Goggles Always wear safety goggles to protect your eyes in any activity involving chemicals, flames or heating, or the possibility of broken glassware.

Lab Apron Wear a laboratory apron to protect your skin and clothing from damage.

Breakage You are working with materials that may be breakable, such as glass containers, glass tubing, thermometers, or funnels. Handle breakable materials with care. Do not touch broken glassware.

Heat-resistant Gloves Use an oven mitt or other hand protection when handling hot materials. Hot plates, hot glassware, or hot water can cause burns. Do not touch hot objects with your bare hands.

Heating Use a clamp or tongs to pick up hot glassware. Do not touch hot objects with your bare hands.

Sharp Object Pointed-tip scissors, scalpels, knives, needles, pins, or tacks are sharp. They can cut or puncture your skin. Always direct a sharp edge or point away from yourself and others. Use sharp instruments only as instructed.

Electric Shock Avoid the possibility of electric shock. Never use electrical equipment around water, or when the equipment is wet or your hands are wet. Be sure cords are untangled and cannot trip anyone. Disconnect the equipment when it is not in use.

Corrosive Chemical You are working with an acid or another corrosive chemical. Avoid getting it on your skin or clothing, or in your eyes. Do not inhale the vapors. Wash your hands when you are finished with the activity.

Poison Do not let any poisonous chemical come in contact with your skin, and do not inhale its vapors. Wash your hands when you are finished with the activity.

Physical Safety When an experiment involves physical activity, take precautions to avoid injuring yourself or others. Follow instructions from your teacher. Alert your teacher if there is any reason you should not participate in the activity.

Animal Safety Treat live animals with care to avoid harming the animals or yourself. Working with animal parts or preserved animals also may require caution. Wash your hands when you are finished with the activity.

Plant Safety Handle plants in the laboratory or during field work only as directed by your teacher. If you are allergic to certain plants, tell your teacher before doing an activity in which those plants are used. Avoid touching harmful plants such as poison ivy, poison oak, or poison sumac, or plants with thorns. Wash your hands when you are finished with the activity.

Flames You may be working with flames from a lab burner, candle, or matches. Tie back loose hair and clothing. Follow instructions from your teacher about lighting and extinguishing flames.

No Flames Flammable materials may be present. Make sure there are no flames, sparks, or other exposed heat sources present.

Fumes When poisonous or unpleasant vapors may be involved, work in a ventilated area. Avoid inhaling vapors directly. Only test an odor when directed to do so by your teacher, and use a wafting motion to direct the vapor toward your nose.

Disposal Chemicals and other laboratory materials used in the activity must be disposed of safely. Follow the instructions from your teacher.

Hand Washing Wash your hands thoroughly when finished with the activity. Use antibacterial soap and warm water. Lather both sides of your hands and between your fingers. Rinse well.

General Safety Awareness You may see this symbol when none of the symbols described earlier appears. In this case, follow the specific instructions provided. You may also see this symbol when you are asked to develop your own procedure in a lab. Have your teacher approve your plan before you go further.

Laboratory Safety

Laboratory safety is an essential element of a successful science class. It is important for you to emphasize laboratory safety to students. Students need to understand exactly what is safe and unsafe behavior, and what the rationale is behind each safety rule.

Review with students the Safety Symbols and Science Safety Rules listed on this and the next two pages. Then follow the safety guidelines below to ensure that your classroom will be a safe place for students to learn science.

◆ Post safety rules in the classroom and review them regularly with students.

◆ Familiarize yourself with the safety procedures for each activity before introducing it to your students.

◆ Review specific safety precautions with students before beginning every science activity.

◆ Always act as an exemplary role model by displaying safe behavior.

◆ Know how to use safety equipment, such as fire extinguishers and fire blankets, and always have it accessible.

◆ Have students practice leaving the classroom quickly and orderly to prepare them for emergencies.

◆ Explain to students how to use the intercom or other available means of communication to get help during an emergency.

◆ Never leave students unattended while they are engaged in science activities.

◆ Provide enough space for students to safely carry out science activities.

◆ Keep your classroom and all science materials in proper condition. Replace worn or broken items.

◆ Instruct students to report all accidents and injuries to you immediately.

Laboratory Safety

Additional tips are listed below for the Science Safety Rules discussed on these two pages. Please keep these tips in mind when you carry out science activities in your classroom.

General Precautions

♦ For open-ended activities such as Chapter Projects, go over general safety guidelines with students. Have students submit their procedures or design plans in writing and check them for safety considerations.

♦ In an activity where students are directed to taste something, be sure to store the material in clean, *nonscience* containers. Distribute the material to students in *new* plastic or paper dispensables, which should be discarded after the tasting. Tasting or eating should never be done in a lab classroom.

♦ During physical activity, make sure students do not overexert themselves.

♦ Remind students to handle microscopes and telescopes with care to avoid breakage.

Heating and Fire Safety

♦ No flammable substances should be in use around hot plates, light bulbs, or open flames.

♦ Test tubes should be heated only in water baths.

♦ Students should be permitted to strike matches to light candles or burners *only* with strict supervision. When possible, you should light the flames, especially when working with younger students.

♦ Be sure to have proper ventilation when fumes are produced during a procedure.

♦ All electrical equipment used in the lab should have GFI switches.

Using Chemicals Safely

♦ When students use both chemicals and microscopes in one activity, microscopes should be in a separate part of the room from the chemicals so that when students remove their goggles to use the microscopes, their eyes are not at risk.

Science Safety Rules

To prepare yourself to work safely in the laboratory, read over the following safety rules. Then read them a second time. Make sure you understand and follow each rule. Ask your teacher to explain any rules you do not understand.

Dress Code

1. To protect yourself from injuring your eyes, wear safety goggles whenever you work with chemicals, burners, glassware, or any substance that might get into your eyes. If you wear contact lenses, notify your teacher.
2. Wear a lab apron or coat whenever you work with corrosive chemicals or substances that can stain.
3. Tie back long hair to keep it away from any chemicals, flames, or equipment.
4. Remove or tie back any article of clothing or jewelry that can hang down and touch chemicals, flames, or equipment. Roll up or secure long sleeves.
5. Never wear open shoes or sandals.

General Precautions

6. Read all directions for an experiment several times before beginning the activity. Carefully follow all written and oral instructions. If you are in doubt about any part of the experiment, ask your teacher for assistance.
7. Never perform activities that are not assigned or authorized by your teacher. Obtain permission before "experimenting" on your own. Never handle any equipment unless you have specific permission.
8. Never perform lab activities without direct supervision.
9. Never eat or drink in the laboratory.
10. Keep work areas clean and tidy at all times. Bring only notebooks and lab manuals or written lab procedures to the work area. All other items, such as purses and backpacks, should be left in a designated area.
11. Do not engage in horseplay.

First Aid

12. Always report all accidents or injuries to your teacher, no matter how minor. Notify your teacher immediately about any fires.
13. Learn what to do in case of specific accidents, such as getting acid in your eyes or on your skin. (Rinse acids from your body with lots of water.)
14. Be aware of the location of the first-aid kit, but do not use it unless instructed by your teacher. In case of injury, your teacher should administer first aid. Your teacher may also send you to the school nurse or call a physician.
15. Know the location of emergency equipment, such as the fire extinguisher and fire blanket, and know how to use it.
16. Know the location of the nearest telephone and whom to contact in an emergency.

Heating and Fire Safety

17. Never use a heat source, such as a candle, burner, or hot plate, without wearing safety goggles.
18. Never heat anything unless instructed to do so. A chemical that is harmless when cool may be dangerous when heated.
19. Keep all combustible materials away from flames. Never use a flame or spark near a combustible chemical.
20. Never reach across a flame.
21. Before using a laboratory burner, make sure you know proper procedures for lighting and adjusting the burner, as demonstrated by your teacher. Do not touch the burner. It may be hot. And never leave a lighted burner unattended!
22. Chemicals can splash or boil out of a heated test tube. When heating a substance in a test tube, make sure that the mouth of the tube is not pointed at you or anyone else.
23. Never heat a liquid in a closed container. The expanding gases produced may blow the container apart.
24. Before picking up a container that has been heated, hold the back of your hand near it. If you can feel heat on the back of your hand, the container is too hot to handle. Use an oven mitt to pick up a container that has been heated.

Using Glassware Safely

♦ Use plastic containers, graduated cylinders, and beakers whenever possible. If using glass, students should wear safety goggles.

♦ Use only nonmercury thermometers with anti-roll protectors.

♦ Check all glassware periodically for chips and scratches, which can cause cuts and breakage.

Using Chemicals Safely

25. Never mix chemicals "for the fun of it." You might produce a dangerous, possibly explosive substance.
26. Never put your face near the mouth of a container that holds chemicals. Many chemicals are poisonous. Never touch, taste, or smell a chemical unless you are instructed by your teacher to do so.
27. Use only those chemicals needed in the activity. Read and double-check labels on supply bottles before removing any chemicals. Take only as much as you need. Keep all containers closed when chemicals are not being used.
28. Dispose of all chemicals as instructed by your teacher. To avoid contamination, never return chemicals to their original containers. Never simply pour chemicals or other substances into the sink or trash containers.
29. Be extra careful when working with acids or bases. Pour all chemicals over the sink or a container, not over your work surface.
30. If you are instructed to test for odors, use a wafting motion to direct the odors to your nose. Do not inhale the fumes directly from the container.
31. When mixing an acid and water, always pour the water into the container first and then add the acid to the water. Never pour water into an acid.
32. Take extreme care not to spill any material in the laboratory. Wash chemical spills and splashes immediately with plenty of water. Immediately begin rinsing with water any acids that get on your skin or clothing, and notify your teacher of any acid spill at the same time.

Using Glassware Safely

33. Never force glass tubing or thermometers into a rubber stopper or rubber tubing. Have your teacher insert the glass tubing or thermometer if required for an activity.
34. If you are using a laboratory burner, use a wire screen to protect glassware from any flame. Never heat glassware that is not thoroughly dry on the outside.
35. Keep in mind that hot glassware looks cool. Never pick up glassware without first checking to see if it is hot. Use an oven mitt. See rule 24.
36. Never use broken or chipped glassware. If glassware breaks, notify your teacher and dispose of the glassware in the proper broken-glassware container. Never handle broken glass with your bare hands.
37. Never eat or drink from lab glassware.
38. Thoroughly clean glassware before putting it away.

Using Sharp Instruments

39. Handle scalpels or other sharp instruments with extreme care. Never cut material toward you; cut away from you.
40. Immediately notify your teacher if you cut your skin when working in the laboratory.

Animal and Plant Safety

41. Never perform experiments that cause pain, discomfort, or harm to animals. This rule applies at home as well as in the classroom.
42. Animals should be handled only if absolutely necessary. Your teacher will instruct you as to how to handle each animal species brought into the classroom.
43. If you know that you are allergic to certain plants, molds, or animals, tell your teacher before doing an activity in which these are used.
44. During field work, protect your skin by wearing long pants, long sleeves, socks, and closed shoes. Know how to recognize the poisonous plants and fungi in your area, as well as plants with thorns, and avoid contact with them. Never eat any part of a plant or fungus.
45. Wash your hands thoroughly after handling animals or a cage containing animals. Wash your hands when you are finished with any activity involving animal parts, plants, or soil.

End-of-Experiment Rules

46. After an experiment has been completed, turn off all burners or hot plates. If you used a gas burner, check that the gas-line valve to the burner is off. Unplug hot plates.
47. Turn off and unplug any other electrical equipment that you used.
48. Clean up your work area and return all equipment to its proper place.
49. Dispose of waste materials as instructed by your teacher.
50. Wash your hands after every experiment.

Using Sharp Instruments

◆ Always use blunt-tip safety scissors, except when pointed-tip scissors are required.

Animal and Plant Safety

◆ When working with live animals or plants, check ahead of time for students who may have allergies to the specimens.
◆ When growing bacteria cultures, use only disposable petri dishes. After streaking, the dishes should be sealed and not opened again by students. After the lab, students should return the unopened dishes to you. Students should wash their hands with antibacterial soap.
◆ Two methods are recommended for the safe disposal of bacteria cultures. *First method:* Autoclave the petri dishes and discard without opening. *Second method:* If no autoclave is available, carefully open the dishes (never have a student do this) and pour full-strength bleach into the dishes and let stand for a day. Then pour the bleach from the petri dishes down a drain and flush the drain with lots of water. Tape the petri dishes back together and place in a sealed plastic bag. Wrap the plastic bag with a brown paper bag or newspaper and tape securely. Throw the sealed package in the trash. Thoroughly disinfect the work area with bleach.
◆ To grow mold, use a new, sealable plastic bag that is two to three times larger than the material to be placed inside. Seal the bag and tape it shut. After the bag is sealed, students should not open it. To dispose of the bag and mold culture, make a small cut near an edge of the bag and cook in a microwave oven on high setting for at least 1 minute. Discard the bag according to local ordinance, usually in the trash.
◆ Students should wear disposable nitrile, latex, or food-handling gloves when handling live animals or nonliving specimens.

End-of-Experiment Rules

◆ Always have students use antibacterial soap for washing their hands.

Star Charts

Autumn Sky

To use this chart, hold it up in front of you and turn it so that the direction you are facing is at the bottom of the chart. This chart works best at 34° north latitude, but can be used at other times and latitudes within the continental United States. It works best at the following times: 10:00 P.M. on September 1; 9:00 P.M. on September 15; 8:00 P.M. on September 30.

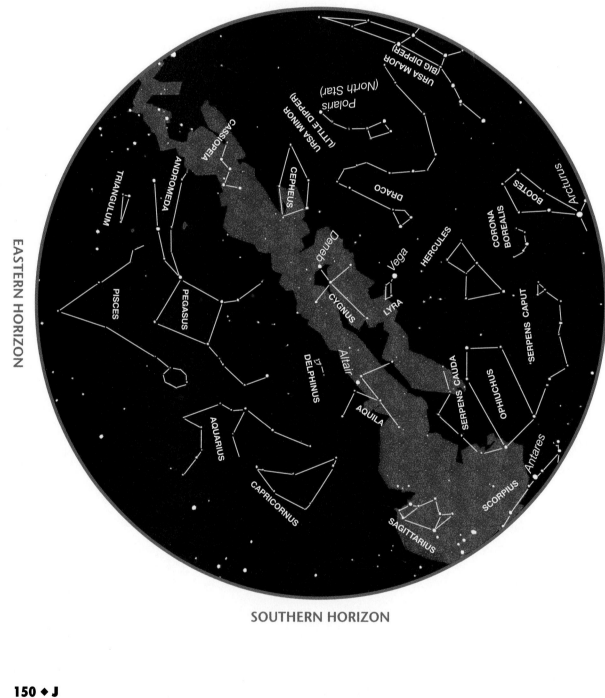

NORTHERN HORIZON

EASTERN HORIZON

WESTERN HORIZON

SOUTHERN HORIZON

Winter Sky

To use this chart, hold it up in front of you and turn it so that the direction you are facing is at the bottom of the chart. This chart works best at 34° north latitude, but can be used at other times and latitudes within the continental United States. It works best at the following times: 10:00 P.M. on December 1; 9:00 P.M. on December 15; 8:00 P.M. on December 30.

NORTHERN HORIZON

EASTERN HORIZON

WESTERN HORIZON

SOUTHERN HORIZON

Spring Sky

To use this chart, hold it up in front of you and turn it so that the direction you are facing is at the bottom of the chart. This chart works best at 34° north latitude, but can be used at other times and latitudes within the continental United States. It works best at the following times: 10:00 P.M. on March 1; 9:00 P.M. on March 15; 8:00 P.M. on March 30.

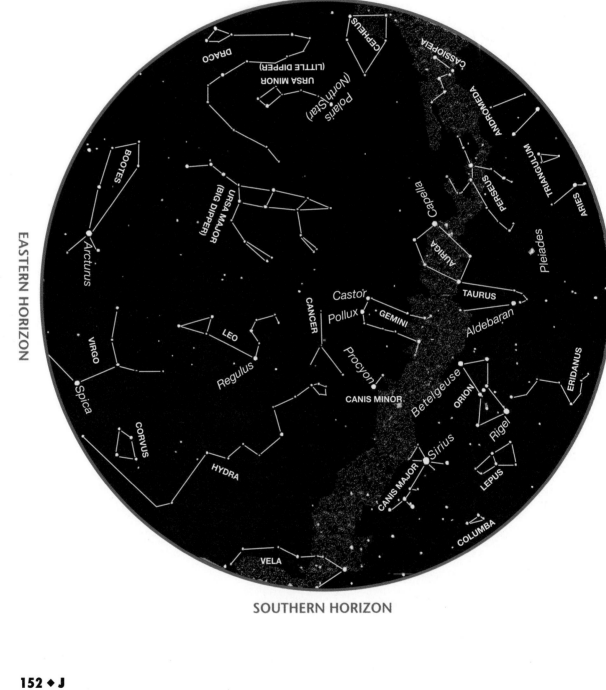

NORTHERN HORIZON

EASTERN HORIZON

WESTERN HORIZON

SOUTHERN HORIZON

Summer Sky

To use this chart, hold it up in front of you and turn it so that the direction you are facing is at the bottom of the chart. This chart works best at 34° north latitude, but can be used at other times and latitudes within the continental United States. It works best at the following times: 10:00 P.M. on June 1; 9:00 P.M. on June 15; 8:00 P.M. on June 30.

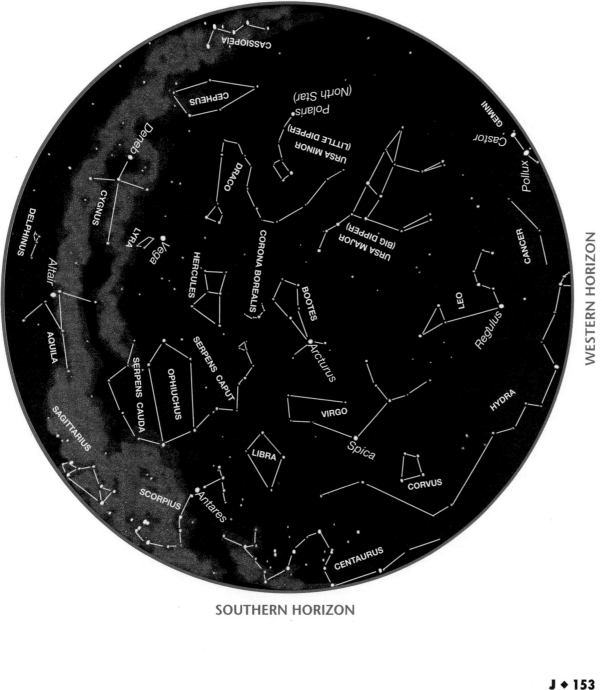

Glossary

absolute magnitude The brightness of a star if it were a standard distance from Earth. (p. 108)

apparent magnitude The brightness of a star as seen from Earth. (p. 107)

asteroid belt The region of the solar system between the orbits of Mars and Jupiter, where many asteroids are found. (p. 82)

asteroids Objects revolving around the sun that are too small and too numerous to be considered planets. (p. 82)

astronomy The study of the moon, stars, and other objects in space. (p. 15)

autumnal equinox The day of the year that marks the beginning of fall in the Northern Hemisphere. (p. 21)

axis An imaginary line that passes through Earth's center and the North and South poles, about which Earth rotates. (p. 15)

big bang The initial explosion that resulted in the formation and expansion of the universe. (p. 122)

binary star A star system that contains two stars. (p. 117)

black hole The remains of an extremely massive star pulled into a small volume by the force of gravity. (p. 115)

chromosphere The middle layer of the sun's atmosphere. (p. 57)

comet A ball of ice and dust whose orbit is a long, narrow ellipse. (p. 80)

constellation A pattern of stars in the sky. (p. 94)

controlled experiment An experiment in which all factors except one are kept constant. (p. 139)

convex lens A piece of transparent glass curved so that the middle is thicker than the edges. (p. 96)

core The central part of the sun, where nuclear fusion occurs. (p. 56)

corona The outer layer of the sun's atmosphere. (p. 57)

crater A round pit on the moon's surface. (p. 41)

eclipse The partial or total blocking of one object by another. (p. 27)

eclipsing binary A star system in which one star periodically blocks the light from another. (p. 118)

electromagnetic radiation Energy that travels through space in the form of waves. (p. 95)

ellipse An elongated circle, or oval shape; the shape of the planets' orbits. (p. 53)

elliptical galaxy A galaxy shaped like a flattened ball, containing only old stars. (p. 120)

equinox The two days of the year on which neither hemisphere is tilted toward or away from the sun. (p. 21)

extraterrestrial life Life that arises outside of Earth. (p. 84)

galaxy A giant structure that contains hundreds of billions of stars. (p. 103)

gas giants The name given to the first four outer planets: Jupiter, Saturn, Uranus, and Neptune. (p. 70)

geocentric A description of the solar system in which all of the planets revolve around Earth. (p. 51)

geosynchronous orbit The orbit of a satellite that revolves around Earth at the same rate that Earth rotates. (p. 37)

giant star A very large star, much larger than the sun. (p. 106)

gravity The attractive force between two objects; its magnitude depends on their masses and the distance between them. (p. 32)

greenhouse effect The trapping of heat by a planet's atmosphere. (p. 66)

heliocentric A description of the solar system in which all of the planets revolve around the sun. (p. 52)

Hertzsprung-Russell diagram A graph relating the temperature and brightness of stars. (p. 108)

hypothesis A possible explanation for a set of observations or answer to a scientific question; must be testable. (p. 139)

inertia The tendency of a moving object to continue in a straight line or a stationary object to remain in place. (p. 53)

irregular galaxy A galaxy that does not have a regular shape. (p. 120)

latitude A measurement of distance from the equator, expressed in degrees north or south. (p. 20)

light-year The distance that light travels in one year. (p. 104)

lunar eclipse The blocking of sunlight to the moon that occurs when Earth is directly between the sun and moon. (p. 29)

main sequence An area on the Hertzsprung-Russell diagram that runs from the upper left to the lower right and includes more than 90 percent of all stars. (p. 108)

manipulated variable The one factor that a scientist changes during an experiment. (p. 139)

maria Dark, flat regions on the moon's surface. (p. 41)

meteor A streak of light in the sky produced by the burning of a meteoroid in Earth's atmosphere. (p. 83)

meteorite A meteoroid that has hit Earth's surface. (p. 83)

meteoroid A chunk of rock or dust in space. (p. 83)

neap tide A tide with the least difference between low and high tides. (p. 33)

nebula A large amount of gas and dust in space, spread out in an immense volume. (p. 113)

neutron star A tiny star that remains after a supernova explosion. (p. 114)

nuclear fusion The process by which hydrogen atoms join together to form helium, releasing energy. (p. 56)

observatory A building that contains one or more telescopes. (p. 97)

operational definition A statement that describes how a particular variable is to be measured or how a term is to be defined. (p. 139)

orbit The path of an object as it revolves around another object in space. (p. 15)

parallax The apparent change in position of an object when seen from different places. (p. 104)

penumbra The part of a shadow surrounding the darkest part. (p. 28)

phase One of the different shapes of the moon as seen from Earth. (p. 25)

photosphere The inner layer of the sun's atmosphere. (p. 57)

prominence A loop of gas that protrudes from the sun's surface, linking parts of sunspot regions. (p. 60)

protostar A contracting cloud of gas and dust; the earliest stage of a star's life. (p. 113)

pulsar A neutron star that produces radio waves. (p. 112)

quasar A distant galaxy with a black hole at its center. (p. 116)

radio telescope A device used to detect radio waves from objects in space. (p. 96)

reflecting telescope A telescope that uses one or more mirrors to gather light. (p. 96)

refracting telescope A telescope that uses convex lenses to gather and focus light. (p. 96)

responding variable The factor that changes as a result of changes to the manipulated variable in an experiment. (p. 139)

retrograde rotation The spinning motion of a planet from east to west, opposite to the direction of rotation of most planets and moons. (p. 65)

revolution The movement of an object around another object. (p. 15)

rotation The spinning motion of a planet about its axis. (p. 15)

satellite Any object that revolves around another object in space. (p. 36)

solar eclipse The blocking of sunlight to Earth that occurs when the moon is between the sun and Earth. (p. 28)

solar flare An explosion of hydrogen gas from the sun's surface that occurs when loops in sunspot regions suddenly connect. (p. 60)

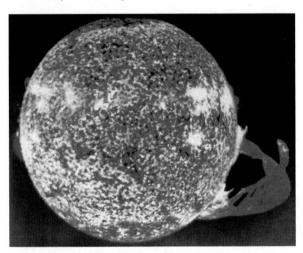

solar wind A stream of electrically charged particles produced by the sun's corona. (p. 58)

solstice The two days of the year on which the noon sun is directly overhead at either 23.5° South or 23.5° North. (p. 20)

spectrograph An instrument that separates light into colors and photographs the resulting spectrum. (p. 99)

spectrum The range of wavelengths of electro-magnetic waves. (p. 95)

spiral galaxy A galaxy whose arms curve outward in a pinwheel pattern. (p. 120)

spring tide A tide with the greatest difference between low and high tides. (p. 33)

sunspot A dark area of gas on the sun that is cooler than surrounding gases. (p. 58)

supernova The explosion of a dying giant or supergiant star. (p. 114)

telescope A device built to study distant objects by making them appear closer. (p. 41)

terrestrial planets The name given to the four inner planets: Mercury, Venus, Earth, and Mars. (p. 62)

tide The rise and fall of the level of water in the ocean. (p. 32)

umbra The darkest part of a shadow. (p. 28)

universe All of space and everything in it. (p. 103)

variable Any factor that can change in an experiment. (p. 139)

vernal equinox The day of the year that marks the beginning of spring in the Northern Hemisphere. (p. 21)

visible light Electromagnetic radiation that can be seen with the unaided eye. (p. 95)

wavelength The distance between the crest of one wave and the crest of the next. (p. 95)

white dwarf The remaining hot core of a star after its outer layers have expanded and drifted out into space. (p. 114)

Acknowledgments

Staff Credits

The people who made up the **Science Explorer** team—representing design services, editorial, editorial services, electronic publishing technology, manufacturing & inventory planning, marketing, marketing services, market research, online services & multimedia development, production services, product planning, project office, and publishing processes—are listed below.

Carolyn Belanger, Barbara A. Bertell, Suzanne Biron, Peggy Bliss, Peter W. Brooks, Christopher R. Brown, Greg Cantone, Jonathan Cheney, Todd Christy, Lisa J. Clark, Patrick Finbarr Connolly, Edward Cordero, Robert Craton, Patricia Cully, Patricia M. Dambry, Kathleen J. Dempsey, Judy Elgin, Gayle Connolly Fedele, Frederick Fellows, Barbara Foster, Paula Foye, Loree Franz, Donald P. Gagnon Jr., Paul J. Gagnon, Joel Gendler, Elizabeth Good, Robert M. Graham, Kerri Hoar, Joanne Hudson, Linda D. Johnson, Anne Jones, Toby Klang, Carolyn Langley, Russ Lappa, Carolyn Lock, Cheryl Mahan, Dotti Marshall, Meredith Mascola, Jeanne Y. Maurand, Karen McHugh, Eve Melnechuk, Natania Mlawer, Paul W. Murphy, Cindy A. Noftle, Julia F. Osborne, Judi Pinkham, Caroline M. Power, Robin L. Santel, Suzanne J. Schineller, Emily Soltanoff, Kira Thaler-Marbit, Mark Tricca, Diane Walsh, Pearl Weinstein, Merce Wilczek, Helen Young.

Illustration

John Edwards & Associates: 19, 25, 26, 28, 29, 33, 54–55, 63t, 71, 82, 106, 115, 118, 119, 122b, 123
Martucci Design: 61, 95b, 100, 112
Jared D. Lee: 104
Morgan Cain & Associates: 15, 18, 22, 27, 35, 36, 37, 47, 59, 63, 75, 81, 91, 101, 105, 109, 111, 122t, 127, 132
Matt Mayerchak: 45, 125
Ortelius Design Inc.: 16, 17
J/B Woolsey Associates: 95t, 96

Photography

Photo Research Kerri Hoar, PoYee McKenna Oster
Cover Image NASA

Nature of Science
Page 8t, Digital Vision; **8b,** Jane Luu; **8b background,** David Jewitt and Jane Luu; **9tr, br,** Jet Propulsion Laboratory; **9mr,** Digital Vision; **10,** John Sanford/Astrostock Art Resource.

Chapter 1
Pages 12–13, NASA; **14t,** Russ Lappa; **14b,** Eric Lessing; **16t,** Corel Corp.; **16b,** Archive Photos; **17t,** Courtney Milne/Masterfile; **17b,** Hazel Hankin/Stock Boston; **20,** Palmer/Kane/TSI; **21,** Art Wolfe/TSI; **23,** Richard Haynes; **24t,** Richard Haynes; **24b,** Larry Landolfi/Photo Researchers; **26mr,** Jerry Lodriguss/Photo Researchers; **26tl, ml, bl, tm, bm, tr, br,** John Bova/Photo Researchers; **28, 29tr, 29br,** Jay M. Pasachoff; **31,** Richard Haynes; **both,** Nancy Dudley/Stock Boston; **34,** Jim Zipp/Photo Researchers; **35t,** Richard Haynes; **36–38,** NASA; **39t,** Richard Haynes; **39b,** NASA; **40t,** John Bova/Photo Researchers; **40b all,** Alastair G.W. Cameron/Harvard-Smithsonian Center for Astrophysics; **41tl,** NASA; **41br,** Jay M. Pasachoff; **42,** N. Armstrong/The Stock Market; **43,** TSI; **44,** NASA.

Chapter 2
Pages 48–49, NASA; **50t,** Russ Lappa; **50b,** Anglo-Australian Observatory, photograph by David Malin; **51–53b,** The Granger Collection, NY; **53t,** Richard Haynes; **57,** Digital Vision; **58,** National Solar Observatory; **58 inset, 60t,** Space Telescope Science Institute; **60b,** National Solar Observatory; **64r,** NASA; **64 inset,** A.S.P./Science Source/Photo Researchers; **65–66,** Digital Vision; **67,** NASA; **68,** Jet Propulsion Laboratory; **69 both,** NASA; **70,** TSI; **72 both,** NASA; **73, 74tr,** Jet Propulsion Laboratory; **74 inset,** Digital Vision; **74b, 75, 76 both, 77,** NASA; **78–80t,** Richard Haynes; **80b,** Space Telescope Science Institute; **82tr,** Jet Propulsion Laboratory; **83tl,** U. S. Geological Survey; **83tr,** Jerry Schad/Photo Researchers; **84,** Ghislaine Grozaz; **85,** James Pisarowicz; **86,** U. S. Geological Survey; **87,** NASA; **88–89,** Jet Propulsion Laboratory.

Chapter 3
Pages 92–93, David Nunuk/Science Photo Library/Photo Researchers; **94t,** Richard Haynes; **94b,** John Sanford/Science Photo Library/Photo Researchers; **96,** Russ Lappa; **97t,** Malin/Pasachoff/Caltech 1992; **97b,** NRAO/Science Photo Library/Photo Researchers; **98tl,** Yerkes Observatory; **98–99tr,** National Astronomy and Ionosphere Center; **98–99br,** John Sanford/Astrostock; **99tr,** NASA; **102,** Silver, Burdett & Ginn Publishing; **103t,** Richard Haynes; **103b,** Roger Harris/Science Photo Library/Photo Researchers; **106 inset,** UCO/Lick Observatory photo/image; **107,** Luke Dodd/Science Photo library/Photo Researchers; **108,** Anglo-Australian Observatory, photograph by David Malin; **112b,** Open University, UK; **113tr,** National Optical Astronomy Observatories; **113br,** Space Telescope Science Institute; **114, 116,** Photo Researchers; **117,** Dennis Di Cicco/Peter Arnold; **118 both,** Richard Haynes; **120t, 120m,** Anglo-Australian Observatory, photograph by David Malin; **120b,** Royal Observatory, Edinburgh/AATB/Science Photo Library/Photo Researchers; **121,** NASA; **124,** David Parker/Science Photo Library/Photo Researchers.

Interdisciplinary Exploration
Page 128t, Jet Propulsion Laboratory; **128b,** U. S. Geological Survey; **129r,** Valerie Ambroise; **129l,** Corbis-Bettmann; **130t,** Pat Rawlings/NASA; **130–131b,** Jet Propulsion Laboratory; **131tr, 131tl,** NASA; **132t,** U. S. Geological Survey; **132b,** NASA/Peter Arnold; **133,** Pat Rawlings/NASA.

Skills Handbook
Page 134, Mike Moreland/Photo Network; **135t,** Foodpix; **135m,** Richard Haynes; **135b,** Russ Lappa; **138,** Richard Haynes; **140,** Ron Kimball; **141,** Renee Lynn/Photo Researchers.

Appendix B
Pages 150–153, Griffith Observer, Griffith Observatory, Los Angeles.